MBLEx
TEST PREP

Complete Study Guide for MBLEx

David Merlino, LMT

wandererstudios.us

ISBN-13: 978-1-7328356-0-3

Photo credits: Amanda Merlino, Desmond Merlino, Steven Merlino,
Starrisa Reyna, Anna Owings, Ashley Capone, Keith Sells, TJ Wilson,
Andrew Briggs, Chara Lawson, Rose Matthews, Jennifer Bessler
Haug, Mike Escobar, Frank Butler. Stock photos via Shutterstock.

Special Thanks: Every school and student who has used any of my guides,
everyone who has supported me in my endeavors, my family, friends,
Fit Reno, Ang Thai Massage, Spavia Reno, Conviction Martial Arts, The
Bodhi Tree Center, and Tim Ferriss.

PUBLISHER'S DISCLAIMER

The material presented in this study guide is for informational purposes
only. Any information regarding Medications, CPR, First Aid, and
Contraindications should be researched by the reader to obtain the most
up-to-date requirements, as these subjects are ever-changing.

INTERNET RESOURCES

Information on how to access internet resources may be found on pages 2
and 3. If these resources are not functioning properly, please email the
author directly at david@mblextestprep.com to notify us of the situation.

ALSO AVAILABLE

Subscribe to the MBLEx Test Prep Podcast on iTunes, Spotify,
Soundcloud, Stitcher, and anywhere else you get podcasts!
Follow us on Facebook at facebook.com/mblextestprep

Published by

2018

Table of Contents

Introduction

Hello! My name is David Merlino, and I am the author of this study guide. A lot of time and energy has gone in to the creation of this guide. I am extremely proud to share this guide with you, and I am honored that you have chosen my study guide to help prepare you for the MBLEx. You have a tall task ahead of you, but it isn't something you can't overcome. Trust me, I've taken, and passed, the MBLEx!

I've been a Licensed Massage Therapist for over 13 years, and I've learned and experienced so much. However, it all began with passing my licensing exam. I understood how to take tests, how to study, and how to give myself the best chance possible to advance into my career. I hope to share this knowledge with you.

In 2011, I began my new career, preparing students to take their massage licensing exams at a career college in beautiful Reno, Nevada. It was here where I honed my craft, helping students achieve a near-90% pass rate on the licensing exam. How did I do this? It's quite simple: I emphasize efficient studying and information over excessive studying and information. Simply put, it's called the minimum effective dose for the MBLEx. I review the information most likely to be seen on the exam, and don't review information I feel isn't necessary, or is unlikely to be seen on the exam. As Olympic pole vaulter Henk Kraaijenhof once said, "Do as little as needed, not as much as possible." This approach makes preparing for the MBLEx much easier to manage.

With this view, my students achieved amazing success. You can too. Before you begin, however, I need to remind you of something: you will be tested on information that isn't present in this study guide. You will be tested on information you have never even seen before. This happened to all of my

students. It even happened to me, someone who had been teaching this information for five years. It's all the luck of the draw. Despite not seeing this information before, you can still do extremely well on these questions. Make sure you check out the Study Skills, Test-Taking Techniques, and Reducing Test Anxiety sections immediately following this page.

I've poured months of my life into the production and creation of this study guide. You are now my student. I believe in you, and I know you will do great.

If you have any questions, I am here to help. Please don't hesitate to send me an email with any questions you may have in regards to the study guide, practice tests, or the MBLEx in general. My personal email address is: **david@mblextestprep.com**. Just note, I am very much willing to help, but if your email is rude or disrespectful in any way, there will be no response from me. Just be cool!

Thank you again. I am honored that you have entrusted me with helping you pass the MBLEx. So let's get started!

Your Instructor,

David Merlino, LMT

How To Use This Study Guide

This study guide is designed to not just TELL information, but to help you, the student, LEARN information. This is achieved in many different ways, including standard study guides, assignments, and practice exams.

To get the complete, most effective and efficient experience from this study guide, I recommend doing the following:

Before starting, figure out the area you need to study most: Massage Therapy, Kinesiology, Pathology, or Anatomy and Physiology. Most people tend to choose Kinesiology first. A common study routine I've helped many students implement is the following(you can change the subjects as you see fit, depending on how comfortable you are with each), with an average of one month of study time before the exam. For this example, we'll say the study order is Kinesiology, Pathology, Anatomy and Physiology, and then Massage Therapy:

Week 1: Study nothing but Medical Terminology and Kinesiology, depending on schedule, for up to 10 hours.
Week 2: Study Pathology for 80% of the time, and study Medical Terminology and Kinesiology the other 20% of the time. So, if you're studying for 10 hours, 8 hours will be dedicated to Pathology, and 2 hours will be dedicated to Medical Terminology and Kinesiology.
Week 3: Study Anatomy and Physiology for 80% of the time, and study Pathology, Medical Terminology, and Kinesiology for the remaining 20% of the time.
Week 4: Study Massage Therapy for 80% of the time, and study Anatomy and Physiology, Pathology, Medical Terminology, and Kinesiology for the remaining 20% of the time.
Final Week: Study every subject an equal amount.

This way of studying, I've found, is great for long-term memory growth in these subjects, as there is a consistent review of information every week.

While studying, especially in the final week before the exam, I highly recommend taking as many practice tests as possible. Go to the following website to take unlimited online practice exams:

http://www.mblextestprep.com/resources.html

Watch video lectures I have created, which puts you in a class-like study session with me as your instructor. Go to the following website to view all available video lectures and follow along while studying:

http://www.mblextestprep.com/resources.html

Utilize pre-made flashcards I've created for you, which cover the most important information you need to study. Go to the following website to utilize flashcards:

http://www.mblextestprep.com/resources.html

While studying, be sure to finish the assignments and practice exams in the book. These are great for assessing your knowledge on the subjects you will have just covered, and help you figure out what you still need to study, and what you've learned.

Online Resources

Make sure you are utilizing the online resources included with your study guide! See below for information on the most important parts!

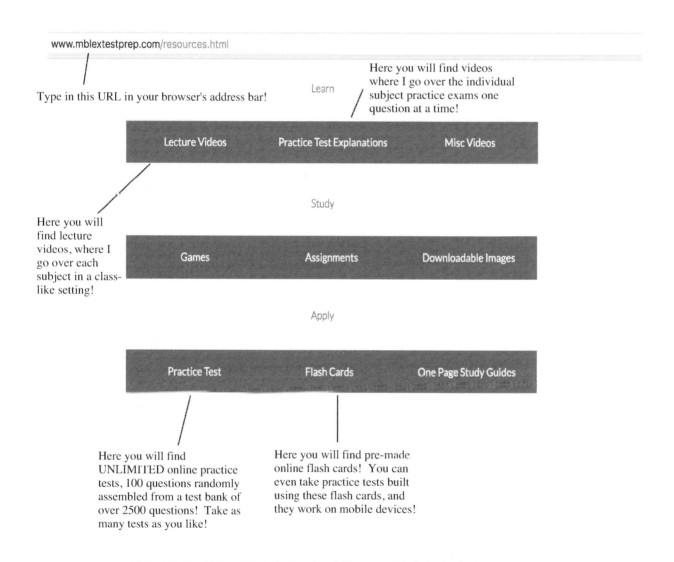

www.mblextestprep.com/resources.html

Type in this URL in your browser's address bar!

Learn

Here you will find videos where I go over the individual subject practice exams one question at a time!

| Lecture Videos | Practice Test Explanations | Misc Videos |

Here you will find lecture videos, where I go over each subject in a class-like setting!

Study

| Games | Assignments | Downloadable Images |

Apply

| Practice Test | Flash Cards | One Page Study Guides |

Here you will find UNLIMITED online practice tests, 100 questions randomly assembled from a test bank of over 2500 questions! Take as many tests as you like!

Here you will find pre-made online flash cards! You can even take practice tests built using these flash cards, and they work on mobile devices!

Study Skills

➢ Do not do all of your studying the night before or day of the test. Study consistently, up to several times per week. Cramming is good for short-term learning, but does not help with long-term learning. The more you study, the more likely you are to retain the information.

➢ Use all of your class and home work as study materials. The information in these assignments is information that might be on your exam.

➢ Take many short breaks as you study. Memory retention is higher at the beginning and end of study sessions than it is in the middle. This is called the Serial Position Effect. Study for no longer than ten minutes, then take a short break.

➢ Focus on one subject at a time while studying. You don't want to confuse yourself by mixing information.

➢ Study the subject you have the most difficulty with more than subjects you are comfortable with. Studying what you aren't weak in doesn't help. If you need work on a specific subject, focus the majority of your time learning that information, even if it means taking away study time from other areas. You're better off being 80% proficient in every subject than 100% in four subjects and only 50% in the last. Not studying this information could prevent you from passing the exam.

➢ While studying, take notes on important information, especially if it's information you don't recognize or remember. Use this information to study with.

➢ Assign yourself tests, reports, assignments and projects to complete. You are more likely to remember information if you write a report on it than if you just read the information.

➢ Teach information you are studying to another person. If you are responsible for someone learning something, you have to know and understand the material, and be able to put that information into the simplest terms possible, so someone else can understand it. This will only help you. Trust me, from personal experience, this really works.

➢ Understand the material you are studying. Do not just try to memorize certain answers you think may be on the test. Certain "key words" might not be on the test. Learn everything about a subject, and you'll never get any question on that subject wrong.

Serial Position Effect: http://www.simplypsychology.org/primacy-recency.html

Test-Taking Tips

➢ Go to the restroom before taking the exam. Using the restroom beforehand ensures that you are 100% focused on the exam, and not on your bladder.

➢ Read the entire question slowly and carefully. Never make assumptions about what a question is asking. Assuming you know what a question is asking may lead to you missing key words in the question that tell you exactly what the question is asking. Read every single word in every single question, multiple times if necessary.

Understand what the question is asking before you try answering it.

➤ Identify key words in each question. Key words are words that tell you exactly what the question is asking. Identify these words easily by reading questions aloud to yourself. The words you find yourself emphasizing while reading aloud are likely the key words.

Here is an example. Read this question:
Q: Which of the following statements is true regarding Swedish massage?
In this question, there are two key words, which are telling you exactly what the question is asking. Now read the question aloud. Which words did you put emphasis on? Most likely, you read the question like this: "Which of the following statements is TRUE regarding SWEDISH massage?" These are the key words.

➤ Do not change your answers, unless you misread the question. Changing your answers puts doubt into your mind, and leads to more changing of answers. The answer you put first is usually correct. Do not change your answers!

➤ Match key words in the answers with key words in the questions. Sometimes it's as simple as matching terms, if you've exhausted all other avenues.

➤ Eliminate answers you know aren't correct and justify the reason they aren't correct. If you can eliminate one answer from each question, that brings your odds of getting that question right up to 33%. If you can eliminate two answers that can't be right, that brings it up to 50%. Then it's just a coin flip!

Here's an example. Read this question, and the answers:
Q: Of the following, which is not contagious?
A. Athlete's Foot
B. Herpes Simplex
C. Influenza
D. Osgood-Schlatter Disease

Have you ever heard of Osgood-Schlatter Disease? Even if you haven't, you can still get this question right by eliminating the other answers. Athlete's Foot is caused by a fungus, and is contagious. That leaves us with three possible answers. Herpes Simplex is caused by a virus, and is contagious. That leaves us with two possible answers. So even if you're guessing at this point, it's only a 50/50 chance you get it right! Influenza is caused by a virus, and is contagious. This process of elimination just gave us the answer: D, Osgood-Schlatter Disease.

➤ Read the entire question before looking at the answers. Again, never make assumptions about what the question is asking.

➤ Come up with the answer in your head before looking at the answers. If the same answer you come up with is in the list of answers, that's most likely the right answer.

➤ Read every answer given to make sure you are picking the most correct answer. Some questions have multiple right answers, and you need to make sure you're picking the most correct answer.

➤ Make sure you are properly hydrated before the test. Studies have been done on the effects of proper hydration on those taking tests. People who are properly hydrated tend to score higher than those who are not.

➤ Exercise for twenty minutes before the exam. Exercise has also been shown to increase test scores.

Exercise and Test-Taking: http://lifehacker.com/20-minutes-of-exercise-before-an-exam-may-boost-your-pe-1541773646

Reducing Test Anxiety

➤ Study consistently. If you understand the material, you won't be as stressed out about the test. There are ways you can study without this book or your class notes as well. An example, whenever you take a bite of food, think about every structure the food passes through in the alimentary canal and what each of the organs do. Another example, whenever you are massaging someone, tell yourself everything about every muscle you work on, like origin, insertion, and action.

➤ Keep a positive attitude while preparing for the test and during the test. If you think you're going to fail, you will not be as motivated to study, you won't adhere to your test-taking techniques, you'll become stressed out during the exam much more easily, and you'll be more likely to fail.

➤ Try to stay relaxed. Utilize deep breathing techniques to calm down if you start feeling nervous or stressed. You will have two hours to finish the exam. You can afford one or two minutes to calm yourself down if you need to.

➤ Exercise consistently up until the day of the test to reduce anxiety. Exercise has been shown to significantly reduce stress, and also helps with memory retention. Try utilizing flash cards while riding an exercise bike.

➤ Take your time on the test. If you find yourself rushing, slow down. Again, you have two hours to finish the exam. Do not rush through it. You may miss important information in the exam and answer questions incorrectly because of this.

Massage Therapy

The MBLEx is a test designed with the massage therapist in mind. There are numerous topics covered on the MBLEx that fall under the general category of Massage Therapy.

In this section, we will discuss many subjects, covering a wide range of information.

Information covered in this section includes:

Massage Technique
Joint Movements
Stretching
Assessment
Precautions
Draping
Bolsters
Body Mechanics
Massage Modalities
Business
Liability Insurance
Types of Employment
Tax Forms
SOAP Notes
Ethics
Communication
Therapeutic Relationship
Psychology

This information is followed by two assignments:

Massage Therapy Matching
Massage Therapy Crossword

The end of the section has a 50 question practice exam on Massage Therapy. These questions ARE NOT the exact same questions you will see on the MBLEx. They are meant to test information that MAY be seen on the MBLEx.

While taking the practice exam, make sure to utilize your test-taking strategies(page 4) to optimize your test scores.

Massage Technique

In western massage, there are **six** main massage strokes, which have been in a constant state of evolution since being developed.

Effleurage is the most common stroke in western massage, consisting of long, **gliding** strokes that are directed **towards the heart**. Effleurage is used to increase circulation of blood and lymph, remove waste from tissues, introduce the therapist's touch to the client, transition between strokes, and apply massage lubricant. Effleurage may be used throughout the massage, but is the main stroke used at the beginning of the treatment. The majority of the time, effleurage is performed by the therapist in the **archer(bow) stance**.

Petrissage utilizes **kneading** movements, lifting and squeezing tissue, to increase circulation, loosen adhesions that may be present in the tissue, and release metabolic waste from tissues. Petrissage is an important stroke to use in post-event sports massage, as it helps flush waste from the muscles and bring fresh oxygen-rich blood into them.

Friction consists of strokes that move **across** tissue. Friction is especially useful in breaking up adhesions and scar tissue, increasing circulation, and stretching muscles. There are many different forms of friction, such as superficial friction (rubbing the surface of the skin), parallel friction, circular friction, and cross-fiber friction.

Tapotement consists of **percussion** strokes, rhythmically affecting the tissues of the body in many different ways. Tapotement increases spindle cell activity in the muscles, which helps activate them and get them ready for use, which makes tapotement a very important stroke to use in pre-event sports massage. Tapotement may also help loosen any phlegm, or mucous, in the respiratory tract, and is very helpful in conditions such as asthma or chronic bronchitis. There are many different forms of tapotement, including hacking, cupping, tapping, and beating.

Vibration is performed by **shaking** a part of the body, using **trembling** actions. Vibration can have different effects on the body, depending on how fine the vibration is. Slow vibration is used to sedate an area(think of massage chairs that vibrate, numbing the area). Fast vibration is used to stimulate an area.

A **nerve stroke** is an **extremely light** form of **effleurage**. Like effleurage, nerve strokes, also called feather strokes, are directed towards the heart. These strokes are primarily used at the end of a massage, or at the end of work on a specific body part, to separate the therapist from the client(ending the massage session), or to transition from one part of the body to another.

Joint Movements

Joint movements describe how a joint is, well, moved! There are four main types of joint movements, performed by the therapist on the client, the therapist and the client working together, the therapist and the client working against one another, or the client performing the action by themselves.

An **active joint movement** involves the client actively performing a movement **without assistance** from the massage therapist. An example would be a massage therapist asking a client to perform a range-of-motion as part of assessment. The therapist does not help with the action, as they would want to see how much movement the client can perform by themselves, and to see where any restrictions may be.

Active assistive joint movements involve the client performing a movement **with assistance** from the massage therapist. Active assistive joint movements are very helpful in rehabilitative settings, allowing the client to move the joint, but making sure someone is there to help move and support the joint to prevent further injury.

Passive joint movements involve the massage therapist moving the joint, with the **client completely relaxed**, not helping at all. Passive joint movements are helpful for performing stretches, feeling for restrictions in movements, and for assisting the client to further relax.

Resistive joint movements are when the client and massage therapist are moving a joint in **opposite directions** at the same time. This creates an isometric contraction(muscle tension increases, length doesn't change, see page 57), which is extremely helpful in a specific type of stretch known as Proprioceptive Neuromuscular Facilitation.

Stretching

Stretching is an exercise that is performed by **elongating,** or lengthening, a muscle. Stretching is extremely beneficial to a person's health.

An **unassisted stretch** is performed by the client stretching into resistance **without any help** from the massage therapist. It is similar to an active joint mobilization, but instead of just moving the joint through its normal range-of- motion, it moves past that point and into a stretch.

An **assisted stretch** is performed by the client, **with assistance** from the massage therapist. Again, this is similar to an active assistive joint movement, where the massage therapist's role is to help the client move the joint into a stretch while stabilizing the joint to ensure there is no damage to the joint.

Proprioceptive Neuromuscular Facilitation(PNF) is a stretch that is very useful in loosening adhesions and scar tissue in muscles, and is very beneficial for athletes. To perform PNF, a massage therapist moves a client's joint into a stretch. Once resistance is met, the client will actively resist the movement being performed by the massage therapist. This puts the muscle into an **isometric contraction**. After holding this resisted movement for 5-10 seconds, the client **relaxes**, and the massage therapist is able to move the stretch further, until resistance is met again. The process is then repeated. PNF allows a highly noticeable increase in the amount of range-of-motion in a joint. *reciprocal inhibition*

Stretch until resistance is met

Isometric contraction

Client relaxes, then the stretch moves further

During stretching and joint mobilizations, we experience **end feels**. An end feel is what causes a joint movement or stretch to not move any further.

A **soft end feel** is the result of **soft tissues**, such as muscles and tendons, pulling back on the joint, preventing any further movement. An example is when stretching the quadriceps. The hip joint is moved into extension until resistance is met. The resistance is due to the quadriceps pulling back on the joint. If the quadriceps are loosened, the joint will move further. This is a soft end feel.

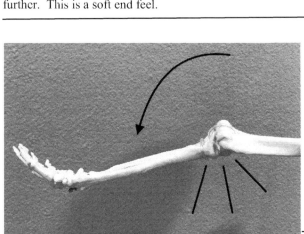

A **hard end feel** is the result of structures, primarily **bone,** preventing a joint from moving further. An example is extension of the knee or elbow. Straightening these joints can only go to a certain point. Bones will prevent these joints from extending any further. That's why hyperextension of these joints may result in broken bones. This is a hard end feel.

An **empty end feel** is caused by neither muscles nor bones interfering with movement. Empty end feels are the result of **trauma** to an area, which prevents movement. An example could be a sprained ankle. With a sprained ankle, inflammation may be present, which immobilizes a joint to prevent further injury. This is an empty end feel.

Easy to Remember: A soft end feel is caused by soft tissues; a hard end feel is caused by hard tissues!

Assessment

Assessments are a vital component of any massage treatment. Assessments are **evaluations** of the client primarily done before a massage, but the therapist is constantly assessing, even during and after a treatment.

Assessments have many different uses, from determining any contraindications the client may have, to tailoring a massage session specifically for that client and what they need. An example could be, if a client complains of low back pain, the therapist could then do visual assessment, range-of-motion exercises, and palpation to determine what the possible cause of the low back pain could be. Then, after the assessment is complete, the therapist may tailor the session to work specifically on the areas of concern(possibly the hamstrings, quadratus lumborum, psoas major, or rectus femoris).

Assessments may be performed in many different ways: *active listening*

Listening to the client and their complaints is the most effective way to determine issues a client may be experiencing.

Visual assessment may be performed, focusing on alignment of specific bony landmarks to determine areas of concern. Some of these areas to compare bilaterally include the ears(possible neck tension), acromion processes (shoulder/back/chest tension), iliac crests(back/hip/thigh tension), anterior superior iliac spines(back/hip/thigh tension), and head of fibulae(back/hip/thigh tension).

Gait analysis may help determine hypertonic muscles unilaterally, and injuries.

Palpation is useful in feeling for adhesions or restrictions in muscles, localized ischemia, and inflammation.

Range-of-motion may be performed by the client for the therapist to determine any restrictions of movement.

Intake forms are extremely helpful in determining contraindications via medical history, medications, any hobbies or jobs that may lead to issues physically or mentally(an example could be the hobby of gardening, which may strain the back or hamstrings).

Common areas of visual assessment. Asymmetry, such as the height of the shoulders which can be seen in the photograph on the left, may be a sign of hypertension in certain areas of the body.

Precautions

During a massage, certain precautions need to be adhered to, to prevent injury or complications to the client.

Endangerment sites are areas of the body that, while massage may be performed on, need to be treated with **extra caution**. These are commonly due to insufficient tissues in the area to support, cushion, and protect important structures like blood vessels and nerves. Endangerment sites include the anterior triangle of the neck, the axilla, the anterior elbow, and the popliteal region.

Local contraindications are areas of the body that must be **avoided** when performing a massage. While endangerment sites allow for massage to be performed, local contraindications do not permit massage on localized areas. Reasons for a part of the body to be considered a local contraindication vary, from inflammation and trauma to infections(such as athlete's foot). The rest of the body may receive massage, but these specific areas must be avoided.

Absolute contraindications prohibit the use of massage. Massage on a person with an absolute contraindication, such as when a person is infected by a virus like influenza, can worsen the condition for the client, cause damage to the body, or even spread an infection or condition to the massage therapists. Do not perform a massage on a client with an absolute contraindication!

Draping

Draping is the use of **linens** to keep a client covered during a massage session. There are many different types of linens that may be used to cover a client. Most commonly, sheets are used. Blankets and towels are other common forms of linens. Draping is a very important step in establishing **boundaries** between the massage therapist and the client. Draping the client tells the client what part of the body the therapist is, and isn't, going to work on, increasing the professionalism required of a massage therapist. Draping also helps the clients establish boundaries, telling the therapist where the client may not want massage to be performed.

Communication is key in establishing boundaries. If there is any question about a client's boundaries with regards to draping, just ask!

Top cover draping refers to the linen placed **atop** the client, which acts as the drape. As previously stated, the most common form is a sheet.

Bolsters

Bolsters are used to place the client into a comfortable position during a massage session. There are many different positions a client may be placed in during a massage, which requires the bolster to be placed in different locations to optimize comfort.

When a client is positioned **supine(face up)** on the massage table, the client may experience low back pain. A bolster should be placed **under the knees** in this case. Low back pain is likely caused by a tight psoas major, iliacus, or rectus femoris. A bolster under the knees produces slight flexion of the hip, which takes pressure off all these muscles.

When a client is positioned **prone(face down)** on the massage table, the client may experience low back pain. A bolster should be placed **under the ankles** in this case. Low back pain is likely caused by tight hamstrings. A bolster under the ankles produces slight flexion of the knee, which takes pressure off the hamstrings.

Side-lying position should be used for pregnant clients, or clients who have difficulty lying prone, such as people with kyphosis. Bolstering for side-lying clients includes placing a bolster between the **knees** to relieve pressure on the hips, under the **arms**, and under the **head**.

Certain clients may need to be placed in a **semi-reclined position**, such as pregnant clients who experience dizziness from lying supine(caused by the fetus placing pressure on the abdominal aorta). When a client is semi-reclined, a bolster should be placed under the **knees**, and behind the **head**.

Body Mechanics

Body mechanics are extremely important for massage therapists. Proper body mechanics prevent the therapist from **injuring** themselves during a massage, which increases the longevity of their career. It makes performing a massage less physically strenuous, and allows the therapist to perform a **better** massage by utilizing pressure and leverage more efficiently.

While performing a massage, the massage therapist's **back** should remain **straight**. **Knees** should be in a **slightly flexed** position. While performing compression, **joints** should be **stacked** to relieve pressure on one specific joint. An important factor in body mechanics that often is overlooked, however, is the **height of a massage table.** The table should be at the proper height for the therapist, based on the type of massage being performed. Deep tissue massages require the table to be slightly lower than Swedish massages.

Body stances are very important while performing massage strokes, making them easier to perform, and makes the strokes flow and transition more smoothly.

The **bow** stance, also called the **archer** stance, is performed with the therapist's **feet** placed **parallel** to the massage table. This allows the therapist to perform long, gliding strokes, such as those seen in effleurage.

The **horse** stance, also called the **warrior** stance, is when the therapist's feet are placed **perpendicular** to the massage table. The feet will face the table, the knees will be slightly flexed. This allows short, powerful strokes to be performed, such as compression and friction.

Massage Modalities

There are many different forms of massage, and many different modalities(specialties) that may be performed by massage therapists. Some require training and certification to perform, and others do not. Check with your local licensing board to determine requirements to perform specific modalities.

Aromatherapy is any treatment utilizing **essential oils**, which may affect the brain's **limbic** system. Essential oils have many different effects on the body, depending on the type of oil used, and how it is administered. Examples include oils having a stimulating effect, such as lemon and grapefruit, having a sedative effect, such as eucalyptus on the respiratory tract, having antiseptic properties, such as tea tree on insect bites, or having calming effects on the brain, such as lavender. Always check with a client for any allergies before using essential oils in a treatment.

Craniosacral Therapy is a very light massage technique that helps to release **blockages** in the flow of **cerebrospinal fluid**, which runs from the **cranium** to the **sacrum**. Blockages in these fluids may cause numerous side effects, including headaches, dizziness, and difficulty processing and understanding information.

Deep Tissue massage is performed by working the **deeper** layers of tissue in the body, including muscles and fascia. Deep tissue may require deeper pressure to be used by the massage therapist to reach deeper structures(an example could be working deeper through the rectus femoris to reach the vastus intermedius).

Hot Stone massage is a treatment that utilizes **heated stones**. The stones may be **placed** on certain parts of the body(hands, feet, lumbar, abdomen), may be used to physically massage a client, or both. Temperature of the stones should be checked by the massage therapist on their own skin(anterior forearm) before attempting to place on the client, to ensure the client does not suffer any burns. Hot stone is used to increase circulation into muscles and tissues, and aids in relaxation.

Hydrotherapy is the use of **water** in any treatment. There are several different types of hydrotherapy, utilizing water in solid(ice), liquid(water), or vapor(steam). **Contrast baths** utilize both a **heated** bath and a **cold** bath. Contrast baths are used to decrease systemic inflammation and increase circulation. A typical contrast bath treatment sees the client use cold water, then hot, then cold, then hot, and end with cold for inflammation relief. A **Vichy shower** is a piece of equipment that hangs over a **water-proof table**. This equipment has seven shower heads attached to it, which can pin-point specific areas of the body to be sprayed.

Lomi Lomi(*Hawaiian "lomi"; massage*) is a **Hawaiian** massage, similar to a Swedish massage, which utilizes rhythmic gliding strokes. These strokes are used on the entire body, and can move from the feet up to the head in one fluid motion. This requires minimal draping, usually nothing more than a hand towel covering the gluteal cleft, exposing the glutes.

Lymphatic Drainage is a technique designed to increase the circulation of **lymph** utilizing very light strokes directed towards the heart. Increasing lymph circulation may help reduce swelling in areas such as the limbs or face.

Myofascial Release is a type of treatment aimed at releasing **restrictions** in **muscles** and **fascia**. Myofascial Release utilizes light strokes that move in the direction of the restriction, helping the muscle "unwind" on its own.

Pregnancy massage is massage for pregnant clients. As discussed earlier, pregnant clients may need to be placed into side-lying or semi-reclined position. Endangerment sites for pregnant clients include the **abdomen** and around the **ankles**.

Reflexology is used to treat **reflex points** on the hands, feet, and ears that correspond to other tissues inside the body, such as **organs**. A map of these locations can be found on page 323.

Reiki is a form of **energy work**, in which the therapist channels universal energy into and throughout the client. In reiki, the therapist primarily(but not always) holds their hands an inch or two **above the client**, and manipulate the client's energy to promote relaxation or other benefits.

Rolfing, developed by **Ida Rolf**, is known as a **structural realignment** technique. The basic principles of Rolfing involve the body being placed back into proper vertical alignment. The Rolfer works on the **fascia** of the body. Loosening the fascia helps the body return to its natural position. Rolfing typically takes place over ten sessions, with a different part of the body worked on during each session.

Sports massage is a massage designed for **athletes**. Sports massage may be performed in many different ways, depending on the needs of the athlete. **Pre-event** sports massage, which may be performed up to 15 minutes before an event, will typically be **stimulating**, increasing circulation into the muscles, and use tapotement to activate spindle cells. Inter-event massage will look to achieve the same results as pre-event massage, but does not utilize tapotement. Using tapotement may result in cramping. **Post-event** massage will be much slower, rhythmic, and relaxing. The primary goal of a post-event massage is to **calm the body** down, remove metabolic waste from tissues, and increase the flow of oxygen-rich blood into the muscles to aid in recovery.

Swedish massage, the most common massage technique in western massage therapy, is mainly focused on **relaxation**. Effleurage is a stroke commonly utilized in Swedish massage, with strokes aimed towards the heart to increase circulation.

Thai massage, originating in Thailand, isn't necessarily what we consider a normal massage. Thai massage is performed with the client wearing loose-fitting clothes, on a mat, on the floor. The therapist's main goal during a Thai massage is to **stretch** the client. Massage may be incorporated into these stretching techniques.

Tuina is the name of **modern Chinese** massage. It is used to balance the eight principles of Chinese medicine. Tuina incorporates rhythmic strokes focused on specific areas of the body. Tuina may help stimulate the body meridians(page 325), and may even incorporate acupressure to help the body heal from musculoskeletal injuries.

Business

Even if you aren't planning on becoming a business owner, understanding how businesses operate is knowledge everyone should have. It can help in retaining clientele, business relationships, and even keep you out of trouble from things like HIPAA violations.

Business for a massage therapist, in most locations, begins with a **certification**. A certification is a credential obtained by completing a certification course, usually in a **school** setting. It also may involve completing a certification exam. Certifications show that you have gained enough knowledge in a given subject to be able to perform that task. In this case, you gain a certificate after completing massage school.

A **license** is a jurisdictional requirement, which is used to **regulate** the practice of massage therapy. Licensing boards set rules and laws that a person is required to follow if they wish to be a licensed massage therapist. Licenses, in most jurisdictions, allow a massage therapist to practice massage therapy and receive money as compensation.

Reciprocity refers to the ability for a massage license in one jurisdiction to be recognized as **valid** in another jurisdiction. Some jurisdictions may require a new license to be obtained, but no more schooling required. Others may require more schooling in addition to paying for a new license.

Liability Insurance

When operating a business at a physical location where there is customer exposure, liability insurance is often required. There are two types of liability insurance: General liability insurance, and Professional liability insurance.

General liability insurance protects the massage therapist in cases such as **accidental falls** by the client that result in bodily injury. **Professional liability insurance** is similar, but instead of protecting the therapist from workplace accidents, it protects the therapist from lawsuits regarding **malpractice** or **negligence**. If a massage therapist knowingly performs a service or treatment they are not authorized, licensed, or certified to perform, this is known as malpractice. If a client tells a therapist not to work on a specific part of the body(say, the feet), and the therapist forgets and works on that area, and injury results, this is considered negligence.

Types of Employment

There are many different types of employment you may encounter as a massage therapist. These are among the most common.

An **independent contractor** is a massage therapist that works independently for themselves, but **contracts** with another person or company to perform work. Independent contractors are not beholden to the same limitations as employees, however. Independent contractors may work whatever schedule they want, charge their own prices, wear their own uniform. Independent contractors do not receive benefits from an employer, however.

Sole proprietors are often categorized similarly to independent contractors. Sole proprietorships are businesses owned by **one person**. Sole proprietors may differ from independent contractors in licensing requirements.

A **partnership** is a business owned by **two or more** people. Ownership may be split differently depending on variables such as money entering into a business relationship, assets, etc.

S Corporations are corporations that pass income and taxes onto the **shareholders**. This requires the shareholders to shoulder the responsibility of reporting income and taxes to the IRS.

Tax Forms

A **W-2** is filed by employees, detailing earnings and money withheld for social security taxes, medicaid, state and federal income taxes. Gratuity may also be reported on the W2, if the gratuity is added to the employee's paycheck.

		Department of the Treasury - Internal Revenue Service	
Form **W-2** Wage and Tax Statement 2017	OMB No. 1545-0008	1 Wages, tips, other compensation 32340.00	2 Federal income tax withheld 455.00
Copy B - To Be Filed With Employee's FEDERAL Tax Return. This information is being furnished to the Internal Revenue Service.	7 Social security tips	3 Social security wages 32340.00	4 Social security tax withheld 200.88
c Employer's name, address, and ZIP code WASHOE COUNTY SCHOOL DISTRICT PO BOX RENO, NV	8 Allocated tips	5 Medicare wages and tips 32340.00	6 Medicare tax withheld 47.00
	9 Verification code	10 Dependent care benefits	11 Nonqualified plans
	12a See instructions for box 12	12b	12c
e Employee's name, address, and ZIP code MEGHAN KENDRICK 123 FOUR FIVE SIX ST RENO, NV 89511	12d	13 Statutory emp / Retirement plan / Third-party sick pay	14 Other
	b Employer Identification Number (EIN) 88-9943740	a Employee's social security number 000-00-0001	
15 State Employer's state ID number	16 State wages, tips, etc.	17 State income tax	18 Local wages, tips, etc. / 19 Local income tax / 20 Locality name

A **1099** is issued to an **independent contractor** by the company they contract with. This statement details the amount of income accrued by the independent contractor through the year.

☐ CORRECTED (if checked)		
PAYER'S name, street address, city or town, province or state, country, ZIP or foreign postal code, and telephone no. Business! 890 One Two Three Street Seattle, WA 00002	1 Rents $	OMB No. 1545-0115
	2 Royalties $ 99,999.99	**2016**
	3 Other income $	4 Federal income tax withheld $
		Form **1099-MISC**
	5 Fishing boat proceeds $	6 Medical & health care payments $
		Miscellaneous Income
PAYER'S federal identification number 01-0000001	RECIPIENT'S identification number XXX-XX-5555	7 Nonemployee compensation $
	8 Substitute payments in lieu of dividends or interest $	**Copy B - For Recipient** This is important tax information and is being furnished to the Internal Revenue Service. If you are required to file a return, a negligence penalty or other sanction may be imposed on you if this income is taxable and the IRS determines that it has not been reported.
RECIPIENT'S name Billy Bob 1234 Five Six Seven Street New York, NY 00001	9 Payer made direct sales of $5,000 or more of consumer products to a buyer (recipient) for resale ☐	10 Crop insurance proceeds $
	11	12
	13 Excess golden parachute payments $	14 Gross proceeds paid to an attorney $
	15a Section 409A deferrals $	15b Section 409A income $
Account number (see instructions) FATCA filing requirement ☐	16 State tax withheld $	17 State/Payer's state no. / 18 State income $
Form 1099-MISC (keep for your records)	www.irs.gov/form1099misc	Department of the Treasury - Internal Revenue Service

A **Schedule C** is filed to the IRS by **sole proprietors**, detailing the amount of money the business made during the previous year.

A **Schedule K-1** is a form filed by individual **partnership members**. It is similar to a W-2, detailing the amount of money each partnership member made during the previous year.

Profit and Loss(income and expense) statements are forms filed by businesses that show how much money was made(**profit**) and how much money was expended(**loss**) during the year.

Gift taxes may be used as deductions on taxes. If a business buys a gift for a customer, no more than **$25** may be claimed as a deduction for that specific client. Other gifts for different clients may also be reported, but each gift reported cannot exceed $25.

SOAP Notes

SOAP notes are the most common form of post-massage documentation. SOAP notes help a massage therapist **document** everything that happened or was said during a massage session. Documenting this information can be helpful in many different ways, from tailoring future massage treatments to protecting the therapist from any malpractice or negligence lawsuits that may arise.

The "**S**" of SOAP stands for "**Subjective**". Under this section of SOAP notes, a massage therapist documents anything the client details about themselves. This can include where they experience pain, their job or hobbies, etc.

The "**O**" of SOAP stands for "**Objective**" or "**Observation**". Under this section of SOAP notes, a massage therapist documents the type of massage or techniques being performed(objective), and anything about the client the therapist can physically see(observe). This can include bruising, inflammation, visual assessments, and gait analysis.

The "**A**" of SOAP stands for "**Assessment**". Under this section of SOAP notes, a massage therapist documents any changes in the client as a result of the massage treatment. An example could be "Pre-massage, right shoulder elevated. Post-massage, right shoulder less elevated".

The "**P**" of SOAP stands for "**Plan**". Under this section of SOAP notes, a massage therapist documents any recommendations for future treatments, or exercises suggested for the client between sessions(such as increase stretching in a specific muscle or area, or increase water intake).

Client files, including intake forms, SOAP notes, and receipts, should be kept by the massage therapist for a minimum of **six** years, per the IRS. This allows for audits to take place by the IRS. Having all documentation stored can help prevent any possible penalties issued by the IRS.

S: Client complains of pain in low back and shoulders, states they work at a computer all day.

O: Elevated right scapula, hypertonic levator scapulae and trapezius bilaterally. Performed stretches on the area, PNF on hamstrings. Swedish massage, focus on scapular region.

A: Client states back feeling better, noticeable scapular depression post-massage. Increased mobility in hip joint and hamstrings.

P: Increase stretching of hamstrings and quadriceps. Increase stretching of pectoralis minor and serratus anterior to help with shoulder pain. Recommended receiving massage at least once a month.

Example of SOAP Notes

Ethics

Ethics are **guiding moral principles**. These guiding moral principles are used to direct a massage therapist in proper course of action in ethical dilemmas. There are many different ethical dilemmas that may arise in the practice of massage therapy. Examples include becoming sexually attracted to a client(refer the client to another therapist) and attempting to sell products or merchandise to a client outside the scope of massage(don't do it).

Scope of practice is performing treatments and techniques you are **qualified to perform**. Working outside of the scope of practice can lead to malpractice lawsuits. Examples of working outside of the scope of practice include performing treatments such as acupuncture or chiropractic work without proper licensing. Stay within your scope of practice at all times!

Boundaries, as discussed earlier, are **limitations** that can be set by the massage therapist and the client. They can be verbally set, such as a client asking a massage therapist to avoid working on a specific part of the body, or non-verbal, such as a client leaving an article of clothing on, which typically means they might not want to have that part of the body worked on. The best way to identify boundaries is to communicate with the client. Ask questions, reinforce the boundaries you or the client have set.

Confidentiality, quite simply, is keeping client information **private and protected**. Client information includes anything that happens or is said during a massage session, client files, intake forms, SOAP notes, and even something as simple as names. This information needs to be kept private. Releasing this information is a violation of HIPAA.

HIPAA(Health Insurance Portability and Accountability Act of 1996) was created by the US Department of Health and Human Services. Inside HIPAA lies the **Privacy Rule**, which is used to **protect** all individually identifiable health information. The Privacy Rule ensures client/patient information is kept private. It does, however, allow this information to be transferred between health care providers when necessary, which allows high-quality health care. Assessments and diagnoses do not need to be re-done, as the information is already present.

Communication

Communication, as we've discussed, is extremely important in the client/therapist relationship. One of the main ways we communicate with clients is by asking questions.

An **open-ended question** is a question used when asking for **feedback** from clients. Often, open-ended questions are meant to extract more detail, more information. It allows the answer to be more open and abstract.

A **close-ended question** is a question used when asking for a **yes-or-no response** only. These questions are used to extract important pieces of information in a short amount of time. During the pre-massage interview, when time is a factor, close-ended questions are primarily used to gather the important information without sacrificing too much time.

Transference and counter-transference occur when one person in the therapeutic relationship begins viewing the other as more than just their client or therapist. **Transference** is when the **client** begins viewing the massage therapist **similarly to a person** in their own personal life. They develop an emotional attachment to the massage therapist. **Counter-transference** is the opposite: a **massage therapist** develops an **emotional attachment** to a client. If either of these occur, it's best to refer the client to another massage therapist, separating the massage therapist from any possible ethical dilemmas.

Self disclosure is when the client shares information about **themselves** during a massage session. This information, which may be documented if relevant, needs to be kept confidential.

Therapeutic Relationship

The relationship a massage therapist shares with a client is known as the **therapeutic relationship**. The relationship between a therapist and client has many complexities. The primary goal of the therapist in the therapeutic relationship is to help the clients achieve goals they may be seeking, whether it be physical or emotional.

In the therapeutic relationship, there exists a **power differential**. The client, while in control of the session in most aspects, gives the therapist the power to perform massage, trusting that they have obtained sufficient training and working knowledge to help achieve the client's goals. The power differential can shift back to the client if the client feels their goals aren't being met, or their boundaries are being violated, such is the drape revealing more of the client than they are comfortable with.

An extremely important part of the therapeutic relationship is communication on both ends, between the client and therapist. If the client does not properly communicate their goals, it becomes difficult for the therapist to design an effective treatment plan. On the other hand, if the therapist fails to communicate reasons for developing a treatment plan based on client goals, the client may feel as if their needs are not being met. It is incumbent on the therapist to direct the flow of communication. The therapist should not be afraid to ask questions or explain reasons for performing specific massage strokes, stretches, or techniques if the client may not understand the reasoning for them.

The therapeutic relationship is the responsibilty of the therapist to guide and cultivate. Ensuring the client is happy with the service received in turn gives the therapist confidence in helping treat the client, which may increase therapist happiness and satisfaction in the job they are performing.

Psychology

A massage may leave a client in a psychologically vulnerable place, and they may exhibit defense mechanisms to help cope with their internal struggles.

Denial, a common defense mechanism, is a **refusal** to acknowledge a given situation, or acting as if something didn't happen.

Displacement is often negative. Displacement is satisfying an impulse by **substitution**. An example could be, you have a very bad day at work or school, you go home, and instead of being upset at school or work, you lash out at a significant other. Releasing your pent-up emotions at something other than what is causing the emotions

Projection is placing one's own internal feelings onto **someone else**. An example could be my wife: when she gets hungry, she becomes easily agitated. She'll then accuse me of being in a bad mood, even though I'm feeling great. This is projection. For the record, this happens a lot.

Regression is taking a **step back** psychologically when faced with stress. An example could be quitting smoking. A person doesn't smoke for a few days, and then they are presented with a stressful situation, which causes them to regress and smoke again.

Repression is subconsciously **blocking out** unwanted emotions. Not even knowing you have something to be upset about. Your mind can erase certain memories to help protect you from stress.

Massage Therapy Matching

__K__: Limitations set by the client or massage therapist

__H__: Refusal to acknowledge a given situation

__M__: Stoppage of range-of-motion due to tight muscles

__E__: Guiding moral principles

__R__: Stance with feet placed perpendicular to the table

__L__: Area of the body that warrants extra caution while massaging

__D__: Gliding strokes directed towards the heart

__A__: Modern Chinese massage

__Q__: Massage therapist moving a joint without assistance from the client

__J__: Protects a massage therapist from malpractice lawsuits

__G__: Percussion Strokes

__I__: Kneading strokes

__O__: Stance with feet placed parallel to the table

__T__: Jurisdictional requirement used to regulate the practice of massage therapy

__N__: Client moving a joint without assistance from the massage therapist

__S__: Stoppage of range-of-motion due to bone

__C__: Massage involving stretching performed on a mat on the floor

__F__: Stoppage of range-of-motion due to trauma

__B__: Client viewing a massage therapist similarly to a person in their early life

__P__: Credential obtained by completing a course in a school setting

A: Tuina

B: Transference

C: Thai Massage

D: Effleurage

E: Ethics

F: Empty End Feel

G: Tapotement

H: Denial

I: Petrissage

J: Professional Liability Insurance

K: Boundaries

L: Endangerment Site

M: Soft End Feel

N: Active Joint Movement

O: Bow Stance

P: Certification

Q: Passive Joint Movement

R: Horse Stance

S: Hard End Feel

T: License

Answer Key on Page 271

Massage Therapy

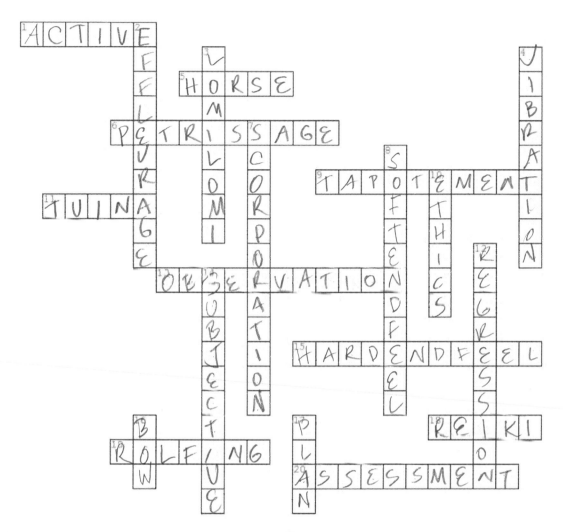

Across

1. Client performing movement without help from the massage therapist
5. Stance in which feet are placed perpendicular to the table
6. Kneading massage strokes
9. Percussion strokes
11. Modern Chinese massage
13. Any observable information the massage therapist can see, SOAP notes
15. Stoppage of range-of-motion due to bones
18. Modality directing universal energy into the client
19. Structural realignment therapy
20. Changes in client due to massage, SOAP notes

Down

2. Long, gliding strokes directed towards the heart
3. Hawaiian massage treatment
4. Shaking or trembling movements
7. Business that passes its income and taxes on to its shareholders
8. Stoppage of range-of-motion due to tight muscles
10. Guiding moral principles
12. Taking a step back psychologically when faced with stress
14. Information the client shares about themselves, SOAP notes
16. Stance in which one foot is placed in front of the other, feet parallel
17. Recommendations for future treatments, SOAP notes

Answer Key on Page 272

Critical Thinking

In this section, you will need to utilize your critical thinking skills to determine the right or wrong response to each of these given scenarios. No massage session is exactly the same, and things may happen during a session that range from unethical to illegal. Knowing when to spot problems is incredibly useful in any stage of a massage therapist's career!

1. Katie is a newly licensed massage therapist, working in a day spa. Today, she is seeing a client for a basic Swedish massage. The client, a regular at the spa, is very nice and polite, respectful of the rules and regulations set forth not just from the spa, but from Katie herself.

The massage goes off without a hitch. Katie works on all of the client's trouble spots, performs some stretches, explains the reasons for her techniques as she goes through the massage whenever the client has a question.

Katie finishes the massage by working on the client's face. The session ends, and the client is extremely happy with Katie's massage. After giving the client instructions for getting off the table and where to go afterwards, Katie opens the door and leaves the room. Katie immediately goes to the rest room and washes her hands. Katie grabs a small cup of water to offer to her client. The client emerges from the massage room, drinks the water, and thanks Katie for the fantastic massage.

After dropping off the client in the changing area, Katie returns to her massage room. She takes the sheets off the table, sprays the table, bolsters, and head rest with a soap and water mixture. After wiping the table off, she then sprays the table with isopropyl alcohol to make sure everything is clean and ready for the next client. Katie gathers the dirty linens. Katie opens the door, disposes of the dirty linens, and is ready for her next client.

Katie meets her next client in the spa waiting area, greets the client, and shakes the client's hand. Katie takes the client in to the massage room to begin the session.

What did Katie do wrong?

didn't dispose linens shook w/ until after cleaned soiled hands

2. Brandon is a long-time massage therapist, owning his own massage establishment for over ten years. Brandon has seen hundreds of different clients, but has a solid regular client base. He is usually booked all week, with only one or two available appointments every week.

A regular client of Brandon's, named Stan, comes in for his weekly massage appointment. The massage is the same massage Brandon always does for Stan, working on all his areas of concern, paying extra attention to his hamstrings because he runs marathons and his thighs tighten up quite a bit during training. He even lets Brandon know he is running a marathon later that week! The session ends, and Stan leaves as happy as ever, feeling great.

Brandon works Tuesday through Saturday. It is now Saturday evening, and Brandon has just finished his last appointment for the week. To help himself relax, Brandon walks to a hole in the wall bar a couple blocks from his massage establishment. He takes a seat at the bar and orders a brewski. He looks to his right, and sees Stan sitting further down the bar with a couple friends.

Brandon grabs his beer and walks over to Stan, greeting him warmly. They shake hands, and Stan introduces Brandon to his friends. After greeting Stan's friends, Brandon turns to Stan and asks about the marathon Stan had just run. Stan tells him he finished in about three hours. Brandon asks how Stan's hamstrings are feeling, and if massage helped him feel better while running. Stan claims the massage did help.

What did Brandon do wrong?

Crossed confidentiality boundaries

3. Johnny works in a chiropractic office as the only massage therapist on staff. He's been working here for over a year, and really enjoys the work. It's a steady job and pays well, and he really enjoys the clientele he gets to work with.

Johnny greets his next client with a very professional demeanor, shaking the client's hand and introducing himself. He brings the client back to the massage room, performs the pre-massage interview and assessment, and instructs the client how he'd like the client on the table. He leaves the room and the client gets on the table as instructed.

Johnny enters the room and begins the massage. While the client is prone, Johnny works on the back. The client enjoys the work on the back, as the client does a lot of manual labor and is constantly lifting heavy objects.

The client seems to be experiencing a small amount of discomfort whenever Johnny massages one specific area in the low back. Johnny asks if the client is all right, and the client says yes, just that it's a little uncomfortable in the area. The client states it feels as if a bone is out of place and needs to be popped back in.

Johnny thinks about this for a second, and remembers watching his boss perform spinal manipulation. Johnny offers to pop the client's back, thinking this could help alleviate the client's pain. The client agrees, and Johnny pushes on the client's back, trying to force the back to pop. He succeeds, and the back does pop. The client thanks Johnny for helping him with his pain. Johnny resumes the massage to completion.

past scope of practice

What did Johnny do wrong?

4. Steph is a massage therapist working for a mountain resort. It is winter time, so it is extremely busy, and the ski slopes are packed. Steph sees many different clients, most of whom she never gets the opportunity to massage again.

A client comes in for a massage scheduled with Steph. Steph greets the client as usual and brings the client back to her massage room. Steph begins the massage, and the client seems to be enjoying it.

During the course of the massage, the client and Steph begin chatting. The client tells Steph that she is in town to ski, but forgot her ski boots at home, and does not want to buy a brand new pair just for this one trip. Steph remembers, she has a couple used pairs of ski boots she never uses any more that she'd be willing to part with. Steph offers to sell the client her used ski boots. The client becomes excited and agrees to buy the boots.

After the session ends, the client and Steph make arrangements to meet at the resort's coffee shop to make the transaction. Later that day they meet at the coffee shop, and the client pays Steph for her used ski boots.

selling items not relevant to massage

What did Steph do wrong?

5. Amber, a massage therapist of six years, has built up a regular clientele base and typically sees the same people at least once every two weeks or so. There is one client in particular she enjoys working on, named James.

James is a good looking man, only a couple years older than Amber. Their personalities mesh, they always have great conversations when he comes in for a massage, and James never misses an appointment. They get along so well, in fact, Amber wonders what might happen if she asks James out on a date.

James comes in for his weekly appointment. Amber has been thinking about James a lot lately, and becomes flustered when she sees him. She brings him in to the massage room, he gets on the table, and the session begins.

The massage is perfectly professional, with no boundaries being crossed by either party. The conversation is delightful as usual. After the massage, Amber meets James outside the massage room with his standard cup of water. James pays for the massage, and books another appointment in one week.

Nervous, Amber stops James before he walks out the door. She states that they've been working with each other for quite a while and have really gotten to know one other well. She continues, asking James if he'd be interested in going out to dinner with her later that week. James smiles and agrees, and they set up a date.

What did Amber do wrong?

past prof. boundaries

6. Jonah has just been hired as a massage therapist at a local membership-based massage establishment. It is his first massage job, and he's excited to begin his career.

Jonah meets all of his fellow co-workers, and feels right at home at his job. Anxiously, he walks to the waiting area and greets his client. He brings his client to the massage room, instructs the client on how he'd like them on the table, then he leaves. The client gets on the table.

Jonah forgets that he left his massage oil and holster in the break room. He walks down the hall to the employee break room, opens the door, and spots a fellow male co-worker looking in a female co-worker's purse. His co-worker looks up, sees Jonah, and immediately looks away from the purse. He makes quick small talk with Jonah, then leaves the break room, all without Jonah taking his eyes off of him. Jonah grabs his massage oil and holster and leaves the break room, heading back to perform his first massage.

Jonah suspects his co-worker of trying to steal from their other co-workers. *must report to supervisor*

What should Jonah do?

7. Charlie is performing a massage on a female client he's never met before. She seems normal, and seems to receive massage quite often. The client complains to Charlie of pain in her low back and glute area.

During the massage, Charlie performs massage on the client, making sure to work on her lower back. The client states that Charlie can work lower, but Charlie states he is already working at the edge of the sheet and cannot work any lower than this.

In an effort to get Charlie to work lower, the client pulls the sheet down further, exposing more of her lower back, but also her underwear.

What should Charlie do? *recover underwear to enforce boundary*

8. Sasha brings a client in for a massage at the local day spa she works at. She has never met the man before, but he seems pleasant.

She begins the massage, working on his back. While working on the trapezius, the client begins making moaning sounds. This is a little strange to Sasha, but nothing she hasn't heard before. Suddenly, she feels the client's hand touch her thigh, and move up towards her buttocks.

What should Sasha do? *reprimand say inappropriate end session*

Answer Key on Page 273

Massage Therapy Practice Exam

1. Essential oil commonly used to aid in treatment of insomnia and chronic fatigue syndrome
A. Eucalyptus
B. Sweet orange
C. Lavender
D. Rosemary

2. A massage table that is able to be folded and transported easily from one location to another
A. Hydraulic
B. Adjustable
C. Pressurized
D. Portable

3. Counter-transference
A. The client viewing a massage therapist as a significant person in their early life
B. The massage therapist bringing their own unresolved issues into the therapeutic relationship
C. Keeping a client's information private and protected
D. Relocating from one office to another

4. A client performing an action with the help of the massage therapist is an example of which joint movement
A. Active
B. Resistive
C. Passive
D. Assistive

5. Stoppage of a range of motion due to muscle and other soft tissues
A. Soft end feel
B. Hard end feel
C. Empty end feel
D. Nervous end feel

6. Gentle rhythmic massage designed to increase lymph circulation, developed by Emil Vodder
A. Lymphatic drainage
B. Swedish massage
C. Sports massage
D. Orthobionomy

7. Lomi Lomi, Craniosacral Therapy, and Rolfing are all forms of
A. Energy techniques
B. Movement techniques
C. Manipulative techniques
D. Kinesiology techniques

8. A massage room should contain all of the following except
A. A music source
B. A bathroom
C. Subdued lighting
D. Comfortable temperature

9. Stance in which the feet run perpendicular to the massage table
A. Bow
B. Archer
C. Horse
D. Swimmer

10. Petrissage
A. Light gliding strokes towards the heart, used to increase circulation and apply lubricant
B. Strokes that move across tissue, used to break up adhesions
C. Kneading strokes, used to release adhesions and increase circulation
D. Percussion strokes, used to stimulate muscle spindle cells

11. Universal precautions should be followed with
A. Clients with allergies
B. Only clients with contagious conditions
C. Every client
D. Clients with no previous medical conditions

12. Questions asked in a pre-massage interview should be
A. Forced
B. Open-ended
C. Abrupt
D. Closed-ended

13. The "A" of "SOAP" stands for
A. Alleviate
B. Assessment
C. Arrangement
D. Alignment

14. A sole proprietorship is a business that has how many owners
A. More than ten
B. Two
C. Four
D. One

15. The most common substance used in body scrubs
A. Salt
B. Sugar
C. Ground coffee
D. Powdered milk

16. A certification is obtained via
A. Passing a jurisprudence exam
B. Paying a fee to a jurisdiction licensing agency
C. Obtaining liability insurance to protect against malpractice
D. Completing educational requirements in a school setting

17. Structural realignment therapy working on muscles and fascia over the course of ten sessions
A. Rolfing
B. Trager method
C. Feldenkrais
D. Myofascial release

18. Massage results in increased production of
A. Cortisol
B. Blood cells
C. Pathogens
D. Water retention

19. Information the client shares about themselves is documented under which section of SOAP notes
A. Objective
B. Subjective
C. Assessment
D. Plan

20. Percussion strokes, used to loosen phlegm in the respiratory tract and activate muscle spindle cells
A. Petrissage
B. Effleurage
C. Friction
D. Tapotement

21. Massage may have all of the following psychological effects except
A. Increased relaxation
B. Decreased stress
C. Increased stress
D. Increased energy

22. After a massage, the massage therapist notifies the client of stretches that the therapist thinks might help with a client's range-of-motion. This information would be documented under which section of SOAP notes
A. Subjective
B. Objective
C. Assessment
D. Plan

23. The primary goal of a massage performed after a sporting event is
A. Move metabolic waste out of tissues
B. Increase circulation
C. Stimulate muscle fibers
D. Break up adhesions between tissues

24. Technique used to treat adhesions found between fascia and muscles
A. Rolfing
B. Myofascial release
C. Deep tissue
D. Osteosymmetry

25. The primary goal of Swedish massage is to
A. Decrease the formation of adhesions between muscles
B. Increase the flow of blood and lymph, and promote relaxation
C. Loosen phlegm in the respiratory tract
D. Decrease sensation in a localized area

26. Business expenses include all of the following except
A. Massages
B. Advertising
C. Electricity
D. Credit card fees

27. Slightly bent knees, straight back, and limp wrists are all examples of
A. Proper massage modalities
B. Improper body mechanics
C. Proper body mechanics
D. Improper massage modalities

28. If a client is unable to withstand any amount of pressure during a massage, a treatment the therapist might recommend would be
A. Reiki
B. Rolfing
C. Myofascial release
D. Lymphatic drainage

29. A massage license from one jurisdiction being recognized as valid in another jurisdiction
A. Reciprocity
B. Certification
C. Liability
D. Malpractice

30. A bolster is placed between the legs and arms and under the head in which position
A. Slightly elevated
B. Supine
C. Prone
D. Side-lying

31. Swedish massage is based on the Western principals of
A. Anatomy and physiology
B. Energy
C. Life force
D. Chi

32. Stretch technique in which a muscle is stretched to resistance, followed by an isometric contraction by the client, then the muscle stretched further after the contraction
A. Active static stretch
B. Proprioceptive neuromuscular facilitation
C. Strain counter-strain
D. Myofascial release

33. A set of guiding moral principles is known as
A. Regulations
B. Scope of practice
C. Ethics
D. Reputation

34. If a Massage Therapist begins to feel sexual attraction towards a client, what should the Massage Therapist do
A. Act upon these urges
B. Do nothing
C. Tell the client
D. Recommend the client see another therapist

35. Goals are
A. Measurable or attainable accomplishments
B. A generalized statement about the purpose of a business
C. The theme of a business
D. Business plans detailing projected income

36. Technique primarily used to work on trigger points
A. Wringing
B. Ischemic compression
C. Cross-fiber friction
D. Myofascial release

37. Areas of the body in which caution is advised during massage of a pregnant client include all of the following except
(A) Face
B. Abdomen
C. Ankles
D. Lumbar

38. Massage stroke directed toward the heart used to increase circulation, transition between strokes, and apply massage lubricant
A. Friction
B. Petrissage
(C) Effleurage
D. Vibration

39. A pre-event sports massage requires the following kinds of strokes to be performed
A. Relaxing
(B) Invigorating
C. Slow
D. Sedative

40. An aura stroke is a massage stroke in which
A. The hands are pressed firmly into the body
B. The hands are touching the body very lightly
(C) The hands are held just above the body
D. The hands are placed on the body without substantial pressure

41. A resistive joint movement
A. Client moves the joint without the assistance of a massage therapist
B. A client moves the joint with the assistance of a massage therapist
(C) A client resists a movement being performed by a massage therapist
D. A massage therapist moves a client's joint without the help of the client

42. Essential oil commonly used to aid in relaxation of smooth muscles in the respiratory tract
(A) Eucalyptus
B. Lavender
C. Lemongrass
(D) Peppermint

43. Protection from malpractice lawsuits is gained by obtaining
A. Limited Liability Corporation
B. Massage certification
C. Licensure
(D) Professional liability insurance

44. With a client lying supine, a bolster should be placed
A. Between the legs and arms, and under the head
B. Under the ankles and neck
(C) Under the knees
D. Under the head only

45. Ability to perform services legally according to occupational standards and licensing
A. Certification
(B) Scope of practice
C. Reciprocity
D. Regulations

46. Gait analysis is observation and interpretation of a person's
(A) Walking pattern
B. Somatic holding pattern
C. Sitting pattern
D. Range of motion

47. Which of the following massage strokes is best in aiding lung decongestion
(A) Tapotement
B. Effleurage
C. Friction
D. Petrissage

48. A client demonstrating range of motion is an example of which joint movement
(A) Active
B. Assistive
C. Passive
D. Resistive

49. A 1099 should be filed quarterly by
A. S Corporations
B. Employees
C. Partnership Members
(D) Independent Contractors

50. A Massage Therapist solicits a product to a client not related to a massage session or treatment. This could be a violation of
(A) Ethics
B. Scope of Practice
C. Licensure
D. Reciprocity

Answer Key on Page 280

30

Medical Terminology

Medical Terminology can be divided into three primary components: Word Roots, Prefixes, and Suffixes.

The Word Root of a medical term is the primary structure involved. It gives us a starting point when breaking down a word. An example is the Word Root "hepat/o", which means "liver".

A Prefix is used to modify a Word Root. An example is "a-", which means "without". A pathology that uses "a-" is "arrhythmia", which means "without rhythm".

A Suffix is used to add description to, or alter, a Word Root. An example is "-itis", which means "inflammation". A pathology that uses "-itis" is "hepatitis". As stated before, the word root "hepat/o" means liver. If we attach "-itis", it becomes "inflammation of the liver".

Many medical terms, prefixes, suffixes, and word roots, have the same meaning. The reason for different terms having the same meaning can be traced back to the origin languages. Modern medical terminology originated in both Latin and Greek, with the majority of words being Greek. When people like Celsus, a Roman physician, began creating medical terminology, they often used Greek terms, but conformed them to be Latin in origin. This is the reason for many terms sharing the same definition.

Medical Terminology

Cardiovascular Word Roots

angi/o:	vessel
aort/o:	aorta
arteriol/o:	arteriole
arteri/o:	artery
ather/o:	fatty plaque
atri/o:	atrium
bas/o:	alkaline
cardi/o:	heart
chrom/o:	color
eosin/o:	rose colored
granul/o:	granule
hemangi/o:	blood vessel
hem/o:	blood
kary/o:	nucleus
leuk/o:	white
lymph/o:	lymph
morph/o:	form
myel/o:	canal
nucle/o:	nucleus
phag/o:	eat
phleb/o:	vein
poikil/o:	irregular
reticul/o:	mesh
scler/o:	hard
sider/o:	iron
sphygm/o:	pulse
thromb/o:	clot
vascul/o:	vessel
ven/o:	vein
ventricul/o:	ventricle

Digestive Word Roots

append/o:	appendix
appendic/o:	appendix
bucc/o:	cheek
cheil/o:	lip
chol/e:	bile
cholangi/o:	bile vessel
cholecyst/o:	gallbladder
choledoch/o:	bile duct
col/o:	large intestine
colon/o:	large intestine
dont/o:	teeth
duoden/o:	duodenum
enter/o:	small intestine
esophag/o:	esophagus
gastr/o:	stomach
gingiv/o:	gums
gloss/o:	tongue
hepat/o:	live
ile/o:	rleum
jejun/o:	jejunum
labi/o:	lip
lingu/o:	tongue
odont/o:	teeth
or/o:	mouth
pancreat/o:	pancreas
pharyng/o:	pharynx
proct/o:	anus
pylor/o:	pylorus
rect/o:	rectum

sial/o.	saliva
sigmoid/o:	sigmoid colon
stomat/o:	mouth

Endocrine Word Roots

aden/o:	gland
adren/o:	adrenal glands
adrenal/o:	adrenal glands
calc/o:	calcium
gluc/o:	sugar
glyc/o:	sugar
gonad/o:	gonads
home/o:	same
kal/i:	potassium
pancreat/o:	pancreas
thym/o:	thymus gland
thyr/o:	thyroid
thyroid/o:	thyroid
toxic/o:	poison
thalam/o:	thalamus

Integumentary Word Roots

adip/o:	fat
albin/o:	white
carcin/o:	cancer
cirrh/o:	yellow
cutane/o:	skin
cyan/o:	blue
derm/o:	skin
dermat/o:	skin
erythem/o:	red
erythemat/o:	red
erythr/o:	red
hidr/o:	sweat
histi/o:	tissue
hist/o:	tissue
ichthy/o:	scaly
jaund/o:	yellow
kerat/o:	hard
leuk/o:	white
lip/o:	fat
melan/o:	black
myc/o:	fungi
onych/o:	nail
pil/o:	hair
scler/o:	hard
seb/o:	sebum
squam/o:	scale
sudor/o:	sweat
trich/o:	hair
ungu/o:	nail
xanth/o:	yellow
xer/o:	dry

Lymphatic Word Roots

aden/o:	gland
adenoid/o:	adenoids
immun/o:	immune
leuk/o:	white
lymph/o:	lymph
lymphaden/o:	lymph gland

lymphangi/o:	lymph vessel
myel/o:	canal
phag/o:	eat
splen/o:	spleen
thym /o:	thymus
tonsill/o:	tonsils

Muscular Word Roots

adhes/o:	stick to
aponeur/o:	aponeurosis
duct/o:	carry
erg/o:	work
fasci/o:	fascia
fibr/o:	fiber
fibros/o:	fiber
flex/o:	bend
is/o:	same
kinesi/o:	movement
lei/o:	smooth
lev/o:	lift
levat/o:	lift
metr/o:	length
quadr/i:	four
quadr/o:	four
rect/o:	straight
rhabd/o:	rod-shaped
ten/o:	tendon
tend/o:	tendon
tendin/o:	tendon
tens/o:	strain
ton/o:	tension
tort/i :	twisted

Nervous Word Roots

astr/o:	star
ax/o:	axon
cephal/o:	head
cerebell/o:	cerebellum
clon/o:	clonus
cortic/o:	cortex
crani/o:	skull
dendr/o:	tree
dur/o:	dura mater
encephal/o:	brain
esthesi/o:	sensation
gangli/o:	ganglion
gli/o:	glue
kinesi/o:	movement
lex/o:	word
lob/o:	lobe
medull/o:	medulla
mening/o:	meninges
ment/o:	mind
mot/o:	move
myel/o:	canal
narc/o:	stupor
neur/o:	nerve
olig/o:	few
phas/o:	speech
phren/o:	mind
psych/o:	mind
spin/o:	spine

synapt/o:	point of contact
tax/o:	order
thalam/o:	thalamus
thec/o:	sheath

Reproductive Word Roots

amni/o:	amnion
andr/o:	male
cervic/o:	neck
colp/o:	vagina
vagin/o:	vagina
embry/o:	embryo
epididym/o:	epididymis
episi/o:	vulva
fet/o:	fetus
galact/o:	milk
genti/o:	genitalia
gynec/o:	woman
hyster/o:	uterus
hymen/o:	hymen
lact/o:	milk
leiomy/o:	smooth muscle
mamm/o:	breast
mast/o:	breast
men/o:	menstruation
metr/o:	uterus
nat/o:	birth
o/o:	egg
oophor/o:	ovary
orch/o:	testicle
ovari/o:	ovary
pen/o:	penis
perine/o:	perineum
prostat/o:	prostate
salping/o:	fallopian tube
sperm/o:	sperm
spermat/o:	sperm
test/o:	testicle
uter/o:	uterus
vagin/o:	vagina
vas/o:	vessel
vesicul/o:	seminal vesicle
vulv/o:	vulva

Respiratory Word Roots

alveol/o:	alveolus
anthrac/o:	black
atel/o:	incomplete
bronch/o:	bronchus
bronchi/o:	bronchus
coni/o:	dust
cyan/o:	blue
embol/o:	plug
emphys/o:	inflate
epiglott/o:	epiglottis
hem/o:	blood
laryng/o:	larynx
lob/o:	lobe
muc/o:	mucous
nas/o:	nose
or/o:	mouth
orth/o:	straight
ox/o:	oxygen
pector/o:	chest
pharyng/o:	pharynx

phon/o:	sound
phren/o:	diaphragm
pleur/o:	pleura
pneum/o:	lung
pneumon/o:	lung
pulm/o:	lung
rhin/o:	nose
sinus/o:	sinus
spir/o:	breathe
steth/o:	chest
thorac/o:	chest
trache/o:	trachea

Skeletal Word Roots

acr/o:	extremity
acromi/o:	acromion
ankyl/o:	crooked
arthr/o:	joint
brachi/o:	arm
calcane/o:	calcaneus
carp/o:	carpals
cephal/o:	head
cervic/o:	neck
chondr/o:	cartilage
clavicul/o:	clavicle
cleid/o:	clavicle
condyl/o:	condyle
cost/o:	ribs
crani/o:	cranium
dactyl/o:	fingers/toes
femor/o:	femur
fibul/o:	fibula
humer/o:	humerus
ili/o:	ilium
ischi/o:	ischium
kyph/o:	hill
lamin/o:	lamina
lord/o:	curve
metacarp/o:	metacarpals
metatars/o:	metatarsals
myel/o:	canal
orth/o:	straight
oste/o:	bone
patell/o:	patella
ped/i:	foot
pelv/i:	pelvis
pelv/o:	pelvis
phalang/o:	phalanges
pod/o:	foot
pub/o:	pubis
rachi/o:	spine
radi/o:	radius
sacr/o:	sacrum
scapul/o:	scapula
scoli/o:	crooked
spondyl/o:	vertebrae
synov/o:	synovium
tal/o:	talus
tars/o:	tarsals
thorac/o:	chest
uln/o:	ulna
vertebr/o:	vertebrae

Urinary Word Roots

| albumin/o: | albumin |

azot/o:	nitrogenous
cyst/o:	bladder
glomerul/o:	glomerulus
kal/i:	potassium
ket/o:	ketone bodies
meat/o:	opening
nephr/o:	kidney
pyel/o:	renal pelvis
ren/o:	kidney
trigon/o:	trigone
ur/o:	urine
ureter/o:	ureter
urethr/o:	urethra
urin/o:	urine
vesic/o:	bladder

Oncology Word Roots

aden/o:	gland
blast/o:	germ cell
carcin/o:	cancer
cauter/o:	burn
chem/o:	chemical
cry/o:	cold
hist/o:	tissue
immun/o:	immunity
leiomy/o:	smooth muscle
leuk/o:	white
mut/a:	genetic change
myel/o:	canal
onc/o:	tumor
rhabdomy/o:	skeletal muscle
sarc/o:	connective tissue

Miscellaneous Word Roots

aur/i:	ear
bi/o:	life
burs/o:	bursa
cerat/o:	horn
chir/o:	hand
corac/o:	crow-like
coron/o:	crown
dextr/o:	right
dors/o:	back
dynam/o:	power
ect/o:	outside
faci/o:	face
glauc/o:	gray
hydr/o:	water
irid/o:	iris
kerat/o:	cornea
lacrim/o:	tear
lapar/o:	abdominal wall
myring/o:	eardrum
omphal/o:	navel
opthalam/o:	eye
phot/o:	light
py/o:	pus
pyr/o:	heat
therm/o:	heat
tympan/o:	eardrum
viscer/o:	internal organs
zo/o:	animal
zym/o:	fermentation

Prefixes

a-:	without
ab-:	away
ad-:	towards
af-:	towards
allo-:	other
an-:	without
ana-:	against
aniso-:	unequal
ante-:	before
anti-:	against
auto-:	self
bi	two
brady-:	slow
cine-:	movement
circum-:	around
contra-:	against
de-:	cessation
di-:	double
dia-:	through
dipl-:	double
dys-:	difficult
ec-:	out
echo-:	repeated sound
ecto-:	outside
ef-:	away
en-:	within
end-:	within
endo-:	within
epi-:	above
eso-:	inward
eu-:	good
ex-:	outside
exo-:	outside
extra-:	outside
hemi-:	half
hetero-:	different
homo-:	same
hyper-:	excessive
hypo-:	below
im-:	not
in-:	in
infra-:	below
inter-:	between
intra-:	inside
iso-:	same
macro-:	large
mal-:	bad
meso-:	middle
meta-:	change
micro-:	small
mono-:	one
multi-:	many
neo-:	new
nulli-:	none
oxy-:	sharp
pan-:	all
para-:	beside
per-:	through
peri-:	around
poly-:	many
post-:	after
pre-:	before
primi-:	first
pro-:	before
pseudo-:	false
quadri-:	four
retro-:	behind
semi-:	half
sub-:	under
super-:	above
supra-:	above
sym-:	together
syn-:	together
tachy-.	rapid
trans-:	through
tri-:	three
ultra-:	excessive
uni-:	one

Suffixes

-ac:	referring to
-acusis:	hearing
-al:	referring to
-algia:	pain
-ar:	referring to
-ary:	referring to
-ate:	form of
-ation:	process
-asthenia:	weakness
-blast:	germ cell
-capnia:	carbon dioxide
-cele:	hernia
-centesis:	puncture
-clasis:	break
-clast:	break
-crine:	secrete
-cusis:	hearing
-cyte:	cell
-desis:	binding
-derma:	skin
-duction:	bringing
-dynia:	pain
-eal:	referring to
-ectasis:	dilation
-ectomy:	removal
-edema:	swelling
-emesis:	vomiting
-emia:	blood
-esis:	condition
-esthesia:	sensation
-ferent:	to carry
-gen:	produce
-genesis:	produce
-globin:	protein
-gnosis:	knowing
-gram:	record
-graph:	recording
-graphy:	recording
-ia:	condition
-iasis:	abnormal condition
-iatry:	medicine
-ic:	referring to
-ical:	referring to
-ician:	specialist
-icle:	small
-ile:	referring to
-ine:	referring to
-ism:	condition
-ist:	specialist
-itis:	inflammation
-kinesia:	movement
-lalia:	speech
-lampsia:	shine
-lepsy:	seizure
-lith:	stone
-logist:	specializing in
-logy:	study of
-lucent:	clear
-lysis:	dissolve
-malacia:	soften
-mania:	frenzy
-megaly:	enlargement
-meter:	measuring tool
-metry:	measuring
-oid:	resembling
-oma:	tumor
-orexia:	appetite
-ory:	referring to
-ose:	referring to
-osis:	condition
-ous:	referring to
-paresis:	partial paralysis
-pathy:	disease
-penia:	deficiency
-pexy:	fixation
-phasia:	speech
-philia:	attraction
-phobia:	fear
-phoria:	feeling
-phylaxis:	protection
-physis:	growth
-plasia:	formation
-plasm:	growth
-plasty:	repair
-plegia:	paralysis
-pnea:	breathing
-poiesis:	formation
-porosis:	porous
-rrhage:	bursting forth
-rrhaphy:	suture
-rrhea:	discharge
-rrhexis:	rupture
-scope:	examining
-spasm:	twitch
-scopy:	visual exam
-stenosis:	narrowing
-stomy:	opening
-tension:	stretch
-thorax:	chest
-thymia:	emotion
-tic:	referring to
-tomy:	incision
-toxic:	poison
-tripsy:	crushing
-trophy:	nourishment
-uria:	urine
-y:	condition

General Medical Terms

A

ABC: References things to check before administering resuscitation efforts, Airway, Breathing, Circulation.
Abscess: A localized collection of pus.
Acute: Sudden, severe onset of a medical condition or disease.
Adhesion: Stuck together.
Ambulant/Ambulatory: The ability to walk.
Arrest: Cessation of bodily activity or function.
Aseptic: Sterile.
Autonomy: Being self-governed.

B

Benign: Does not spread.
Biopsy: Surgically removing tissue to examine microscopically.

C

Cachexia: Loss of appetite, weight, with muscle atrophy, usually associated with a serious medical condition such as cancer.
Carcinogen: A substance that may cause cancer.
Chronic: A disease or condition that persists over a period of time.

D

Diagnosis: Determination of the cause of a disease.

E

Edema: An excessive accumulation of fluid in an area.
Etiology: The study of the cause of a disease.
Excision: Surgically removing a structure or tissue.

F

Febrile: Presence of a fever.
Fistula: Location where an organ has developed an opening into another organ.

I

Idiopathic: An unknown cause of disease.
Incision: Cutting in to, typically with a scalpel.
Incontinence: Loss of control of the bladder and/or bowels.
In Situ: "In original place", commonly references cancer that is still in its place of origin, such as the epithelium of the skin.
Intravenous: Inside a vein, usually referencing injections.
Ischemia: Lack of blood flow to an area, which may result in necrosis.

M

Malaise: General unwell feeling or discomfort.
Malformation: A structure that is not formed properly.
Malignant: Spreading of cancer from one area to another.

N

Necrosis: Death of tissue.
Neopathy: A new disease

P

Pallor: General paleness.
Palsy: Paralysis.
Peptic: Referring to the stomach.
Phlegm: Secretions expelled from the lungs, also known as sputum.
Phobia: Fear of a person, thing, or situation.
Prognosis: Predicted outcome of a disease and recovery rate.
Pulse: Expansion of an artery as blood passes through.
Pyrogenic: Producing fever.

S

Sepsis: An infection.
Sign: Observable indications of an illness.
Sinus: A cavity.
Sputum: Secretions expelled from the lungs, also known as phlegm.
Symptom: A physical manifestation of an illness.
Syndrome: Groups of symptoms caused by a disease.

T

Transient: Short duration.
passing

Word Root Matching

R : necr/o

M : leuk/o

G : melan/o

J : cost/o

K : spondyl/o

L : gastr/o

P : derm/o

Q : chondr/o

C : adip/o

B : hepat/o

H : gloss/o

A : my/o

D : nephr/o kidney

E : brachi/o

T : cardi/o

S : erythr/o

I : encephal/o brain

F : hem/o

O : pneum/o

N : phleb/o

A. Muscle my —o

B. Liver hepa

C. Fat adi

D. Kidney nephr-o

E. Arm brachi

F. Blood hemo

G. Black melan

H. Tongue gloss

I. Brain encephal

J. Rib cost.

K. Spine spondy

L. Stomach gast

M. White leuk

N. Vein phleb

O. Lung pneum

P. Skin derm

Q. Cartilage chondr

R. Death necro

S. Red eryth

T. Heart cardi

Answer Key on Page 271

Prefix Matching

S. : auto-

C. : a-

P : hyper-

B. : meta-   *change*

O : mal-

A : syn-

J. : homeo-   (J) *same*

K. : hypo-

T. : inter-

G : dia-

D. : bi-

K : macro-   *homeo*

I. : brady-   *slow*

M : micro-

E. : anti-

H : iso-   (H) *equal*

N. : circum-

Q. : endo-   *within Q.*

L. : ad-

F. : epi-

A. Together

B. Change

C. Without

D. Two

E. Against

F. Above

G. Through

H. Equal

I. Slow

J. Same

K. Large

L. Towards

M. Small

N. Around

O. Bad

P. Excessive

Q. Inside

R. Below

S. Self

T. Between

Answer Key on Page 271

Suffix Matching

_M_ : -ectomy   _I_ : -plegia

_L_ : -blast   _C_ : -gen

_R_ : -pnea   _Q_ : -phagia

_S_ : -crine _endocrine_   _K_ : -globin

_O_ : -cision   _J_ : -clast

_A_ : -trophy   _D_ : -edema

_P_ : -algia   _F_ : -osis

_H_ : -stasis _standing still_   _T_ : -cyte

_B_ : -emia   _E_ : -oid

_G_ : -derma   _N_ : -lysis

A. Nourishment   K. Protein

B. Blood   L. Germ Cell — _clast_

C. Production   M. Removal

D. Swelling   N. Dissolve

E. Resembling   O. Cutting

F. Condition   P. Pain

G. Skin   Q. Eating

H. Standing Still   R. Breathing

I. Paralysis   S. Secrete

J. Break   T. Cell

Answer Key on Page 271

Break down the following diseases by their word roots, prefixes, and suffixes, giving the definition of each part in the blank spaces.

1. Arteriosclerosis: __arteries__ / __hardening__ / __condition__   _nephr Kidney_
2. Pyelonephritis: __renal pelvis__ / __Kidney__ / __inflammation__
3. Encephalitis: __brain__ / __inflammation__
4. Lymphedema: __lymph__ / __swelling__
5. Hyperthyroidism: __excessive__ / __thyroid__ / __condition__
6. Cholecystitis: __bile gall__ / __bladder__ / __inflammation__
7. Hepatitis: __liver__ / __inflammation__
8. Phlebitis: __vein__ / __inflam__

Build the name of the following diseases just using their definition. Remember, not every disease has a prefix or suffix!

1. Without blood: __an__ / __emia__
2. Fatty plaque hard condition: __athero__ / __scler__ / __osis__
3. Stomach inflammation: __gastr__ / __itis__
4. Black tumor: __mela__ / __noma__
5. Fiber muscle pain: __fibro__ / __my__ / __algia__
6. Bone joint inflammation: __osteo__ / __arthr__ / __itis__
7. Bladder inflammation: __cys__ / __itis__
8. Without breath: __a__ / __pnea__

Answer Key on Page 271

40

Anatomy and Physiology

Anatomy and Physiology is a large part of the MBLEx, with so many body systems and body parts that may be covered during the test.

In this section, we will discuss many subjects, covering a wide range of information.

Information covered in this section includes:

Homeostasis
Regional Anatomy
Body Planes
Body Regions
Cells
Tissue
The Cardiovascular System
The Digestive System
The Endocrine System
The Integumentary System
The Lymphatic System
The Muscular System
The Nervous System
The Reproductive System
The Respiratory System
The Skeletal System
The Urinary System

This information is followed by two assignments:

Anatomy and Physiology Matching
Anatomy and Physiology Crossword

The end of the section has a 50 question practice exam on Anatomy and Physiology. These questions ARE NOT the exact same questions you will see on the MBLEx. They are meant to test information that MAY be seen on the MBLEx.

While taking the practice exam, make sure to utilize your test-taking strategies(page 4) to optimize your test scores.

Anatomy and Physiology

Anatomy and Physiology, two extremely important aspects of the human body. **Anatomy**, simply put, is the study of the **structure** of the human body. All of the parts that make up the body constitute anatomy, from bones, muscles, and nerves, to cells, tendons, ligaments, and everything in between.

Physiology is the study of the **function** of the body. How do the parts of the body that make up the body's anatomy function? What do they do? This is physiology. Anatomy and physiology go hand-in-hand.

What are they
+ what do they do.

Homeostasis

Homeostasis is the existence and maintenance of a **constant internal environment.** The body's internal environment is constantly changing and responding to various stimuli. Examples of stimuli are temperature, hormones, diet, and the body's pH level. These stimuli that change the body's internal environment in some way are known as **homeostatic variables**. As the variables change, so too does the internal environment.

How does the body respond to these changes? Using **homeostatic mechanisms**, such as sweating and shivering. An example, when your body temperature gets too high, your body mechanically(physically) responds by sweating. Sweat evaporates off the skin, which cools the body down, lowering body temperature. When the body becomes too cold, the body responds by mechanically increasing the amount of twitching in the skeletal muscles. This increased twitching, which is normally undetectable, results in shivering, which produces body heat, raising body temperature.

The body's internal environment is constantly changing, and the body constantly adjusts certain aspects of itself to respond to these changes. If temperature is an example, the **set point**(normal range) of a body's temperature is 98.6 degrees Fahrenheit. The internal body temperature is never set right at 98.6 degrees. It is constantly fluctuating around it, maintaining a normal range of optimal body function.

Regional Anatomy

Regional Anatomy is the study of the structures of the body, broken down into different parts. When describing the position of one structure in the body in relation to another structure or structures, we use **directional terms**. An example, using the term "medial condyle" instead of just "condyle" lets us communicate effectively which condyle is being discussed.

The main directional terms are:
- **Superior**: Above.
- **Inferior**: Below.
- **Anterior**: Front.
- **Posterior**: Back.
- **Proximal**: Closer to the midline.
- **Distal**: Further from the midline.
- **Medial**: Middle.
- **Lateral**: Side.
- **Deep**: More internal.
- **Superficial**: Towards the surface.

Body Planes

Body planes are important for viewing structures from different aspects. These can be used when doing simple visual assessment, or in instances such as surgery or cadaver dissection.

There are four main body planes: A **midsagittal**, or **median** plane, runs down the **midline** of the body, splitting the body into **equal left and right sides**. This is the only location for a midsagittal plane.

A **sagittal** plane also splits the body into left or right sides, but **not equally**. It can be located anywhere along the body except down the midline.

A **transverse**, or **horizontal** plane, splits the body into **superior and inferior** portions. It does not have to be at the waist. It can split the body into superior and inferior at any point along the body.

A **frontal**, or **coronal** plane, as the name suggests, splits the body into front and back, or **anterior and posterior**. If a person wanted to dissect the heart and make all four chambers visible, they would cut the heart into a frontal or coronal plane. See photo on page 49.

Body Regions

The body, as stated earlier, can be broken down into different parts, or regions. There are three main body regions: the **central** body region, the **upper limb**, and the **lower limb**.

The **central** body region contains all of the structures located in the center of the body: the **head**, the **neck**, and the **trunk**. Take away the arms and legs, and you're left with the central body region.

The **trunk** can be further divided into three regions: the **thorax**, or chest, the **abdomen**, and the **pelvis**. The thorax contains the heart, lungs, esophagus, thymus, and major blood vessels connecting to the heart. The abdomen contains the majority of our digestive organs, including the stomach, liver, gallbladder, pancreas, small intestine, and large intestine. It also contains the kidneys and ureters. The pelvis contains the urinary bladder, urethra, and reproductive organs.

The **upper limb** can be broken down into four regions: the **arm**, **forearm**, **wrist**, and **hand**. The arm contains the humerus. The forearm contains the radius and ulna. The wrist contains the carpals. The hand contains the metacarpals and phalanges.

The **lower limb** can also be broken down into four regions: the **thigh**, **leg**, **ankle**, and **foot**. The thigh contains the femur. The leg contains the tibia and fibula. The ankle contains the tarsals. The foot contains the metatarsals and phalanges.

Midsagittal Plane

Transverse/Horizontal Plane

Frontal/Coronal Plane

Cells

Cells are the functional **units** of all tissues. Cells are responsible for performing all essential life functions, from synthesizing nutrients to destroying pathogens and debris. Cells **divide** via a process known as **mitosis**. During mitosis, the cell splits from one single mother cell into two separate daughter cells. These daughter cells then divide further into daughter cells of their own, and the cycle repeats until enough cells are present to form a tissue.

Inside each cell are **organelles**, structures that help regulate function of the cell.

The **nucleus** regulates the **overall function** of the cell. Inside the nucleus is **DNA**(deoxyribonucleic acid), which is the building block for life. Also inside the nucleus is the **nucleolus**, which contains **RNA**(ribonucleic acid). RNA is vital in transmitting signals from DNA to ribosomes for protein synthesis.

Mitochondria are responsible for the production of **adenosine triphosphate(ATP)**, the molecule that provides **energy** to the body by transporting chemical energy to parts of the body that require it.

Golgi apparatus allows proteins and lipids to be bundled and **transported** within the cell itself.

The **smooth endoplasmic reticulum** is responsible for synthesizing **carbohydrates** and **lipids** for use in producing new cell membranes.

Lysosomes are responsible for **breaking down** several different substances inside the cell, including protein and waste products.

Ribosomes, which contain protein and RNA, are responsible for **synthesizing cell proteins**.

Cytoplasm is found inside the cell, and is a **gel-like substance**. It allows organelles, nutrients, and waste products to move throughout the cell.

Tissue

The body is constructed by smaller parts making bigger parts, until we have an organism. The organization of the body is: cells > tissues > organ > organ system > organism. A **tissue** is made of a group of **cells** with **similar function and structure**. When these cells, all formed roughly the same way, which perform the same action, come together, they form a tissue. There are **four** types of tissue in the human body: **epithelial**, **muscular**, **nervous**, and **connective**.

• **Epithelial** tissue forms most **glands**, the **digestive tract**, the **respiratory tract**, and the **epidermis**. Anywhere there is a mucous membrane, there is epithelium. Epithelial tissue is responsible for **protection**(the epidermis protects the body from pathogens and trauma), **secretion**(glands secrete substances, from hormones to mucous), and **absorption** of nutrients(the linings of the small intestine are made of epithelium, which allows nutrients to be absorbed into the blood stream). Epithelial tissue is also **avascular,** which means there is no direct blood supply to the tissue. This is what allows layers of the epidermis to be peeled away without any bleeding.

EPITHELIAL CELLS

Simple squamous

Simple cuboidal

Simple columnar

Ciliated columnar

• **Muscular** tissue creates **muscles**. There are three types of muscles: **skeletal** muscles, so named because they connect to the skeleton, **cardiac** muscles, which create the heart, and **smooth** muscles, which are abundant in several locations in the body.

Skeletal muscles, as the name implies, attach to the **skeleton**. Another name for skeletal muscle is "**striated**" muscle, due to its appearance under a microscope. These muscles are **voluntary**, meaning you can control them. When these muscles contract, they pull on the bones they attach to, which allows movement.

Skeletal muscles are **always in a state of twitching**, even if you can't feel it. It's this twitching, very fine contractions, that produces **body heat**. When body temperature drops, the skeletal muscles increase the amount of contraction, which produces high body temperature, with the twitching of the muscles becoming more apparent. This is what happens when you shiver!

Cardiac muscle is the muscle that makes the heart. Another name for cardiac muscle is "**branching**" muscle, due to its appearance under a microscope. Cardiac muscle is **involuntary**, meaning you can't control it. Cardiac muscle is powerful, shooting **blood** out of the heart with each contraction. The only function of cardiac muscle is to send blood from one place to another.

Muscle tissue

Cardiac muscle   Smooth muscle   Skeletal muscle

Smooth muscle is found in several locations throughout the body. Another name for smooth muscle is "**non-striated**" muscle, due to its appearance under a microscope. Smooth muscle is **involuntary**, meaning you can't control it. Smooth muscle, because it is found in several different regions of the body, has several different functions. Smooth muscle can be found in the **walls** of **hollow organs** such as the stomach and intestines. When these muscles contract, they force food through the digestive system, which is known as **peristalsis**.

Other locations smooth muscle can be found are in the skin, and in the eyes. In the skin, smooth muscle attaches to hair. When these muscles contract, they stand hair up, producing goosebumps. These muscles are known as the arrector pili muscles. In the eyes, smooth muscles help to dilate the iris and pupil.

• **Nervous** tissue forms the **brain**, **spinal cord**, and **nerves**. The primary cell of nervous tissue is known as a **neuron**. Neurons process nervous impulses, sending these impulses to other tissues, such as muscles, or between other neurons.

Neurons receive **action potentials** (electric impulses), which are brought into the cell by **dendrites**, branch-like projections coming off the cell body of the neuron. Once the nucleus processes the information coming into the cell, it sends the impulse out of the cell to its destination by way of the **axon**, a long projection coming off the cell body. The axons terminate at other neurons, or help innervate muscles.

Neuron Structure

CONNECTIVE TISSUES

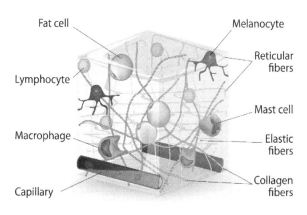

Fat cell
Melanocyte
Reticular fibers
Lymphocyte
Mast cell
Macrophage
Elastic fibers
Collagen fibers
Capillary

• **Connective** tissue is the most abundant form of tissue in the body. There are several different structures made by connective tissue, including **tendons**, **ligaments**, **fascia**, **bones**, **lymph**, **cartilage**, and **blood**. Connective tissue, as the name suggests, is responsible for **connecting** tissues. In addition to connecting tissues, it helps to **separate** tissues, as seen in serous membranes and cartilage.

Connective tissue contains two specific types of cells known as **blast** cells and **clast** cells. These cells play a very important role in the health of connective tissue. Blast cells are germ cells that are responsible for **building** connective tissue. Blast cells divide and build tissue until the structure is complete. Once the structure is complete, the blast cells mature, and stop dividing. Clast cells are responsible for **breaking down** tissue, which is very important in keeping the tissue healthy. If a person suffers a fracture, clast cells will enter the area and destroy the dead tissue, cleaning the area, which allows blast cells a clean surface to build new tissue on.

Blood is the most **abundant** form of connective tissue in the body. Blood is mainly a mode of **transportation** for blood cells, hormones, nutrients, and waste products. There are four parts of blood: **erythrocytes**, **leukocytes**, **thrombocytes**, and **plasma**.

Erythrocytes, also known as red blood cells, are responsible for **transporting oxygen** and **carbon dioxide** throughout the body. The cytoplasm of erythrocytes is made of a protein known as **hemoglobin**, which is primarily made of iron. Hemoglobin is what oxygen and carbon dioxide attach to. In the lungs, when the erythrocytes are exposed to the alveoli, carbon dioxide detaches from the erythrocytes, and oxygen then attaches in its place. This is how gas exchange occurs in erythrocytes.

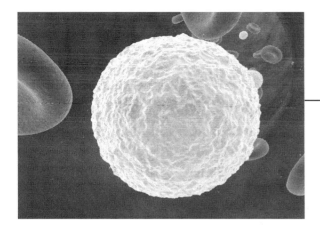

Leukocytes, also known as white blood cells, are the body's primary **defense** against **pathogens**. There are several different types of leukocytes, ranging from T-cells to basophils. These cells eat pathogens(such as bacteria), dead cells, and debris floating in the blood stream.

Thrombocytes, also known as **platelets**, have one function: to **clot the blood**. This is vitally important when a person is bleeding. If the blood does not clot, the person could continue bleeding until they lose too much blood.

Plasma is the **fluid** portion of blood. The majority of blood, around 56%, is made of plasma. Plasma is what allows all of the blood cells, hormones, nutrients, and waste to move throughout the body. Without plasma, these substances would go nowhere!

Serous Membranes

Serous membranes are forms of connective tissue that are used to **separate** organs from one another, **preventing friction**. They accomplish this by **surrounding** the organ or body cavity

Inside the thorax, there are two serous membranes: the **pericardium**, which surrounds the **heart**, and the **pleural** membranes, which surround the **lungs**. These membranes help protect these organs from injury.

Inside the abdomen and pelvis, there is one serous membrane: the **peritoneum**. This membrane keeps the organs inside the abdomen and pelvis from being injured, and provides a pathway for many blood vessels, lymph vessels, and nerves to travel.

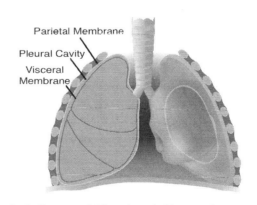

Parietal Membrane
Pleural Cavity
Visceral Membrane

Inside of a serous membrane is a thick fluid, known as **serous fluid**. This fluid helps the membranes absorb shock. Holding the fluid in place are two walls. The inner wall, which comes into contact with the organs, is known as the **visceral serous membrane**. The outer wall, which comes into contact with other structures such as bones or other organs, is known as the **parietal serous membrane**.

Test It Out!: To get a visual of a serous membrane, find a balloon, and fill it about halfway with some sort of oil, tying it off. Gently push a finger into the balloon, so it wraps around your finger. The part of the balloon that is pressed up against your finger would be the visceral serous membrane. Inside the balloon is the serous fluid. The outside of the balloon would be the parietal serous membrane. NOTE: Do this over a sink, in case the balloon accidentally breaks!

Cardiovascular System

The Cardiovascular System is one of the most important organ systems in the body, responsible for **transportation** of nutrients such as oxygen and hormones to tissues. It also allows for waste to be moved to areas of the body where it can be eliminated, such as the lungs, liver, and kidneys. Wastes include carbon dioxide and urea.

The primary organ of the Cardiovascular System is the **heart**. The heart, a large, powerful muscle, has one function: to **pump blood** throughout the body.

When blood first enters the heart, it is deoxygenated, and enters into the **right atrium**. It then passes through the **tricuspid valve**(which separates the right atrium from the right ventricle), into the **right ventricle**. The cardiac muscle in the right ventricle contracts, and it sends the deoxygenated blood out of the heart to the lungs through the **pulmonary arteries**. Despite carrying deoxygenated blood, these vessels are still called arteries because they carry blood away from the heart. After blood cycles through the lungs, exchanging oxygen and carbon dioxide, the blood returns back to the heart through the **pulmonary veins**. Again, despite carrying oxygenated blood, these vessels are called veins because they carry blood towards the heart. The blood re-enters the heart into the **left atrium**. It passes through the **bicuspid/mitral valve**(which separates the left atrium and left ventricle), into the **left ventricle**. An extremely powerful contraction occurs in the left ventricle, which shoots blood out of the heart to the rest of the body through the **aorta**, the **largest artery** in the body.

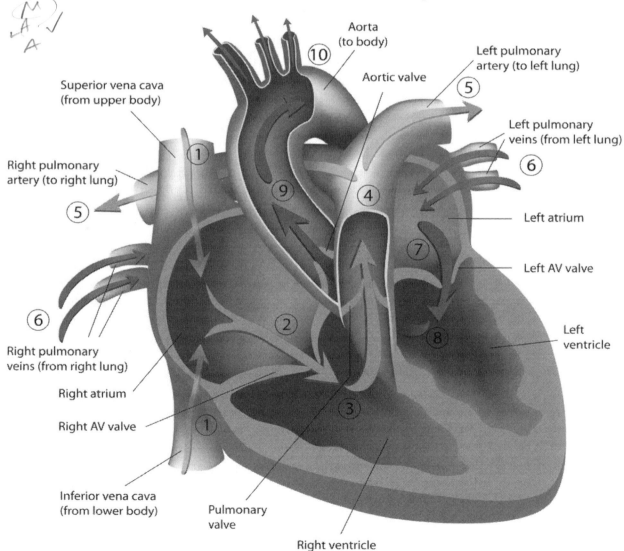

The pathway of blood flow through the heart

Blood vessels are the main mode of transportation for not only blood, but other substances, such as hormones. These substances are carried throughout the body in blood vessels. The largest types of blood vessels are known as **arteries**. Arteries primarily carry oxygenated blood away from the heart, to tissues. Arteries are the deepest blood vessels due to their size and importance. Tissues surrounding the arteries help to protect them from damage, which could result in severe bleeding and loss of oxygen.

Veins are blood vessels that primarily carry deoxygenated blood towards the heart, where it can replace carbon dioxide with oxygen. Veins are much more superficial than arteries, often visible under the skin, whereas most arteries cannot be seen.

Capillaries are microscopic arteries, and are where gas exchange takes place between blood vessels and tissues.

Major arteries and veins are often named after their location in the body, such as the brachial artery/vein(in the arm), femoral artery/vein(in the thigh), abdominal aorta(in the abdomen), etc.

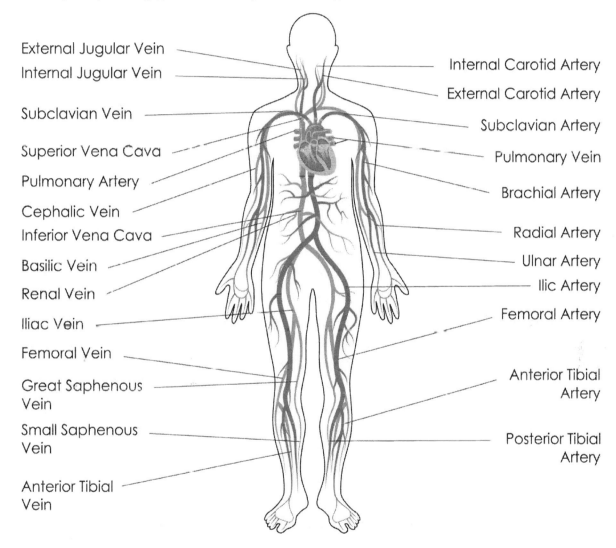

External Jugular Vein

Internal Jugular Vein

Subclavian Vein

Superior Vena Cava

Pulmonary Artery

Cephalic Vein

Inferior Vena Cava

Basilic Vein

Renal Vein

Iliac Vein

Femoral Vein

Great Saphenous Vein

Small Saphenous Vein

Anterior Tibial Vein

Internal Carotid Artery

External Carotid Artery

Subclavian Artery

Pulmonary Vein

Brachial Artery

Radial Artery

Ulnar Artery

Ilic Artery

Femoral Artery

Anterior Tibial Artery

Posterior Tibial Artery

*The **aorta** is the **largest artery** in the body!*

*The **great saphenous vein** is the **longest vein** in the body!*

Digestive System

The Digestive System has many structures, organs, and functions. It is one of the most important systems in the body, responsible for bringing nutrients **into** the body, **digestion** of food, **absorption** of nutrients into the body's tissues, and **elimination** of waste products.

Structures of the Digestive System include the **mouth, pharynx, esophagus, stomach, liver, gallbladder, pancreas, small intestine,** and **large intestine.**

Digestion

The **mouth**, also known as the **oral cavity**, is the first place digestion begins taking place. The **teeth** manually break down food by **chewing, or mastication.** The food mixes with **saliva**, which contains digestive enzymes such as **amylase**, that help to break down carbohydrates. The **tongue** assists with mastication by pressing food against the teeth. Once food has been properly chewed, it is swallowed.

After food is swallowed, it moves from the mouth into the **pharynx**, also known as the **throat**. The pharynx is simply a passage-way for food, water, and air on the way to their respective destinations. Food leaves the pharynx and enters the esophagus.

The **esophagus** is a long tube that runs from the pharynx inferiorly, passes through the diaphragm, and connects to the **stomach**. The esophagus, much like the pharynx, has one function: transporting food. The esophagus, and every hollow organ of the Digestive System, are lined with smooth muscle. When the smooth muscle rhythmically contracts, it forces food further along in the organ. This is known as **peristalsis**.

Once food reaches the **stomach**, both ends of the stomach close off, and the stomach begins **digesting** the food. Powerfully, it churns the food, breaking it down manually. Stomach acids like hydrochloric acid and pepsin mix with the food inside the stomach and further help to break down the food. Once food is properly digested, the stomach opens at the pylorus, the bottom of the stomach, and food exits the stomach and enters into the small intestine.

The **small intestine** is where the majority of **absorption** of nutrients occurs. **Accessory organs** produce substances that help aid the small intestine in digestion. These accessory organs are the liver, gallbladder, and pancreas.

The **liver**, the heaviest internal organ, mainly acts as a **blood detoxifier**. It filters harmful substances from the blood. However, it aids in digestion by producing **bile**, a yellowish substance that aids in the emulsification of fats. Connecting to the liver is the gallbladder. Once the liver produces bile, it empties the bile into the gallbladder, where it is stored until it is needed.

The **gallbladder** simply has one function: to **store bile** and empty bile into the small intestine through the bile duct, which connects to the duodenum, the first section of the small intestine.

The **pancreas** creates **pancreatic juice,** which aids in the digestion of proteins, lipids, and carbohydrates. These substances empty into the small intestine through the same path as bile, the bile duct.

Food moves from the stomach into the **small intestine**. The first section of the small intestine is known as the **duodenum**. The duodenum is the last section of the Digestive System that digestion of food takes place. Bile, glucagon, and insulin all mix with food in the duodenum and further break down substances. Peristalsis forces the food from the duodenum further into the small intestine, into the middle portion, known as the **jejunum**. The jejunum is where the majority of nutrient absorption takes place in the small intestine. As the food is forced through the small intestine, it moves into the final section, known as the **ileum**. Final absorption occurs in the ileum. Food moves through the ileum and into the large intestine.

The **large intestine** has two primary functions: **absorption** of **water**, and **elimination** of **waste**. As feces moves through the large intestine, water is absorbed. If too much water is absorbed, constipation may result. If not enough water is absorbed, diarrhea may result. The large intestine has four sections: the **ascending colon**, the **transverse colon**, the **descending colon**, and the **sigmoid colon**. As the feces leaves the sigmoid colon, it enters the rectum, where it is ready to be eliminated from the body.

Digestive System

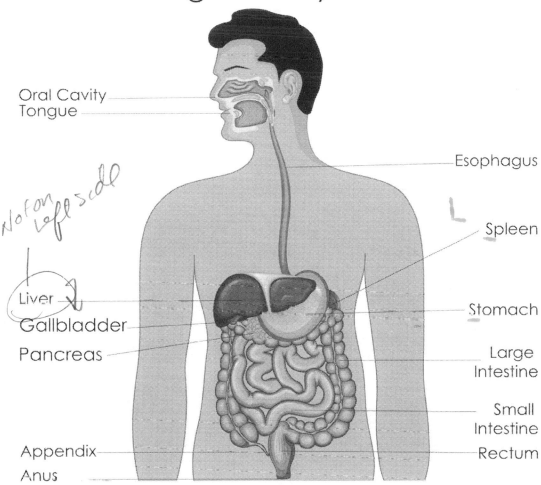

Oral Cavity
Tongue

Esophagus

Spleen

Liver
Gallbladder
Pancreas

Stomach

Large Intestine

Small Intestine

Appendix
Anus

Rectum

No for on left side (handwritten)

Sphincters

In the Digestive System, there are **ring-like** bands of **muscle** between digestive organs, known as **sphincters**. Sphincters function to allow food to enter into an organ, or to keep food from moving backwards.

There are four primary sphincters in the Digestive System:

The **esophageal** sphincter is located between the **pharynx** and the **esophagus**. It opens and allows food to move down into the esophagus.

The **cardiac** sphincter is located between the **esophagus** and the **stomach**. It is named after the region of the stomach it connects to, which is known as the cardia. When food enters the stomach, the cardiac sphincter closes, preventing food and stomach acid from ascending into the esophagus.

The **pyloric** sphincter is located between the **stomach** and the **small intestine**. It is named after the region of the stomach it connects to, which is known as the pylorus. When food enters the stomach, the pyloric sphincter closes, preventing food from leaving the stomach before digestion has taken place. When food has been properly digested, the pyloric sphincter opens, and food leaves the stomach and enters the small intestine.

The **ileocecal** sphincter is located between the **small intestine** and the **large intestine**. It is named after the parts of the two organs that come together, the ileum(small intestine) and cecum(large intestine).

secrete within

Endocrine System

The Endocrine System is responsible for coordinating specific activities of cells and tissues by releasing **hormones** into the body. Endocrine glands differ from exocrine glands in two specific ways: endocrine glands create and secrete hormones, while exocrine glands create and secrete things like sweat, saliva, and oil. Endocrine glands secrete hormones directly into the **blood stream**, while exocrine glands secrete their substances onto a **surface**(such as the surface of the mouth or skin).

Endocrine glands have many different functions that help regulate body function and homeostasis.

Glands

hats on kidneys

The **adrenal** glands, located atop the kidneys(*ad-: towards; renal: kidney*), secrete **epinephrine** and **norepinephrine**. These hormones help to elevate blood pressure, heart rate, and blood sugar. They are considered stress hormones, and are secreted when the body is under stress, or in the sympathetic nervous response.

The **hypothalamus** produces **dopamine**, an important hormone that increases blood pressure and heart rate. It is considered the reward center hormone. If you win at a game or contest, your hypothalamus may release dopamine, which gives a sensation of excitement.

The **ovaries** are the female gonads. They create **estrogen** and **progesterone**, two hormones important to female development and bone growth.

Pancreatic Islets are the parts of the pancreas that create **glucagon**, which increases blood sugar levels, and **insulin**, which decreases blood sugar levels. Glucagon is created by **alpha cells**, and insulin is created by **beta cells**.

Gabi

The **pineal** gland is responsible for the production of **melatonin**, the hormone that regulates the body's wake/sleep cycle.

The Endocrine System

Pineal gland — Hypothalamus
Pituitary gland
Thyroid gland
Thymus
Pancreas
Adrenal glands
Testes (male)
Ovaries (female)

The **pituitary** gland, which many consider the "master gland", secretes **growth hormone**, which regulates the amount of growth a person may experience. It also secretes **prolactin**, which stimulates milk production, and **follicle- stimulating hormone**, which influences production of female egg cells and male sperm cells.

The **testes** are the male gonads. The testes secrete **testosterone**, the primary male hormone, responsible for increasing bone and muscle mass.

The **thyroid** is a gland in the neck that produces **calcitonin**, which aids in decreasing the levels of calcium in the blood stream. Too much calcium in the blood may weaken the bones and cause kidney stones.

Integumentary System

The Integumentary System is the body's first line of defense against pathogens and trauma. Its primary function is to protect the body. It also secretes substances, may absorb certain substances, and even eliminates waste.

Skin

The **skin**, which is the body's largest organ, is the main structure of the Integumentary System. The skin **protects** the body by creating a thick barrier that prevents pathogens from entering, and helps to cushion the body from blunt trauma.

Aiding the skin in protection are the **nails**. Finger and toe nails are made of **keratin**, the same cells that create thick layers in the skin called calluses. The nails prevent damage to the distal phalanges.

Hair also aids in protection, but in a different way. Hair is used to regulate temperature. When body temperature drops, smooth muscle that attaches to each hair, known as **arrector pili**, contract, forcing the hair to stand up. This creates an insulating layer, which is meant to trap warmth underneath the hair, much like a blanket. This does little for humans, but is utilized by animals to retain heat in cold environments.

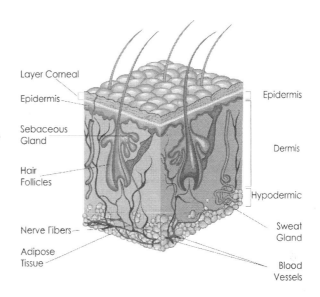

Glands

Inside the skin are glands, which also aid in protection. **Sudoriferous** glands emerge from deep in the skin to the surface directly through tubes. Sudoriferous glands create and secrete **sweat**. Sweat is mostly made of water, but may also contain salt and waste products such as ammonia. Sweat is used to lower body temperature by evaporating off the surface of the skin. The evaporation cools the skin, which helps lower the internal body temperature.

Sebaceous glands are glands that connect to hair, and produce **oil(sebum)**. Oil helps to protect the body from pathogens and debris in the air. Blockage of a sebaceous gland, however, may lead to a bacterial infection, and acne.

Sensory Receptors

Inside the skin, there are many types of receptors that detect certain sensations, relaying the information to the brain. Sensory receptors aren't exclusive to the skin, but there are an abundance of them in the skin.

Nociceptors are a type of sensory receptor that detects the sensation of **pain**. Pain, while unpleasant, is actually vital in protection of the body. The term "noci-" is Latin for "hurt".

 Easy to Remember: Nociceptors detect pain. Remember the old saying "No pain, No gain".

Meissner's Corpuscles are sensory receptors that are very superficial in the skin, and detect **light pressure**. Massage strokes such as effleurage and feather strokes are detected by Meissner's Corpuscles.

Pacinian Corpuscles are sensory receptors that are very deep in the skin, and detect **deep pressure**. Deep massage strokes, such as compression, are detected by Pacinian Corpuscles.

 Easy to Remember: Pacinian Corpuscles detect deep pressure. Match up "Paci" of Pacinian with "Paci" of Pacific Ocean. The Pacific Ocean is deep.

flows only to ♡

Lymphatic System

The Lymphatic System is vital in the body's **defense** against pathogens and disease. Not only are leukocytes abundant in lymph, but antibodies are created in the Lymphatic System. The Lymphatic System contains **lymph**, **lymph nodes**, **lymph vessels**, and **lymph organs**.

Lymph, the primary structure of the Lymphatic System, is a fluid composed of **water**, protein, leukocytes, urea, salts, and glucose. Lymph allows **transport** of all of these substances through the body, ultimately dumping into the blood stream. Lymph is made of **interstitial fluid**, fluid found between cells.

Lymph travels throughout the body through **lymph vessels**. Lymph vessels are similar to blood vessels, but only flow in one direction, towards the heart. Lymph vessels absorb foreign bodies and nutrients from tissues, bringing them into the lymph to be transported to the blood stream or lymph nodes. The **largest lymph vessel** in the body is located in the trunk. It is known as the **Thoracic Duct**. The Thoracic Duct drains lymph into the **left subclavian vein**, where it joins with blood.

Lymph nodes are large **masses** of lymphatic tissue. They are responsible for production of **antibodies**, and help destroy any foreign objects that enter the lymph. During an infection, lymph nodes may become tender and swollen.

The **thymus**, located in the chest, is responsible for production of **T-lymphocytes**, or T-cells. T-cells are vital in regulation of the body's immune system. If a person contracts HIV, the virus destroys the T-cells, which essentially disables the immune system.

The **spleen** is an organ of the Lymphatic System responsible for **destroying** dead or dying **red blood cells** from the blood stream, in addition to destroying pathogens and debris.

Spleen Recycles R Blood cells.

Cervical lymph nodes

Right jugular trunk

Right lymphatic duct

Right subclavian trunk

Right subclavian vein

Axillary lymph nodes

Left jugular trunk

Left subclavian trunk

Left subclavian vein

Thoracic duct

Cisterna chyli

Right lumbar trunk

Left lumbar trunk

Inguinal lymph nodes

Intestinal trunk

DID YOU KNOW?

The **Thoracic Duct** is the **largest lymph vessel** in the body!

Muscular System

Muscles have numerous actions in the body, primarily **producing body heat**, contracting to allow **movements**, and constricting **organs** and **blood vessels**.

Muscle Structure

Skeletal muscles are broken down into the following components:

- **Sarcomeres** are the functional units of skeletal muscle. When they shorten, the muscle contracts.

- **Actin** is part of a sarcomere, known as the **thin** filament. Actin is what myosin attaches to during a muscle contraction. Actin anchors to the **Z-Line** in a sarcomere.

- **Myosin** is part of a sarcomere, known as the **thick** filament. Myosin resembles a golf club head, and attaches to actin during a muscle contraction. The entire span of the thick filaments in one sarcomere is known as the **A-Band**.

- **Tropomyosin** is a protein that **covers** the attachment sites myosin attaches to actin on during a contraction. **Calcium ions** are responsible for removing the tropomyosin from the actin, allowing the myosin to attach to the actin and initiate a contraction.

Muscle contractions begin with **action potentials** sent from the brain. Action potentials terminate at the **neuromuscular junction**, releasing **acetylcholine(aCh)** into the synapse. This results in the aCh binding to certain receptors in the muscle fiber, which in turn allows sodium ions to enter the muscle fiber. The sodium ions come into contact with the sarcoplasmic reticulum, which causes a release of **calcium ions**. The calcium ions enter into the working unit of muscles, known as sarcomeres. A sarcomere contains thick filaments, known as myosin, and thin filaments, known as actin. When a muscle isn't in a state of contraction, the myosin and actin do not interact due to the presence of tropomyosin preventing myosin from attaching to actin. When the body wants to allow the muscle to contract, calcium ions bind to tropomyosin, causing them to reveal the attachment sites on the actin for the myosin. Once the tropomyosin is removed, the myosin attaches to the actin, pulling the Z-lines closer together. This causes the sarcomere to shorten. The shortening of all the sarcomeres in a muscle fiber result in the entire muscle contracting.

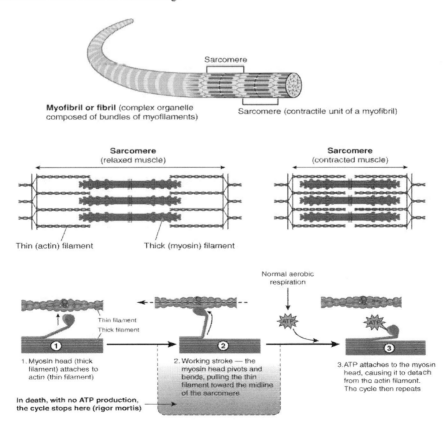

Myofibril or fibril (complex organelle composed of bundles of myofilaments)

Sarcomere (contractile unit of a myofibril)

Sarcomere
(relaxed muscle)

Sarcomere
(contracted muscle)

Thin (actin) filament   Thick (myosin) filament

Normal aerobic respiration

1. Myosin head (thick filament) attaches to actin (thin filament)

Thin filament
Thick filament

In death, with no ATP production, the cycle stops here (rigor mortis)

2. Working stroke — the myosin head pivots and bends, pulling the thin filament toward the midline of the sarcomere

3. ATP attaches to the myosin head, causing it to detach from the actin filament. The cycle then repeats

Muscle Shapes

Muscles have numerous different shapes. These include:

Circular: Circular muscles are arranged in a **circular** manner. Examples include orbicularis oris and orbicularis oculi.

Convergent: Convergent muscles are **spread out** on one end and **merge** together at another end. An example is pectoralis major.

Parallel: Parallel muscles have muscle fibers that all run in the **same direction**. Examples include sartorius and coracobrachialis.

Pennate: Pennate muscles have an appearance resembling a **feather**. These muscles can be **unipennate**(one feather), **bipennate**(two feathers), or **multipennate**(multiple feathers). Examples include flexor pollicis longus(unipennate), rectus femoris(bipennate), and deltoid(multipennate).

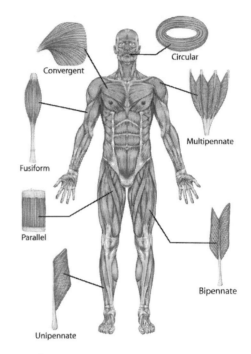

Muscle Contractions

When there is **tension** in a muscle, it is **contracting**. A muscle can contract without moving, though. There are four types of muscle contractions.

Isometric Contraction: Iso means "**same**" or "**equal**". Metric means "**length**". When an isometric contraction occurs, as the name implies, the length of the muscle **stays the same**, but tension in the muscle **changes**. An example: imagine trying to lift something that is too heavy for you to lift. The muscles required to lift the object increase in tension, but because the muscles aren't strong enough, the length of the muscles don't change.

Isotonic Contraction: Iso means "**same**" or "**equal**". Tonic means "**tension**". When an isotonic contraction occurs, as the name implies, the tension in the muscle **stays the same**, but the muscle length **changes**. There are two separate types of isotonic contractions:

Concentric Contraction

Eccentric Contraction

Concentric Contraction: When a concentric contraction occurs, several things take place. The tension in the muscle **initially increases** until the amount of tension required to perform the action is reached, then the tension **remains constant**. While the tension remains constant, the muscle **length decreases**. An example is performing a biceps curl.

Eccentric Contraction: When an eccentric contraction occurs, several things take place. The tension in the muscle **initially decreases** until the amount of tension required to perform the action is reached, then the tension **remains constant**. While the tension remains constant, the muscle length **increases**. An example is extending the elbow and lowering the weight down after the biceps curl in a concentric contraction.

 General Rule of Thumb: With concentric contractions, the muscle length decreases. With eccentric contractions, the muscle length increases.

Muscle Actions

Muscles perform numerous actions on the body, depending on which muscle is contracting. To see examples of all of these actions, refer to page 177. Muscle actions include the following:

Flexion: **Decreasing** the **angle** of a joint.

Extension: **Increasing** the **angle** of a joint.

Adduction: Moving a structure **towards** the **midline**.

Abduction: Moving a structure **away** from the **midline**.

Protraction: Moving a structure **anteriorly**.

Retraction: Moving a structure **posteriorly**.

Inversion: Turning the **sole** of the foot **in** towards the **midline**.

Eversion: Turning the **sole** of the foot **out** away from the **midline**.

Elevation: Moving a structure **superiorly**.

Depression: Moving a structure **inferiorly**.

Supination: Rotating the **palm** so it is facing **upwards**.

Pronation: Rotating the **palm** so it is facing **downwards**.

Rotation: **Turning** a structure around its **long axis**.

Circumduction: **Turning** a structure around the **circumference** of a joint.

Opposition: Moving structures in **opposite** directions.

Lateral Deviation: Moving a structure from **side-to-side**.

Plantarflexion: Pointing toes **down**.

Dorsiflexion: Pointing toes **up**.

DID YOU KNOW?

Davis's Law states that when going through periods of **unuse**, muscle and tendon strength will **decrease**!

When a muscle performs an action, other muscles associate with the muscle in different ways.

A **Prime Mover/Agonist** is the muscle that primarily performs a specific action. An example: when plantarflexion is performed, the **strongest** muscle performing it is the gastrocnemius. That means gastrocnemius is the prime mover/agonist.

A **Synergist** is the muscle that **assists** the prime mover/agonist in performing the action. Synergists are not as strong as prime movers. An example: when plantarflexion is performed, soleus contracts to allow more strength, assisting gastrocnemius in performing the action. That means soleus is the synergist.

An **Antagonist** is a muscle that performs the **opposite** action of the prime mover/agonist. Every muscle has an antagonist. An example: gastrocnemius contracts, performing plantarflexion. To return the foot to the starting position, gastrocnemius relaxes, and tibialis anterior contracts, which performs dorsiflexion. This makes tibialis anterior the antagonist to gastrocnemius.

A **Fixator** is a muscle that **stabilizes** an area or joint while an action is being performed. Stabilizing the joint prevents things like injury and allows optimal movement to occur. An example: Supraspinatus stabilizes the head of the humerus in the glenoid fossa, keeping the joint together during the numerous movements the glenohumeral joint performs.

Easy to Remember: Just think of it like this: Batman is the Agonist, the main character. Robin is the Synergist, the helper. The Joker is the Antagonist, who does the opposite of Batman. Alfred is the Fixator, who helps hold Batman together.

Nervous System

Nerves are structures in the **Nervous System**, made of nervous tissue. Nerves have many functions, from regulating vital functions within the body, to controlling muscles.

There are two divisions of the Nervous System: the **Central Nervous System**, and the **Peripheral Nervous System**. The Central Nervous System consists of the **brain** and **spinal cord**. The Central Nervous System is under involuntary control, responsible for interpretation of sensations and mental activity.

Nerve impulses are categorized as **sensory** or **motor**. Sensory impulses are detected by sensory receptors throughout the body(such as nociceptors, olfactory receptors, etc), and travel **to the brain** and/or spinal cord for processing. These impulses are called **afferent** impulses. In the case of reflexes, these impulses only reach the spinal cord, due to the immediacy of the required response. This is why reflexes are involuntary! Once the impulse reaches the brain and/or spinal cord, the brain and/or spinal cord interpret the sensation, and send a **motor** impulse back down the body to tell the body **how to respond** to the stimulus. These impulses are called **efferent** impulses.

Easy to Remember: Just remember "SAME". You can pair up "Sensory" with "Afferent", and "Motor" with "Efferent"!

DID YOU KNOW?

Hilton's Law states that a nerve innervating a muscle that crosses and takes action on a joint will also **innervate the joint** and skin of the joint!

Hilton's everywhere Surround y

Central Nervous System

The brain consists of three parts: the **cerebrum**, which is the largest part of the brain and split into left and right hemispheres, the **cerebellum**, located at the back and bottom of the brain, and the **brain stem**, which connects the brain to the spinal cord.

Each side of the **cerebrum** is divided into **lobes**, named after the bones atop them: **frontal** lobe(processes motivation, aggression, mood), **temporal** lobe(processes memory, hearing, and smell), **parietal** lobe(processes most sensory information), and **occipital** lobe(processes vision).

The **cerebellum** is responsible for regulation of **muscle tone**, **balance**, **coordination**, and control of **general body movements**.

The **brain stem**, which consists of(in descending order) the **midbrain**, the **pons**, and the **medulla oblongata**, controls the **vital functions** of the body, such as breathing, heart rate, coughing, sneezing, vomiting, and blood vessel diameter.

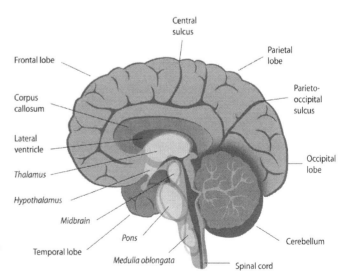

Median section of the brain

Peripheral Nervous System

The Peripheral Nervous System consists of the body's **nerves**. There are two divisions of the Peripheral Nervous System: **Cranial Nerves** and **Spinal Nerves**. Cranial Nerves, as the name suggests, emerge from the brain, and help to regulate the functions of the head and face. There are **twelve pairs** of Cranial Nerves, each numbered in Roman Numerals:

- Olfactory(I)
- Optic(II)
- Oculomotor(III)
- Trochlear(IV)
- Trigeminal(V)
- Abducens(VI)
- Facial(VII)
- Vestibulocochlear(VIII)
- Glossopharyngeal(IX)
- Vagus(X)
- Accessory(XI)
- Hypoglossal(XII)

Spinal Nerves are much more numerous than Cranial Nerves. There are **31 pairs** of Spinal Nerves. The Spinal Nerves, as the name suggests, emerge from the spinal cord, and are responsible for controlling skeletal muscle.

A bundle of Spinal Nerves that emerge from the spinal cord is known as a **Plexus**. There are three plexi in the body: **Cervical Plexus, Brachial Plexus, Lumbosacral Plexus**. The Cervical Plexus emerges from the spinal cord in the range of **C1-C4**. The primary nerve of the Cervical Plexus is known as the **Phrenic Nerve**.

The Phrenic Nerve descends inferiorly from the Cervical vertebrae and innervates(provides nervous stimulation to) the **Diaphragm**.

The Brachial Plexus emerges from the spinal cord at **C5-T1**. As the name suggests, the nerves of the Brachial Plexus move distally, controlling the muscles of the **upper limb**. There are five primary nerves of the Brachial Plexus:

- Radial
- Musculocutaneous
- Axillary
- Median
- Ulnar

The **Radial Nerve** is located on the posterior arm and forearm, and innervates the triceps brachii, anconeus, brachioradialis, and wrist extensors.

The **Musculocutaneous Nerve** is located in the anterior arm, and innervates the biceps brachii, brachialis, and coracobrachialis.

The **Axillary Nerve** is primarily located in the armpit, and innervates the teres minor and deltoid.

The **Median Nerve** is located in the anterior arm, forearm, and hand, and innervates the wrist flexors, and most muscles on the lateral side of the hand.

The **Ulnar Nerve** is located on the anterior arm, medial forearm, and medial hand, and innervates the wrist flexors and most muscles on the medial side of the hand.

The Lumbosacral Plexus, as the name suggests, emerges from the **entire span** of the lumbar and sacral vertebrae. The major nerves of the Lumbosacral Plexus include:

- Sciatic
- Femoral
- Obturator
- Tibial
- Common Peroneal
- Deep Peroneal
- Superficial Peroneal

The **Sciatic Nerve** is a large nerve located on the posterior thigh. The Sciatic Nerve is actually both the Tibial Nerve and the Common Peroneal Nerve bundled together. Once the Sciatic Nerve reaches the back of the knee, it branches off into two separate nerves. The Sciatic Nerve innervates the hamstring muscle group.

The **Femoral Nerve** is located on the anterior thigh, and innervates the quadriceps muscle group, iliacus, sartorius, and pectineus.

The **Obturator Nerve** is located on the medial portion of the thigh, and innervates the adductor muscle group.

The **Tibial Nerve**, after branching off the Sciatic nerve, runs down the posterior leg, and innervates the gastrocnemius, soleus, tibialis posterior, and plantaris.

The **Common Peroneal Nerve**, after branching off the Sciatic Nerve, actually branches off into two other nerves of its own: The Deep Peroneal and Superficial Peroneal Nerves.

The **Deep Peroneal Nerve** is located on the anterior leg, and innervates the tibialis anterior.

The **Superficial Peroneal Nerve** is located on the lateral portion of the leg, running along the fibula, and innervates the peroneus longus and peroneus brevis.

The Cranial Nerves

Olfactory nerve fibers (I)
Optic nerve (II)
Oculomotor nerve (III)
Trochlear nerve (IV)
Trigeminal nerve (V)
Abducens nerve (VI)
Facial nerve (VII)
Vestibulocochlear nerve (VIII)
Glossopharyngeal nerve (IX)
Vagus nerve (X)
Accessory nerve (XI)
Hypoglossal nerve (XII)

Pons
Medulla

The Cervical Plexus

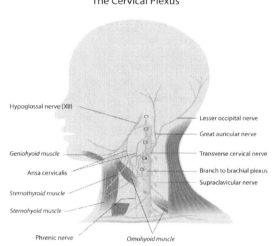

Hypoglossal nerve (XII)
Geniohyoid muscle
Ansa cervicalis
Sternothyroid muscle
Sternohyoid muscle
Phrenic nerve
Omohyoid muscle

C1
C2
C3
C4
C5

Lesser occipital nerve
Great auricular nerve
Transverse cervical nerve
Branch to brachial plexus
Supraclavicular nerve

The Brachial Plexus

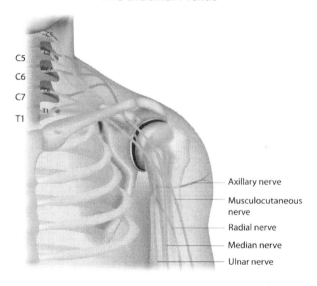

C5
C6
C7
T1

Axillary nerve
Musculocutaneous nerve
Radial nerve
Median nerve
Ulnar nerve

The Lumbar Plexus

Anterior divisions
Posterior divisions

Iliohypogastric nerve
Ilioinguinal nerve
Genitofemoral nerve
Lateral femoral cutaneous nerve
Saphenous nerve
Obturator nerve
Femoral nerve

T12
L1
L2
L3
L4
L5

Autonomic Nervous System

The autonomic nervous system helps to regulate **homeostasis** by release of hormones, controlling heart rate, breathing rate, and other bodily functions. There are two divisions of the autonomic nervous system: the **Sympathetic Response**, and the **Parasympathetic Response**.

The Sympathetic Response is also known as "**fight-or-flight**". When the body is in a state of **stress**, the Sympathetic Response helps the body respond by releasing **norepinephrine** into the blood stream, which increases heart rate and blood sugar. The digestive organs will also shut down, and blood will be pulled from these organs and supplied to the muscles for use.

The Parasympathetic Response is also known as "**rest-and-digest**". When the body is in a state of **relaxation**, the Parasympathetic Response helps the body to calm itself. It decreases the body's heart rate, and increases blood flow to the digestive organs to increase **peristalsis**. The Parasympathetic Response, decreasing heart rate, and peristalsis are all controlled by Cranial Nerve X, the **Vagus Nerve**.

Reproductive System

The Reproductive System is responsible for **reproduction,** or the creation of offspring. Many organs and structures in the reproductive system are shared with other body systems, such as the urethra, testes, and ovaries.

There are two subcategories: the **Male Reproductive System** and **Female Reproductive System**. Each vary in structures and function.

The **Male Reproductive System** is responsible for the production of **spermatozoa**(sperm) and male hormones, such as testosterone. Major structures of the Male Reproductive System include the penis, testes, scrotum, and ducts that carry sperm.

The **penis** is the primary organ of the Male Reproductive System, responsible for **sexual intercourse**, which allows passage of sperm outside the body through the urethra. The penis also allows for urine to leave the body. During sexual arousal, nerves cause blood vessels in the penis to dilate, which then causes the penis fills with blood. This results in an erection.

The **testes**, as discussed in the endocrine system, are responsible for the production of **testosterone**. They are also responsible for **spermatogenesis**, or sperm production. After the testes produce sperm, it is stored in a tube located atop each testicle, known as the **epididymis**. Upon ejaculation, the sperm leaves the epididymis and enters the vas deferens.

The **vas deferens** are tubes that connect the epididymis to the **urethra**. During ejaculation, smooth muscle in the walls of the vas deferens contract rhythmically(known as peristalsis), forcing sperm into the urethra. The sperm mixes with secretions from structures such as the prostate, which creates semen.

The **prostate** is a gland, located near the bladder, that produces secretions that join with sperm to create **semen**.

The **Female Reproductive System** is responsible for the production of **egg cells**, estrogen, progesterone, and **fetal development**. Major structures of the Female Reproductive System include the vagina, ovaries, fallopian tubes, uterus, and cervix.

The **vagina** is the **passageway** located between the cervix and the opening to the outside of the body. The vagina is often confused with the outer, visible portion, known as the vulva. The vagina allows a passageway for the penis during sexual intercourse.

The **ovaries**, as discussed in the endocrine system, are responsible for the production of estrogen and progesterone. The ovaries are also the structures that produce and release **egg cells(oocytes)** in women. Eggs are typically released once a month from one ovary.

The **fallopian tubes** allow **passage** of oocytes from the ovaries to the uterus. Fertilization most commonly occurs in the fallopian tubes.

The **uterus** is an inverted pear-shaped organ responsible for the **development of a fetus**. Upon fertilization, the embryo attaches to the wall of the uterus. The placenta develops, which connects to the embryo, providing it with blood flow and nutrients to help it grow. During childbirth, the placenta detaches from the uterus and exits through the cervix and vagina.

The **cervix** is a narrow, circular passage that connects the **vagina to the uterus**. During pregnancy, the cervix is closed by a thick layer of mucous. During childbirth, the cervix dilates widely, which allows a passage for the child to pass through.

Respiratory System

The Respiratory System has one essential function: to bring **oxygen** into the body, and eliminate wastes, such as **carbon dioxide**, from the body. The main organs of the Respiratory System are the **lungs**. The left lung has two lobes and is smaller than the right lung, which has three lobes. This is due to the presence of the heart on the left side of the chest.

Conduction of air is controlled by the **nose**. Air enters the body through the nose, and is filtered by **hair** and **mucous**. The nose also warms the air as it enters the body.

The **larynx**, also known as the voice box, is a short tube located inferior to the pharynx. As air passes over the vocal cords in the larynx, the vocal cords vibrate, which produces **speech**.

Sitting atop the larynx is a flap of tissue known as the **epiglottis**. Upon swallowing, the epiglottis lies on top of the larynx, blocking any food or fluid from entering the larynx, which **prevents choking**.

Connecting to the larynx inferiorly is a tube of cartilage known as the **trachea**, or the wind pipe. The trachea is the primary passageway for air to enter into the lungs.

Once air enters the lungs, it goes into each lung through **bronchial tubes**, which branch off of the trachea. These tubes branch into smaller tubes called bronchioles. Bronchial tubes secrete **mucous**, which helps to trap any dirt or debris that have made it into the lungs.

At the end of the bronchioles are tiny **air sacs**, known as **alveoli**. The alveoli resemble a cluster of grapes. Capillaries attach to the alveoli and move blood across the surface of the alveoli. This allows carbon dioxide to detach from the erythrocytes and exit the blood stream, and also allows oxygen to enter the blood stream and attach to erythrocytes. Alveoli are where **gas exchange** occurs in the Respiratory System.

Respiration is accomplished by contraction of the **diaphragm**, a large muscle connected to the rib cage that separates the chest from the abdomen. The diaphragm creates a **vacuum** inside the chest. When it contracts, it descends, pulling the chest down. This allows air to enter into the lungs. When the diaphragm relaxes, it ascends up into the chest, which forces air out of the lungs.

The Respiratory System

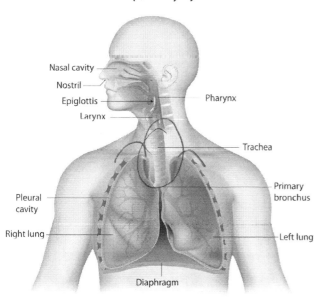

Human Lung Anatomy and Function

There are only three major structures that pass through the diaphragm: the **descending aorta**, the **inferior vena cava**, and the **esophagus**!

Skeletal System

The Skeletal System is a vital component of movement. We wouldn't be able to move if we didn't have bones! Muscles attach to bones, and when a muscle contracts, it pulls on a bone(or bones), which performs an action. Bones also produce blood cells, provide stability for the body, and protect structures and organs in the body. Needless to say, bones are extremely important!

There are **206** bones in the human body. Each bone can be classified as one of the following: **Long** bone, **Short** bone, **Irregular** bone, **Flat** bone, **Sesamoid** bone.

- **Long** bones appear **longer** than they are **wide**. There are numerous long bones in the body, including, but not limited to, the clavicle, humerus, femur, metatarsals, and phalanges.

- **Short** bones are **as long** as they are **wide**. Examples include the carpals and tarsals.

- **Irregular** bones are bones that have generally **unusual shapes**. Examples include the mandible, vertebrae, and pubis.

- **Flat** bones are named after how they look: **flat**. They are typically thin and flat. Examples include the scapula, ribs, and cranial bones.

- **Sesamoid** bones are bones embedded **inside tendons**, and named after what they look like. They are rounded, and resemble **sesame seeds**. The primary examples are the patella and pisiform.

Long bones consist of three main parts: the **epiphyses**, the **metaphyses**, and the **diaphysis**. The epiphyses can be found on the **ends** of the long bone, and are where the bone articulates with other bones. The epiphyses are covered with cartilage to prevent friction between the articulating bone surfaces. The epiphyses are primarily made of spongy bone, which allows certain bones to withstand extreme pressure without fracturing.

The **metaphyses** are the sections between the epiphyses and the diaphysis. Inside the metaphyses, there is a line of cartilage called the **epiphyseal plate/line**, and it is where **growth** in the bone takes place during childhood and adolescence. As a person grows, eventually the cartilage ossifies and becomes part of the bone, and growth in the bone no longer occurs.

The **diaphysis** is the **shaft** of the bone. Inside the shaft of the bone is the medullary cavity. The medullary cavity contains **red bone marrow** during childhood, which is the site of **red blood cell formation**. When the child ages, the red bone marrow is converted into yellow bone marrow, which is mainly just fat. The diaphysis is made of compact bone to provide as much strength as possible around the medullary cavity, while still giving enough space for the cavity itself to fill with marrow.

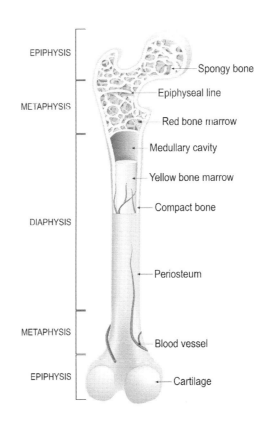

EPIPHYSIS

METAPHYSIS

DIAPHYSIS

METAPHYSIS

EPIPHYSIS

Spongy bone
Epiphyseal line
Red bone marrow
Medullary cavity
Yellow bone marrow
Compact bone
Periosteum
Blood vessel
Cartilage

Joints

Where bones come together is known as an **articulation**. Another name for articulation is "**joint**". Joints are where **movements** occur. We don't flex muscles, we flex joints!

All joints are classified as one of the following: **Synarthrotic**, **Amphiarthrotic**, or **Diarthrotic**. Synarthrotic joints are joints with little to **no movement** in them, such as the sutures in the skull. Amphiarthrotic joints are joints that are **slightly movable**, such as the intervertebral joints. Diarthrotic joints are **freely movable** joints, and have no real movement restrictions, such as in the shoulder or hip.

 *Easy to Remember: To remember the joint classifications, just think of "**SAD**". This tells you the joint classifications in order from least movable joint to most movable joint. **S**ynarthrosis, **A**mphiarthrosis, **D**iarthrosis.*

Joints have several structures that help create and support them. Between bones that articulate, on the **epiphyses**, there is **articular cartilage**. This type of cartilage is known as **hyaline** cartilage. It is a dense form of cartilage, very thick, and is a shock-absorber. Hyaline cartilage also **prevents friction** between the articulating bones, so bones don't rub against each other during movement.

Certain joints have a specific type of cartilage in them known as **a labrum**. The labrum, found in the glenohumeral joint and iliofemoral joint, is used to **deepen** the joint, providing a deeper socket for these ball-and-socket joints. This provides more **strength** and **stability** for the joint.

Ball + Socket → Labrum cartilage

Bones are held together by **ligaments**. Ligaments are avascular, meaning they are not supplied with blood by blood vessels. Ligaments are strong, but do not stretch very far before injury can occur. Tearing of ligaments such as the Anterior Cruciate Ligament is common in activities such as sports, or in car accidents.

Four of the most important joints joined together by ligaments are located in the skull, between the cranial bones. These synarthrotic joints are called **sutures**. The **sagittal** suture runs along a sagittal plane on the top of the head, connecting the two **parietal bones**. The **coronal** suture runs on a coronal plane, connecting the **frontal** bone to the **parietal** bones. The **squamous** suture runs on a sagittal plane, but is located on the side of the skull, connecting the **parietal** and **temporal** bones together. Finally, the **lambdoid** suture, named for its resemblance to the Greek letter "lambda", connects the **occipital** bone to the **parietal** bones.

Coronal Suture

Squamous
Suture

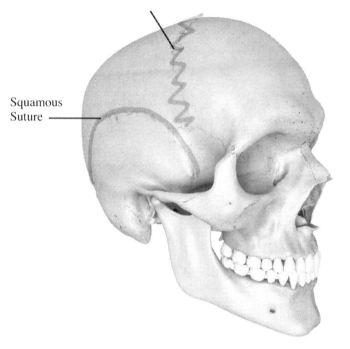

Sagittal Suture

Lambdoid
Suture

Synovial joint of the knee

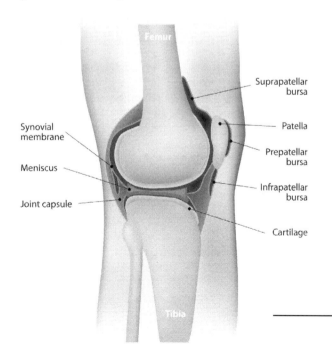

Femur

Suprapatellar
bursa

Synovial
membrane

Patella

Prepatellar
bursa

Meniscus

Infrapatellar
bursa

Joint capsule

Cartilage

Tibia

Inside the joint itself, a membrane is present, known as the **synovial membrane**. The synovial membrane produces a fluid that helps to lubricate the joint, known as the **synovial fluid**. Lubrication of the joint is key in keeping the joint functioning optimally. Surrounding the entire joint is thick, dense connective tissue known as the **joint capsule**. The joint capsule keeps everything inside the joint, such as the synovial fluid, and provides even more strength and support for the joint.

Muscles are held to bones via **tendons**. Tendons are similar to ligaments, but have a much more rich blood supply, and able to stretch further before injury occurs.

Types of Diarthrotic Joints

- There are **six** different types of diarthrotic joints.

Ball-and-Socket joints feature one bone with a **ball** at the epiphysis, and another bone with a **socket**. The ball fits in the socket, creating a ball-and-socket joint. Examples include the shoulder and hip joints. Ball-and- socket joints have the most amount of movement, able to move the joint in really any direction.

Hinge joints act much like the hinge on a door, only opening and closing. Hinge joints only allow movement in **one plane**, allowing only **flexion** and **extension**. Examples include the elbow and knee joints.

Pivot joints allow only one type of movement: **rotation**. All they do is allow structures to turn. An example is the atlantoaxial joint, which lets us shake our head "no". This is rotation.

Plane/gliding joints are produced when the articulating bones have **flat** surfaces, and there is a **disc of cartilage** between the bones. This allows the joint to move, or glide, in any direction, although with slight movement. Examples include the joints between the carpals and tarsals.

Saddle joints are only located in one part of the body: the **metacarpophalangeal joint** of the **thumb**. Saddle joints are named after the appearance of the articulating bones. The articulating surfaces are both shaped like saddles. The two bones that create the saddle joint are the **first metacarpal** and the **trapezium**.

Ellipsoid/condyloid joints are extremely similar to ball-and-socket joints. On one bone, there is a **condyle**, which resembles a ball, but isn't as pronounced. This condyle fits into an **elliptical cavity** on another bone, which is similar to a socket, but not as deep. This allows movements such as flexion, extension, adduction, abduction, and circumduction. An example is the radiocarpal joint.

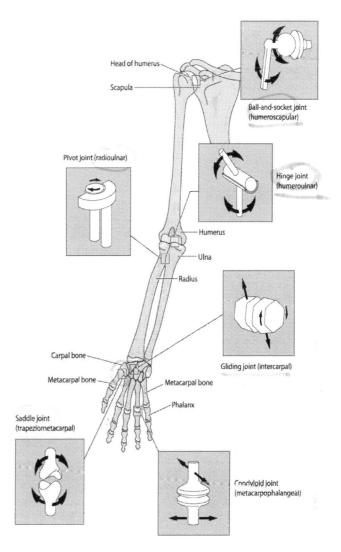

Skeleton Divisions

There are two divisions of the skeleton: the **Axial Skeleton** and the **Appendicular Skeleton**.

The Axial Skeleton contains all of the bones that do not correspond to any appendages: the **skull**, **vertebral column**, and **thoracic cage**. These bones make up the trunk.

The Appendicular Skeleton contains all of the bones that correspond to the appendages: the **humerus, radius, ulna, carpals, metacarpals, phalanges, femur, tibia, fibula, metatarsals, phalanges**, the **pectoral girdle**(clavicles and scapulae) and **pelvic girdle**(ilium, ischium, pubis, and sacrum).

Bones of the Axial Skeleton

Skull

The skull's primary function is to **protect the brain**. The bones that make up the skull are:

Parietal   Mandible
Frontal   Vomer
Temporal   Ethmoid
Occipital   Sphenoid
Zygomatic   Nasal
Maxilla   Lacrimal

Vertebral Column

The vertebral column consists of **26** individual bones. Its primary function is to **protect the spinal cord,** which runs through it. There are five different regions of the vertebral column. They are:

Cervical(7 vertebrae)
Thoracic(12 vertebrae)
Lumbar(5 vertebrae)
Sacral(1 vertebrae)
Coccygeal(1 vertebrae)

Cervical Vertebrae

Thoracic Vertebrae

Lumbar Vertebrae

Sacrum and Coccyx

Easy to Remember: To remember how many vertebrae are in the cervical, thoracic, and lumbar regions, just think of **breakfast, lunch,** *and* **dinner**. *You have breakfast(cervical) at* **7**, *lunch(thoracic) at* **12**, *and dinner(lumbar) at* **5**.

Chest

The chest consists of the **rib cage**. The primary function of the rib cage is to **protect vital organs** inside the thorax, and assist in breathing by giving the diaphragm a place to attach. The rib cage consists of:

True ribs(superior seven ribs) *1-7*
False ribs(inferior five ribs) *8 - 12*
Floating ribs(ribs 11 and 12) *11 +12*

Bones of the Appendicular Skeleton

Pectoral Girdle

The pectoral girdle is responsible for holding the upper limbs to the body. The pectoral girdle consists of four bones:

Scapulae(two bones)
Clavicles(two bones)

Scapula   Clavicle

Pelvic Girdle

The pelvic girdle is primarily responsible for holding the lower limbs to the body. The pelvic girdle contains:

Ilium(two bones)
Ischium(two bones)
Pubis(two bones)
Sacrum(one bone)

Arm

The arm contains one bone:

Humerus

The humerus is the **funniest** bone in the body! Get it? Humerus?

Forearm

The forearm contains two bones:

Radius
Ulna

Radius   Ulna

Wrist

The wrist is located distally to the forearm, and it contains the **carpal** bones. The carpal bones are divided into two separate lines, each containing four bones. The proximal line is listed first, then the distal line:

Proximal Line:
Scaphoid
Lunate
Triquetrum
Pisiform

Distal Line:
Trapezium
Trapezoid
Capitate
Hamate

Capitate
Hamate
Pisiform

Trapezoid
Trapezium
Scaphoid

Triquetrum
Lunate

DID YOU KNOW?

The **carpometacarpal joint** of the **thumb**, made by the **trapezium** and **first metacarpal**, is the only place in the body you find the **saddle joint!**

Easy to Remember: To remember the order of the carpals, think of this old saying: **S**ome **L**overs **T**ry **P**ositions **T**hat **T**hey **C**an't **H**andle (**S**caphoid, **L**unate, **T**riquetrum, **P**isiform, **T**rapezium, **T**rapezoid, **C**apitate, **H**amate)

Hand

The hand contains **19 bones** in each hand:

Metacarpals(5 bones)
Phalanges(14 bones)

Metacarpals   Proximal Phalanges   Middle Phalanges   Distal Phalanges

Thigh

The thigh contains one bone:

Femur

*The femur is the **longest**, and **strongest**, bone in the body!*

Leg

The leg contains two bones:

Tibia
Fibula

Wolff's law
wt-bearing / strength training
↓ ↑ bone density

Fibula   Tibia

Ankle

The ankle is located distally to the leg, and it consists of the bones of the **tarsals**:

Calcaneus   Cuneiform I
Talus   Cuneiform II
Navicular   Cuneiform III
Cuboid

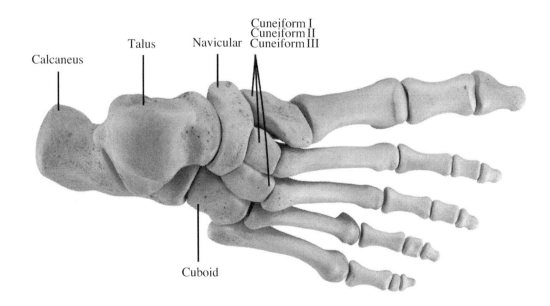

Calcaneus   Talus   Navicular   Cuneiform I / Cuneiform II / Cuneiform III

Cuboid

Foot

The foot contains **19 bones** in each foot:

Metatarsals(5 bones)
Phalanges(14 bones)

Metatarsals

Proximal Phalanges

Middle Phalanges

Distal Phalanges

Urinary System

The Urinary System is primarily responsible for **elimination** of **waste** from the body. It also assists in regulating the **pH level** of the body, and may also assist in reabsorption of substances back into the body. The four main structures of the Urinary System are(in descending order) the **kidneys, ureters, urinary bladder**, and **urethra**.

Blood enters the kidneys through the renal arteries. Inside the kidneys, blood is **filtered** through the **nephrons,** which pulls waste products such as **urea** out of the blood. Inside each kidney, there are over one million nephrons. The waste products filtered out of the blood by the nephrons become **urine**. The nephrons also allow nutrients and water to be reabsorbed back into the blood stream.

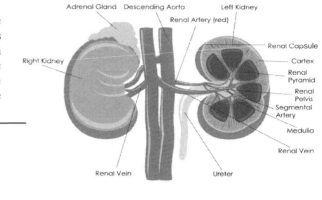

The pH Scale

pH values of some common substances

BASE

14	Drain cleaner (pH14)
13	Bleach (pH13,5)
12	Ammonia solution (pH11,5)
11	Antacid (pH10)
10	
9	Baking soda (pH8,5)
8	Egg (pH7,6 - 8,0)
7	Water and Blood (pH7 - 8)
6	Milk (pH6,6 - 6,9)
5	Coffee and tea (pH5 - 5.5)
4	Beer (pH4,5)
3	Wine (pH3,5)
2	Lemon juice (pH2)
1	Gastric acid (pH1)
0	Electrolyte (pH0)

NEUTRAL 7

ACID

A **pH scale** is used to determine the **acidity** or **alkalinity** of a substance. If a substance reads between **7-14** on a pH scale, it is base, or **alkaline**. The higher the number, the more alkaline a substance is. An example, bleach is highly basic, and comes in at 12.6. Blood is slightly basic, and comes in at 7.4. On the other hand, if a substance comes in between **0-7** on a pH scale, it is **acidic**. The lower the number, the more acidic a substance is. An example, hydrochloric acid(the kind of acid in the stomach that helps digest food) comes in at 2.0, so it is highly acidic. Black coffee registers at about 5.0, so it is slightly acidic. The kidneys help regulate substances in the body that make the body's fluids either too acidic or too basic by filtration.

Once urine has been created, it is sent from the kidneys to the urinary bladder through two small tubes known as ureters. The ureters only function as a **passageway** for urine.

Urine **collects** in the urinary bladder, until it is ready to be eliminated from the body. The urinary bladder expands as more urine is added to it. The urinary bladder can typically hold between 300-500 ml of fluid. Once urine is released from the urinary bladder, it passes through the urethra.

The urethra, much like the ureters, is a small tube that has one function: **transporting urine** from the urinary bladder **out of the body**.

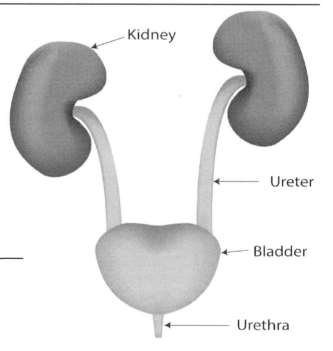

Anatomy and Physiology Matching

C : Constant internal environment

K : Suture connecting the two parietal bones

E : Organ that creates bile and detoxifies blood

T : Tissue responsible for separating structures

O : Sensory receptor that detects pain

D : Organ that filters blood and creates urine

M : "Rest-and-digest" response

L : Muscle contraction with constant tension and decreasing muscle length

B : Gland responsible for the creation of T-Cells

Q : Muscle contraction with constant tension and increasing muscle length

P : Region of the vertebral column with five bones

N : Suture connecting the occipital bone and parietal bones

A : Cell responsible for transporting oxygen and carbon dioxide

H : Tissue responsible for protection, secretion, and absorption

S : "Fight-or-flight" response

J : Glands responsible for production of estrogen and progesterone

F : Region of the vertebral column with seven bones

G : Body plane that splits the body into superior and inferior

I : Largest lymph vessel in the body

R : Body plane that splits the body into anterior and posterior

A: Erythrocytes

B: Thymus

C: Homeostasis

D: Kidneys

E: Liver

F: Cervical Vertebrae

G: Transverse Plane

H: Epithelial Tissue

I: Thoracic Duct

J: Ovaries

K: Sagittal Suture

L: Concentric Contraction

M: Parasympathetic Response

N: Lambdoid Suture

O: Nociceptor

P: Lumbar Vertebrae

Q: Eccentric Contraction

R: Frontal Plane

S: Sympathetic Response

T: Connective Tissue

Answer Key on Page 271

Anatomy and Physiology

Across

1. Anatomical law stating bone strength will increase when placed under pressure
4. Ends of long bones that articulate with other bones
6. Region of the vertebral column with twelve bones
9. Contraction in which the muscle tension remains constant, and the length increases
10. Type of joint that allows only flexion and extension
11. Study of the structures of the body
13. Gland that produces oil
14. Nervous response that lowers heart rate and stimulates peristalsis
17. Carpal that articulates with the first metacarpal, creating the saddle joint
18. Portion of the small intestine where the majority of nutrient absorption takes place
19. Hormone produced by the ovaries
21. Suture connecting the occipital and parietal bones
22. Blood cell responsible for transport of oxygen and carbon dioxide
23. The entire span of the myosin in a single sarcomere
24. Tissue responsible for protection, secretion, and absorption

Down

2. Organ that produces bile and detoxifies blood
3. Organs responsible for urine production via blood filtration
5. Structure found in joints that produces fluid that lubricates the joints
7. Contraction in which the muscle tension remains constant, and the length decreases
8. Shaft of a long bone
11. Where gas exchange occurs in the lungs
12. Gland that produces calcitonin, which reduces calcium levels in the blood
15. Largest lymph vessel in the body
16. Structure in the brain responsible for controlling muscle tone, coordination, and balance
20. Largest artery in the body

Answer Key on Page 275

79

Anatomy and Physiology Practice Exam

1. The sympathetic nervous response is also referred to as
A. Housekeeping
B. Rest and digest
C. Fight or flight
D. Central

2. A sudoriferous gland is a type of exocrine gland that produces what substance
A. Oil
B. Sweat
C. Testosterone
D. Milk

3. The longest vein in the body, located on the medial aspect of the leg and thigh
A. Great saphenous
B. Femoral
C. External iliac
D. Brachial

4. The pituitary gland produces all of the following hormones except
A. Growth hormone
B. Testosterone
C. Follicle-stimulating hormone
D. Prolactin

5. Perirenal fat surrounds the
A. Rectum
B. Bladder
C. Liver
D. Kidneys

6. Primary function of a gland
A. Secretion
B. Protection
C. Absorption
D. Contraction

7. Branching muscle tissue is also called
A. Smooth
B. Skeletal
C. Cardiac
D. Striated

8. What aspect of the body is being studied in anatomy
A. Structure
B. Function
C. Diseases
D. Movement

9. Mastication is more commonly known as
A. Chewing
B. Swallowing
C. Sneezing
D. Defecating

10. The pulmonary arteries carry blood from the right ventricle to
A. Left atrium
B. Rest of the body
C. Aorta
D. Lungs

11. Beta cells produce
A. Bile
B. Glucagon
C. Somatostatin
D. Insulin

Gabi

12. Where two bones come together
A. Fracture
B. Articulation
C. Contracture
D. Ellipsoid

13. T-lymphocytes are produced by which gland
A. Thymus
B. Thalamus
C. Pituitary
D. Pineal

14. Light pressure is detected by
A. Nociceptors
B. Pacinian corpuscles
C. Merkel discs
D. Meissner's corpuscles

15. The phrenic nerve emerges from the
A. Neck
B. Chest
C. Lumbar
D. Brain

16. Another name for a leukocyte is
A. Thrombocyte
B. Red blood cell
C. Platelet
D. White blood cell

17. The cervical plexus emerges from which sets of vertebrae
A. C1-C7
B. C1-C4
C. T1-T6
D. L1-S4

18. There are seven vertebrae in which region of the vertebral column
A. Thoracic
B. Cervical
C. Lumbar
D. Coccygeal

19. Erythrocytes
A. Carry oxygen and carbon dioxide throughout the body
B. Are also called neutrophils and perform phagocytosis
C. Produce thrombi at an area of trauma
D. Allow transport of blood cells throughout the body

20. Storage of bile is controlled by the
A. Gallbladder
B. Liver
C. Small intestine
D. Stomach

21. Absorption of nutrients primarily takes place in what part of the small intestine
A. Jejunum
B. Ileum
C. Duodenum
D. Cecum

22. The superior seven pairs of ribs are also called
A. Inferior ribs
B. False ribs
C. Superior ribs
D. True ribs

23. Waste moves through the large intestine in the following order
A. Transverse colon, ascending colon, sigmoid colon, descending colon
B. Sigmoid colon, descending colon, transverse colon, ascending colon
C. Ascending colon, transverse colon, descending colon, sigmoid colon
D. Descending colon, ascending colon, transverse colon, sigmoid colon

24. Peristalsis is controlled by which of the following types of muscle
A. Cardiac
B. Skeletal
C. Smooth
D. Striated

25. Vitamin D is produced in the following organ
A. Liver
B. Skin — D synthosis
C. Pancreas
D. Spleen

26. Glucagon is produced by
A. Delta cells
B. Beta cells
C. Alpha cells
D. Theta cells

27. Part of the respiratory passage that divides into the left and right bronchus
A. Larynx
B. Pharynx
C. Trachea
D. Epiglottis

28. Which of the following is not one of the four types of tissue
A. Nervous
B. Connective
C. Epithelial
D. Skeletal

29. The largest internal organ in the body
A. Liver
B. Stomach
C. Brain
D. Spleen

30. Enzyme located in the saliva which aids in digestion of carbohydrates
A. Epinephrine
B. Prolactin
C. Amylase
D. Parotid

31. The esophagus passes through the following structure on its way to the stomach
A. Peritoneum
B. Liver
C. Pericardium
D. Diaphragm

32. Heat creation is produced by which type of muscle tissue
A. Smooth
B. Cardiac
C. Skeletal
D. Adipose

33. The functional unit of tissue is called
A. Cell
B. Nerve
C. Blood
D. Muscle

34. Most superior portion of the sternum
A. Costal cartilage
B. Body
C. Xiphoid process
D. Manubrium

35. Which of the following molecules attaches to hemoglobin
A. Nitrogen
B. Oxygen
C. Helium
D. Argon

36. Breaking down food, absorption of nutrients, and elimination of waste is the function of which body system
A. Urinary
B. Digestive
C. Cardiovascular
D. Lymphatic

37. Non-striated muscle is
A. Involuntary
B. Voluntary
C. Controlled easily
D. Controlled by concentration

38. Connective tissue connecting bone to bone
A. Fascia
B. Tendon
C. Ligament
D. Dermis

39. There are how many pairs of spinal nerves in the peripheral nervous system
A. 24
B. 12
C. 18
D. 31

40. All of the following carry blood away from the heart except—
A. Capillaries
B. Arteries
C. Arterioles
D. Veins

41. The ovaries and testes are examples of
A. Exocrine glands
B. Digestive organs
C. Endocrine glands
D. Cardiovascular vessels

42. Chyme moves from the stomach into the small intestine through which sphincter
A. Ileocecal
B. Cardiac
C. Pyloric
D. Esophageal

43. Epithelial tissue
A. Holds tissue together and separates tissues
B. Provides protection, secretes substances, and absorbs substances
C. Is found inside joints and helps to lubricate joints
D. Allows nerve impulses to be transmitted from the brain to muscles

44. The adrenal glands are located atop which organs
A. Large intestine
B. Small intestine
C. Kidneys
D. Ureters

45. Dopamine is an example of a
A. Hormone
B. Synapse
C. Neuron
D. Dendrite

46. The largest veins in the body, responsible for returning deoxygenated blood to the heart
A. Aorta
B. Vena Cava
C. Pulmonary arteries
D. Pulmonary veins

47. Function of serous membranes
A. Secreting sebum
B. Connect organs
C. Creating blood
D. Separate organs

48. Which of the following is not a structure in the digestive system
A. Gallbladder
B. Spleen
C. Liver
D. Pancreas

49. The first cervical vertebrae is also called the
A. Occiput
B. Axis
C. Atlas
D. Dens

50. Pepsin is located in the
A. Stomach
B. Small intestine
C. Pancreas
D. Gallbladder

Answer Key on Page 280

Pathology

On the MBLEx, you will be asked several questions about pathology. These questions are meant to ensure you, the student, understand diseases and the disease process, and can properly assess a client and determine any potential contraindications.

In this section, we will discuss many subjects, covering a wide range of information.

Information covered in this section includes:

Medications
Medical Tests and Equipment
Pathology of the Cardiovascular System
Pathology of the Digestive System
Pathology of the Endocrine System
Pathology of the Integumentary System
Pathology of the Lymphatic System
Pathology of the Muscular System
Pathology of the Nervous System
Pathology of the Respiratory System
Pathology of the Skeletal System
Pathology of the Urinary System
Cancers
Psychological Disorders
CPR
First Aid

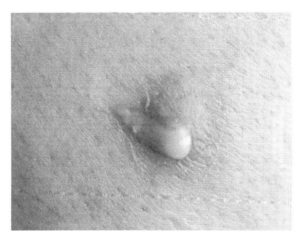

This information is followed by three assignments:

Pathology Matching
Pathology Crossword
Medications Word Search

The end of the section has a 50 question practice exam on Pathology. These questions ARE NOT the exact same questions you will see on the MBLEx. They are meant to test information that MAY be seen on the MBLEx.

While taking the practice exam, make sure to utilize your test-taking strategies(page 4) to optimize your test scores.

Medications

There are many different types of medications used to treat many types of illnesses, diseases, and infections. Among the most common are:

Analgesics, which help to **relieve pain**. Examples include acetaminophen and non-steroidal anti-inflammatory drugs. These help treat symptoms of conditions that cause pain, such as cancer.

Antacids, which reduce the activity of **acids** in the stomach. These help treat conditions such as Gastroesophageal Reflux Disease.

Antibiotics, which are used to combat **bacterial** growth. Examples include penicillin, amoxicillin, and erythromycin. These are used to treat infections in the body, such as cellulitis, impetigo, and diverticulitis.

Anticoagulants, which are used to reduce the formation of **blood clots**. Examples include aspirin, heparin, and warfarin. These are used to treat conditions such as deep vein thrombosis, and phlebitis.

Antifungals, which aid in destroying **fungus**. Examples include terbinafine and fluconazole. These are used to treat any type of fungal infection, such as Tinea Pedis(Athlete's Foot) or Tinea Capitis.

Antihistamines, which reduce the effects of **histamines** on the body, including runny nose and itching. These are used to treat allergic reactions.

Anti-inflammatory agents, which help to reduce **inflammation**. Examples include non- steroidal anti-inflammatory drugs such as ibuprofen. These are used to help treat inflammation in conditions such as bronchitis, and potentially Alzheimer's Disease.

Antipyretics, which help to reduce **fever**. Examples include ibuprofen and aspirin. These are used to treat symptoms of fever and other systemic infections.

Antivirals, which aid in preventing **virus** reproduction. Examples include amantadine and rimantadine. These are used to combat virus reproduction in conditions such as encephalitis.

reduce BP **Beta blockers**, which help to reduce **blood pressure**. Examples include acebutolol. nadolol, and nebivolol. These are used to treat conditions such as hypertension, arrhythmia, and myocardial infarction.

Bronchodilators, which aid in **dilation** of the **bronchial tubes**. Examples include albuterol and salmeterol. These are used to treat conditions such as asthma, and bronchitis.

Decongestants, which reduce **inflammation** in the **nasal cavity**. Examples include pseudoephedrine and phenylephrine. These are used to treat congestion caused by allergies.

Diuretics, which increase the production of **urine**. Examples include bumetanide, amiloride, and mannitol. These are used to treat conditions such as edema, and hypertension.

Insulin, which **lowers** the amount of **sugar** in the blood stream. Insulin is primarily used to treat Diabetes.

Local anesthetics, which are used to **numb** an area. They are most commonly administered via **needle injection**. Examples include lidocaine and nitracaine. These are typically used before performing a surgical procedure around the area of incision.

Sedatives, which are used to **calm** and **relax** the body. Examples include diazepam and clonazepam. These are typically used to calm a person before a painful or uncomfortable procedure is performed, such as a colonoscopy.

Statins, which aid in **lowering cholesterol** levels in the blood stream. Examples include atorvastatin, rosuvastatin, and lovastatin. These are used to treat and/or prevent heart disease and its various symptoms, including **hypertension** and stroke.

Medical Tests and Equipment

AED(Automated External Defibrillator): An AED is a portable defibrillator, used to send **electric shocks** to the heart in a person who is suffering from sudden cardiac arrest. The person will have two sticky pads attached to their skin that connect to the AED, one pad placed on the chest and one on the left side of the trunk. The AED sends a shock to the person through the pads, directly into the heart, which can help return the heart to its normal rhythm.

Arthroscopy: Arthroscopy is used to view the inner structures of a **joint**. It is performed by making a small incision, and inserting a tube with a **camera** attached directly into the joint. This allows a view of any structural damage that may occur, such as torn ligaments. If surgery is being performed, it may be performed arthroscopically, where all the instruments being used are inserted into the joint through small holes, without making a large incision.

Arthroscopy

Bone Graft: A bone graft, similar to a skin graft, is the removal of a small amount of bone tissue from one part of the body, placing the removed tissue on another bone that may be lacking in sufficient tissue. This can be done if part of a bone is removed during surgery, or in cases such as joint replacements to help the new structures anchor in to the bone more securely. The new bone sets, and the area where the graft is located becomes stronger.

Catheter: A catheter is a small tube inserted in to a part of the body to help fluid drain. The most common form is a urinary catheter. These are inserted into the urethra and into the urinary bladder. From there, fluid is able to drain freely from the bladder.

Centrifuge: A centrifuge is a medical device used to separate solids from liquids. This is especially useful in separating plasma from the blood cells in blood. Centrifuges accomplish this by spinning in circles extremely fast, forcing the solids in a substance to move to the bottom of the vial, and the liquids move to the top.

Centrifuge

Chemotherapy: Chemotherapy is the use of certain chemicals to destroy cancerous cells and tumors in the body. Chemotherapy may be administered at different times and different ways, depending on the cause of the cancer. It may be used to destroy some cancer cells and shrink a tumor to aid with pain relief, or to make surgery on the tumor more successful. After a tumor is removed, chemotherapy may be used to destroy any remaining cancerous cells in the body and prevent it from recurring or spreading elsewhere. Chemotherapy is usually given intravenously, but may also be given orally or topically.

Compression Devices: Compression devices are used to mimic the lymphatic system, and rhythmically compress the legs to increase the flow of lymph. This can decrease lymphedema. Examples of typical compression devices include compression socks, and cuffs that wrap around the legs.

Cryotherapy: Cryotherapy is the use of cold or ice in a treatment. Cryotherapy can be used to reduce inflammation, increase circulation after a short period of application, destroy tissues such as warts, or even destroy nerves that may be causing pain. Cryotherapy can be applied many different ways, from the use of cold packs, to ice baths.

Computerized Axial Tomography(CT/CAT Scan): Computerized Axial Tomography, also known as CT or CAT Scan, is an imaging technique in which a snapshot is taken of a part of the body on a given body plane. This allows viewing of structures in the body from differing points of view. CT is extremely similar to MRI, but uses X-ray to produce images instead of magnetic fields.

Echocardiogram: An echocardiogram is a type of ultrasound performed on the heart in order to view all the structures and chambers of the heart. This can be used to determine if there are any issues with the heart, such as valve defects, how strong the heart muscle is, or if there are any abnormal holes in the heart.

Echocardiogram

Holter Monitor

Electrocardiogram(ECG/EKG): If a doctor feels as if a patient needs to have their heart rhythm monitored, they may administer and ECG/EKG. During this procedure, ten pads attached to electrodes are attached to the patient's bare skin on specific points around the trunk. The ECG/EKG picks up the electrical activity of the heart, and produces a visualization that shows each wave of electrical activity. The first wave seen is known as the P wave, and shows the contraction of the atria. Next is the QRS wave, which shows the depolarization and contraction of the ventricles. Following that is the T wave, which represents re-polarization of the ventricles.

In some cases, a person may need to have heart activity recorded over 24-48 hours. In these cases, a Holter Monitor is used. These are portable machines that remain attached to a patient, continuously recording heart activity. These can be used if a person has irregular heart rhythms that come and go, and aren't present during an initial ECG/EKG reading.

Electroencephalogram(EEG): An electroencephalogram is a test used to detect the electrical activity of the brain. It uses electrodes placed around the head that attach directly to the scalp to detect electric activity. Electroencephalograms are performed to help diagnose brain disorders, such as encephalitis, tumors, epilepsy, and damage to the brain from concussions.

Electromyography(EMG): Electromyography is a test used to detect the proper functioning of muscles and the nerves that innervate the muscles. This is done to assess any nerve or muscle damage that may be present, or if communication between the nerve and muscle has been impaired. Electromyography is performed by several different means. A needle may be placed directly into the muscle to read electrical activity. Adhesive pads may be placed on the skin above the muscle to detect nervous conduction as well.

Electromyography

Endoscope: An endoscope is a procedure in which a tube is inserted into a part of the digestive tract with a camera and light attached, allowing a doctor to see inside the organs. Commonly, this is performed to view the esophagus, stomach, and small intestine. An endoscope used to view the large intestine is known as a colonoscopy.

Epidural: An epidural is a medical procedure used to block pain and sensation in the lower body. It is performed by injecting analgesics and anesthetics around the spinal cord in the lumbar region. The medications are delivered via a catheter inserted into the site of injection. Epidurals are commonly used during labor to eliminate pain associated with child birth.

Lithotripsy: Lithotripsy is the use of sound waves administered via ultrasound to break up or destroy deposits building up in the body, such as kidney stones and gallstones. Lithotripsy is typically only performed if one of these deposits is too large to pass from the body on its own. The sound waves produced break up the deposit, and allow it to be passed normally. These sound waves are produced by a machine known as a lithotripter.

Magnetic Resonance Imaging(MRI): Magnetic Resonance Imaging is the use of high powered magnetic fields to help produce images of structures and organs inside the body. These images are typically much more detailed than X-rays, especially when viewing organs. MRI is used to help diagnose conditions such as tumors, issues with the digestive system, and issues with the heart and blood vessels. The MRI machine is a large tube in which a person lies for an extended period of time, which allows a thorough image to be produced.

MRI Machine

Mammogram: A mammogram is a procedure used to detect breast cancer in patients who are not showing any symptoms. It uses an X-ray to view the internal breast tissue. A mammogram is typically performed by placing the breast between two glass plates that compress the tissue. Compressing the tissue allows the X-ray to view all of the breast without missing anything.

Mohs Surgery: Mohs surgery is a type of surgery performed on skin cancer. During this treatment, thin layers of a tumor in the skin are removed one at a time, until eventually nothing but healthy tissue remains. This type of procedure is performed to reduce the amount of damage done to surrounding tissues while ensuring the tumor has been effectively removed. The area may be stitched closed, receive a skin graft, have skin pulled over from an adjacent area to cover the site, or may be left to heal on its own.

Myelogram: A myelogram is an imaging procedure used to view issues that may be occurring in the spinal canal. Special dyes are injected into the spinal column, and the patient is given X-rays, which allow the structures inside the spinal canal to be properly viewed. Myelograms are used to examine conditions such as herniated discs, infections such as meningitis, and tumors in the brain or spinal cord.

Pacemaker

Pacemaker: If a patient suffers from severe arrhythmia, a pacemaker may be implanted into the body to help regulate heart rhythm. The pacemaker is usually placed under the skin on the upper left side of the chest, just inferior to the clavicle. A pacemaker is a small metal device with a battery inside that sends electric shocks to the heart when it detects the heart rhythm is not functioning properly. It accomplishes this with the use of leads that travel through the superior vena cava directly into the heart. The leads go into the atrium, ventricle, or both, depending on the type of arrhythmia a person has. The battery in a pacemaker typically lasts between five and ten years, and can be replaced.

Radiation Therapy: Radiation therapy is a type of treatment used to destroy cancerous tissue. It is performed by exposing the affected portion of the body to a highly concentrated beam of radiation. The machine responsible for administering the radiation is pointed directly at the spot to be treated, and uses X-rays to destroy cancerous cells. It may also destroy healthy tissue, however. Radiation therapy may also be used to make tumors smaller and prevent a tumor from growing or spreading before surgery may be performed.

Radiation Therapy

Skin Graft: A skin graft is transplanting skin from one location on the body to another where skin has been lost, commonly from burns or injuries. A thin layer of epidermis is removed using a shaver(similar to a potato peeler), then placed on the area where skin is needed. The area is covered in bandages to allow healing. Over time, the skin adheres to the injured area and becomes new skin for the area.

Sphygmomanometer: When measuring blood pressure, a sphygmomanometer is wrapped around a person's arm. The cuff around the arm inflates, and the pressure of the blood passing through the arteries can be felt. The sphygmomanometer produces two numbers: the systolic number and diastolic number. The systolic number reads systolic pressure, which is the pressure felt as blood is pumped from the heart and passes through the arteries. The diastolic number reads diastolic pressure, which is the pressure felt when the heart is at rest and blood is not passing through that portion of the arteries at that time. A normal blood pressure is 120/80 mmHg, in which the systolic pressure is 120 mmHg, and the diastolic pressure is 80 mmHg.

Sphygmomanometer

Ultrasound

Ultrasound: An ultrasound, also known as sonography, is an imaging technique utilizing sound waves to produce pictures of structures inside the body. Commonly, ultrasound is used to view the development of a fetus during pregnancy, but may also be used to examine infections inside the body, liver and gallbladder function, and heart conditions. The part of the machine that is used to perform the scanning is known as the transducer.

X-Ray: An X-ray is an imaging technique using radiation to view structures that light typically does not pass through. Structures most commonly viewed using X-rays are bones and metals. X-rays allow visual examination of structures that may be broken, damaged, or infected.

X-Ray

Cardiovascular System Pathologies

Anemia
(an-: without; -emia: blood)

Anemia is a disease of the blood, resulting in a **lack** of **oxygen** and an over-abundance of carbon dioxide in the blood. There are many different types of anemia, ranging from iron-deficient anemia, to sickle cell anemia. Anemia is the most common blood condition in the United States, with an estimated 3.5-4 million people afflicted with it.

Iron-deficient anemia is the most common form of anemia. The cells in the blood that are responsible for carrying oxygen and carbon dioxide throughout the body are the erythrocytes, or red blood cells. In the cytoplasm of erythrocytes, there is a protein present known as hemoglobin, which is made of iron. The hemoglobin attracts oxygen and carbon dioxide, allowing these molecules to attach to the erythrocytes.

Causes

In iron-deficient anemia, the primary cause is a lack of iron being consumed. Less iron being consumed results in less **hemoglobin** in the erythrocytes, which in turn causes a lack of oxygen and carbon dioxide attaching to the red blood cells.

Sickle cell anemia is an inherited form of anemia, in which the erythrocytes have a sickle shape, as opposed to a normal erythrocyte, which is circular. This shape can cause the erythrocytes to become stuck in blood vessels, and reduce adequate blood flow to tissues.

Symptoms

People with anemia may feel sluggish, tired, have an increased heart rate, may show paleness in the skin, shortness of breath, and experience dizziness, all due to a lack of sufficient oxygen reaching tissues.

Sickle cell anemia may also result in the further development of infections due to damage caused to the spleen, pain in the thorax and abdomen(known as crises) due to blockage of blood vessels in these locations, and a lack of nutrients to the body, which can stunt growth.

People whose diet lacks proper amounts of iron or vitamin B-12 may develop anemia. Pregnancy, and a lack of folic acid, may result in anemia in pregnant women. Sickle cell anemia is primarily seen in African-Americans, resulting from a genetic defect.

Treatments

Treatments for anemia vary depending on the type, but may include increasing iron intake, bone marrow transplants, or blood transfusions. Pregnant women may require an increased intake of folic acid. People with sickle cell anemia face less treatment options. The only potential cure is through a bone marrow transplant. Often times, the only treatment is trying to minimize the number of crises a person may experience. Antibiotics and pain relievers may help in preventing infections in younger patients and reducing pain experienced during crises.

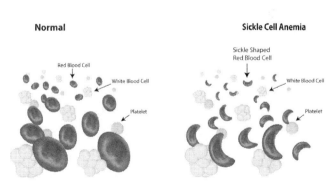

Contraindications

Massage is indicated for a client with anemia. Massage helps increase circulation and oxygen intake, which provides the body with needed nutrients.

Aneurysm
(Greek "aneurysma": a widening)

An aneurysm is a condition of the arteries, resulting in a **bulge** in the wall of an artery. There are several different forms and causes of aneurysms. Different types of aneurysms include Aortic(bulge in the wall of the aorta), Cerebral(bulge in an artery supplying blood to the brain), and Ventricular(bulge in the wall of the heart).

Causes

Aneurysms are the result of a part of an arterial wall becoming weakened. When the wall of the artery becomes weakened, it forces the wall out, creating a pouch or bubble. Most commonly, aneurysms are the result of hypertension putting too much pressure or strain on the artery. Ventricular aneurysms are most commonly caused by myocardial infarction, which can weaken the heart muscle.

When the arterial wall stretches due to weakness, it makes it much easier for the artery to rupture. Because the artery carries oxygen-rich blood, this makes aneurysms very dangerous, as any rupture will severely cut off blood flow to the structure supplied with blood by the artery.

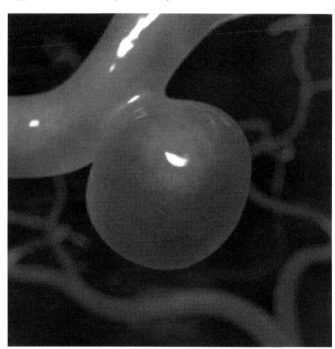

Symptoms

Unfortunately, aneurysms that have not ruptured are asymptomatic. In fact, aneurysms themselves, unless very large, cause no symptoms at all. When an aneurysm ruptures, however, a person may experience severe chest or back pain, low blood pressure, severe headache, tachycardia, and lightheadedness.

People may develop aneurysms for many different reasons, including obesity, hypertension, diabetes, advanced age, and alcoholism. Some people develop aneurysms for no apparent reason at all.

Treatments

Common locations for aneurysms include the abdominal aorta and the brain. Aneurysms may be treated surgically before rupture to prevent major medical emergencies in the future. Beta blockers are commonly used as medications before surgery is required.

Contraindications

Massage is indicated with a doctor's note. Any massage that increases blood pressure should be avoided, such as deep tissue, because it can put pressure on arteries, which may lead to bursting of an aneurysm.

Arrhythmia
(a-: without; rhythm: rhythm)

Arrhythmia is a condition of the heart, which results in the heart's natural **rhythm** being altered. There are several different forms of arrhythmia. Some of the most common forms of arrhythmia are Atrial Fibrillation, Bradycardia, and Tachycardia.

Causes

Atrial fibrillation, the most common form of arrhythmia, results when the atria, the heart's upper chambers, contract irregularly, which sends blood into the ventricles at uncoordinated times. This is caused by an electrical signal from the SA Node not firing correctly, which disrupts the timing of the atria contracting. This can affect the ability of the heart to consistently deliver oxygenated blood to the body.

Bradycardia*(brady-: slow; -cardia: heart)* results in the heart rate being reduced to a rate of contraction that is considered too slow to deliver substantial oxygen to the body.

Tachycardia*(tachy-: rapid; -cardia: heart)* results in the heart rate being increased to a rate of contraction that is considered too rapid. In tachycardia, the ventricles of the heart are contracting too rapidly, which may cause a lack of oxygen-rich blood from reaching the body, as the quick contractions do not allow the ventricles to properly fill with blood before being pumped out to the rest of the body. Older adults, those over age 60, are more likely to develop arrhythmia than younger adults and children. Heart diseases are a main contributing factor towards older adults developing arrhythmia. Other diseases may also play a role in the development of arrhythmia, so people who have had myocardial infarction may be more prone to developing the disease. Diabetes, sleep apnea, and hypertension all have contributed to the development of arrhythmia.

Symptoms

There are many different symptoms seen with arrhythmia. Symptoms include dizziness, fatigue, shortness of breath, pain in the chest, lightheadedness, and fainting. Arrhythmia may also, in severe cases, result in cardiac arrest.

Cardiac arrhythmia

Sinus node

Normal electrical pathways

Atrioventricular node

Atrial fibrillation impulses

Chaotic signals

Rapid ventricular impulses

Normal heart   **Atrial Fibrillation**

Treatments

Treatments vary, depending on the type of arrhythmia a person suffers from. Medical devices, such as pacemakers, may be implanted into the body to help regulate and control heart rhythm(IE, if a person's heart rate drops too low, the pacemaker will stimulate the heart muscle and cause it to contract, increasing heart rate back to safe levels). Alternative methods to controlling arrhythmia, such as massage therapy and yoga, may be applied in some cases.

Contraindications

Untreated arrhythmia is an absolute contraindication for massage therapy. If a client has a pacemaker, massage may be performed. A client may have discomfort while lying prone due to pressure on the pacemaker, which may call for side-lying massage to be performed, or pillows to be used to take pressure off the area. Avoid massaging the site of the pacemaker(upper left chest just below clavicle).

Arteriosclerosis/Atherosclerosis
(arterio: artery; scler-: hard; -osis: condition);
(athero: fatty plaque; scler-: hard; -osis: condition)

Arteriosclerosis is a **hardening** of the walls of arteries, a condition that progresses slowly over time. Atherosclerosis is a build-up of **fatty plaque** inside the arteries. These two conditions are often caused by one another, and are often interchangeable.

Causes

Arteriosclerosis has many different contributing factors, including hypertension, high cholesterol, and smoking. Each of these can damage an artery. The body's response to this damage is to increase the thickness of the artery to prevent further damage. When this occurs, the artery becomes much harder and unable to move and stretch normally. This may also lead to increased deposits of plaque in the arteries, a condition known as atherosclerosis. This increased plaque, along with the hardening of the artery, may restrict blood flow and lead to conditions such as angina pectoris and myocardial infarction.

Symptoms

Symptoms include angina pectoris, shortness of breath, fatigue, and pain in any area of the body that may have any sort of restriction in the arteries.

Treatments

Medications are effective treatments, including beta-blockers, statins, calcium channel blockers, and diuretics. If an increased plaque buildup is severe, an angioplasty may be performed, or a stent may be placed inside the artery to increase blood flow. Plaque may be surgically removed, or a bypass surgery may be performed to increase circulation into areas that may be experiencing ischemia.

Contraindications

Massage for atherosclerosis/arteriosclerosis may be performed. Certain medications may require a lighter massage to be performed, because they may thin the blood and damage to a blood vessel can lead to increased bleeding internally.

STAGES OF ATHEROSCLEROSIS

Healthy artery

Build-up begins

Plaque forms

Plaque ruptures; blood clot forms

Deep Vein Thrombosis
(thromb/o: clot; -osis; condition)

Deep Vein Thrombosis(DVT) is a condition in which **blood clots(thrombi)** form in the **veins** deep in the body, typically the legs. These blood clots can block blood flow in the veins, which can lead to several serious issues.

Causes

There are various causes for DVT. Primary causes are injury to a vein, surgery, impaired or limited mobility, and certain medications. An injury to a vein can result in blood clots, especially if there is significant damage to the vein. Surgery, which can result in cutting through veins, can also lead to blood clots. Post-surgery, if a patient is immobilized for extended periods, circulation starts to decrease in efficiency, which can lead to blood pooling in the veins of the legs. This pooling of blood can result in clots. It is this same reason people who have paralysis may develop blood clots as well.

Symptoms

Although symptoms may not be present in someone with DVT, others do show symptoms, which include a warm sensation in the affected area, pain in the affected area that can increase in intensity, and discoloration in the affected area. Most commonly, DVT affects the lower limb, so this is where a person will most likely experience these symptoms.

Deep Vein Thrombosis

Treatments

The primary treatment for DVT is medication. Certain medications can help reduce the chance of developing DVT in the future, or even remove the blood clot from the body. Intravenous anticoagulants such as heparin help to thin the blood. Other anticoagulants, such as warfarin, work extremely well in conjunction with injectable anticoagulants.

If the blood clot is severe, the patient might be given a thrombolytic, a type of medication that destroys blood clots. These are typically only given in serious cases of blood clots, such as those that result in pulmonary embolism.

Compression socks, which compress the leg up to the knee, can help reduce the amount of swelling a patient might experience with DVT.

Contraindications

Deep vein thrombosis is typically a local contraindication. Avoid the site of the thrombus, as dislodging the clot may lead to circulation being cut off in organs such as the lungs, brain, or heart. Massage that increases blood pressure may be contraindicated, and deeper massages may be contraindicated due to the use of anticoagulants and thrombolytics.

Heart Murmur
(murmur: to mutter)

A heart murmur is a condition of the heart, which results in blood flowing **backwards** in the heart. A "murmur" refers to the sound of blood flowing through the heart. There are two types of heart murmurs: Innocent and Abnormal. Innocent heart murmurs are seen in children and infants, usually the result of congenital heart disease. Abnormal heart murmurs are much more serious, most likely due to the development of heart disease or valve malfunction.

Causes

Heart murmurs may not require any medical attention, depending on the cause. Other times, medical attention may be needed. Most commonly, heart murmurs are the result of a **bicuspid/mitral valve** prolapse, where the valve is pulled backwards into the left atrium.

This allows blood to flow backwards in the heart, which may reduce the ability of the heart to pump enough oxygen-rich blood to the body.

People who have developed endocarditis or Rheumatic fever often develop heart murmurs due to damage to the valves in the heart.

Symptoms

While most heart murmurs aren't serious, abnormal heart murmurs may present with symptoms such as cyanosis in the fingers, chest pain, dizziness, shortness of breath, and fainting.

Treatments

Heart murmurs may require the person to take anticoagulants to prevent the formation of blood clots, may be treated for hypertension if it is resulting in heart murmurs, or may need surgery to repair the malfunctioning valve.

Contraindications

Massage may be performed on a client with a heart murmur.

Hypertension
(hyper-: above; -tension: tension)

Hypertension is a condition of the cardiovascular system, resulting in **elevated blood pressure**. There are numerous factors that may contribute to the development of hypertension. For an average healthy adult, systolic blood pressure(pressure felt in arteries when the heart beats) is around 120 mmHg, and diastolic pressure(pressure felt in arteries when the heart is at rest) is around 80 mmHg. To be diagnosed with hypertension, a person's systolic pressure would be 140 mmHg and diastolic pressure would be 90 mmHg.

Causes

Hypertension may have no underlying cause, or may be the result of factors such as dysfunction of the adrenal glands or thyroid, dietary issues such as obesity or high sodium intake, kidney disease, and alcohol consumption.

Hypertension is most commonly associated with people who smoke, drink excessive amounts of alcohol, are overweight, are older in age, consume excessive salt, and more.

Symptoms

Unfortunately, hypertension is largely asymptomatic. Only in extreme cases, where the heart's blood pressure spikes extremely highly, will someone experience symptoms, such as dizziness and headaches. Most symptoms people associate with hypertension are actually side effects of medications.

Treatments

Untreated, hypertension may lead to numerous serious medical conditions, such as myocardial infarction, stroke, atherosclerosis, and aneurysm. Luckily, hypertension is very easy to detect, and very treatable. Often times, treatment is as simple as making lifestyle or dietary changes, such as consuming less sodium and increasing exercise. Other times, hypertension may require the use of medications such as beta blockers, statins, and diuretics.

Contraindications

Hypertension is generally not contraindicated for massage. Massage that increases blood pressure, such as deep tissue or hot stone, may be contraindicated if the client is not taking medication to control hypertension. Light massage, which promotes lowering blood pressure, should be performed.

Migraine Headaches

Migraine Headaches are a type of headache that affect the brain, which results in most side effects experienced.

Migraines have been referred to as "**vascular** headaches", due to the involvement of blood vessels. In migraines, when the brain is stimulated by a trigger, neurons rapidly send impulses which affects the blood vessels surrounding the meninges, three layers of connective tissue that surround and protect the brain. At first, the blood vessels constrict, which does not result in pain. A short time after constricting, the blood vessels will dilate, which places immense pressure on the meninges, which results in severe pain.

Causes

Migraines have numerous causes, which may be from exposure to substances like tyramine(a naturally occurring chemical found in foods such as aged cheese, alcoholic beverages, and cured meats), caffeine, stress, or even hormonal imbalance during stages such as menstruation. Migraines may even be considered hereditary.

Symptoms

Symptoms include nausea, fatigue, extreme pain, loss of sight, blurred vision, sensitivity to sound, and pain on one side of the head. Not everyone that experiences a migraine experiences all of the symptoms detailed, as each migraine is different.

Treatments

If a migraine is in the beginning stages, taking pain medication such as aspirin or ibuprofen can help reduce the symptoms of mild migraines. Other medications, called triptans, can help to constrict blood vessels, which can help reduce the effects of migraines.

Preventative drugs may be taken to reduce the chances of developing a migraine in the future. These medications include beta blockers, non-steroidal anti-inflammatory drugs, and even antidepressants.

Contraindications

Migraine headaches are generally not contraindicated for massage.

Myocardial Infarction
(myo-: muscle; -cardia: heart; infarct: obstruction of blood flow)

A Myocardial Infarction, or heart attack, is a condition that affects the heart muscle, reducing blood flow throughout the body.

An infarction is an obstruction of blood flow to a specific part of the body. In this case, blood flow to the heart is obstructed. The two arteries that supply blood to the heart muscle are known as the coronary arteries. When an abundance of substances such as plaque build up inside these arteries, it restricts blood flow to the heart muscle. When blood flow is restricted, the tissue does not receive adequate oxygen, which results in **necrosis** of the affected tissue. When too much cardiac muscle dies, the body experiences a myocardial infarction, or heart attack.

Causes

Myocardial infarctions may be the result of atherosclerosis(*athero-: fatty plaque*), a condition which causes the artery walls to harden and thicken, due to a build-up of plaque in the arteries. Hypertension, smoking, and obesity may also contribute to the development of atherosclerosis.

Symptoms

Symptoms of myocardial infarction may be acute, or build up over a period of days leading up to the myocardial infarction. In the preceding days, a person may experience malaise, fatigue, and discomfort in the chest. Acute stages of myocardial infarction include intense chest pain, pain in the neck and left arm, and increased heart rate.

Treatments

A person who has suffered from a myocardial infarction may have a coronary bypass surgery performed, an angioplasty or stent placed in the affected artery, or may not need any surgery and only require medications such as aspirin, beta blockers, and statins.

Contraindications

Massage is an absolute contraindication during a myocardial infarction. After a myocardial infarction has occurred and a client has been treated, it is a good idea to get a note from a doctor before proceeding. Depending on the severity of the infarct and treatment, certain massages should not be performed due to strain they may place on the heart when increasing blood pressure.

Anatomy of a heart attack

Healthy artery

Atherosclerotic plaque with blood clot

Phlebitis
(phleb : vein; -itis: inflammation)

Phlebitis is a condition of the cardiovascular system, affecting the **veins**, causing them to become **inflamed**. Blood clots may form in these veins.

Causes

Phlebitis may have numerous causes, including trauma to a vein, and immobility. Trauma to a vein results in what is known as superficial phlebitis, usually the result of IV catheters being placed into a vein via needles.

Deep vein thrombosis is another type of phlebitis, taking place deeper in the body. Deep vein thrombosis(DVT) is most commonly caused by immobility of a limb. The body's veins move and stretch with the rest of the body during movement. If the veins are immobilized, they will become irritated due to blood pooling in the veins. The blood pooling may result in blood clot formation. If a blood clot dislodges from its location and flows freely in the blood stream, it is known as an embolus, which could become lodged in other blood vessels throughout the body, cutting off blood flow and resulting in ischemia. Depending on the part of the body this takes place, it could even lead to possible death.

Symptoms

Symptoms of superficial phlebitis include tenderness and swelling around the injured vein, often with the affected vein presenting with a red line in the skin following the vein. The vein may feel hard to the touch due to inflammation.

Deep vein thrombosis may present with pain in the entire affected limb(usually the leg), along with swelling. If infection results, people may have fever.

Treatments

Treatments of phlebitis include anticoagulants for deep vein thrombosis such as heparin, ibuprofen, and antibiotics for superficial phlebitis.

Deep vein thrombosis requires immediate medical attention, as it may result in embolism, which could potentially be fatal.

Contraindications

Phlebitis should be treated as a local contraindication. Because medications may be prescribed that thin the blood, lighter massage should be performed to prevent internal bleeding from damaged blood vessels. Massaging the site of phlebitis may dislodge a clot, which can result in an embolism.

Raynaud's Syndrome

Raynaud's Syndrome is a condition that results in **constriction** of the blood vessels in the **fingers** and **toes**, reducing **circulation** to these areas. This constriction is known as "vasospasm". Primary Raynaud's Syndrome occurs independently, while Secondary Raynaud's Syndrome is typically associated with other conditions.

Causes

The primary contributors to Raynaud's Syndrome are cold temperatures, stress, and cigarette smoking. Raynaud's Syndrome is typically not a debilitating disease. During a flare-up, the skin typically turns white, the person may experience numbness or pain, and the affected areas become very cold.

Secondary Raynaud's Syndrome may be associated with conditions such as lupus or scleroderma, and develops later in life than Primary Raynaud's Syndrome.

Symptoms

Symptoms of Raynaud's Syndrome include discoloration of the skin in affected areas, cold fingers and/or toes, numbness, and stinging pain upon warming of the area.

Treatments

Treatments for Raynaud's Syndrome include exercise, reducing stress, not smoking, and avoiding cold temperatures whenever possible. Secondary Raynaud's Syndrome may require medications such as statins to help regulate blood pressure and cholesterol.

Contraindications

Contraindications

Raynaud's Syndrome is indicated for massage. Using heat should be avoided, as sensation in the affected area may be decreased and tissue damage may result. Massaging the area can help dilate blood vessels and bring blood back into the fingers and toes. Increasing the temperature of the massage room may also help dilate blood vessels.

Varicose Veins
(varicose: abnormally swollen)

Varicose veins are the abnormal swelling of veins in the body, most commonly seen in the **legs**, but may be present in any vein. There are many different types, ranging from regular varicose veins, to spider veins, and even hemorrhoids.

Causes

Inside the veins, there are valves that push deoxygenated blood back up to the heart. Typically, as a person ages, the valves stop working as efficiently, which allows blood to pool **backwards** in the veins. This added pressure causes irritation and swelling of the veins. Blood pooling in the veins may also lead to complications such as the development of blood clots.

Because veins are much more superficial than arteries, when a vein becomes swollen, it is often visible. Varicose veins often present with a purple color, may look cord-like, and may even cause pain and discomfort. Causes of varicose veins include sitting or standing for prolonged periods, age, and even pregnancy.

Symptoms

Often times, varicose veins occur with no symptoms other than visual symptoms, such as discoloration of veins. If a varicose vein becomes painful, a person may experience burning, itching, edema, and cramping in the legs around the site of the varicose vein.

Treatments

Treatment is often unnecessary, outside of self-care. Self-care may include wearing compression socks, exercise, diet, and elevating the legs to help circulation. If treatment is required, there are a number of different things that can be done, all the way up to removing the varicose vein from the body.

Contraindications

Varicose veins are a type of phlebitis, and are considered a local contraindication. Working on a swollen vein may dislodge a clot, which could become an embolism.

Digestive System Pathologies

Cholecystitis
(chole-: bile; cyst-: bladder; -itis: inflammation)

Cholecystitis is **inflammation** of the **gallbladder**. If untreated, cholecystitis may lead to extremely serious conditions, such as rupture of the gallbladder.

Causes

Most commonly, cholecystitis is the result of formation of **gallstones**. Gallstones can block the cystic duct, which connects the gallbladder to the bile duct on its way to the duodenum, causing inflammation of the gallbladder as bile backs up in the organ.

There is no consensus on what causes gallstones to form. Some theories state gallstones form because the bile contains too much cholesterol, too much bilirubin, or the gallbladder doesn't properly empty bile into the duodenum.

Symptoms

Symptoms of cholecystitis include severe abdominal pain in the upper right quadrant near the liver, nausea, vomiting, fever, and pain in the right shoulder/back. These symptoms often occur after ingesting large meals.

Treatments

A diagnosis of cholecystitis almost always results in a hospital stay. Treatments may include antibiotics to fight off any associated infection, pain medication to reduce discomfort, and fasting to let the gallbladder rest and reduce inflammation.

Cholecystitis often recurs, and therefore, most people who are diagnosed with cholecystitis require surgery to completely remove the gallbladder. The liver is then connected directly to the duodenum, allowing bile to enter into the small intestine.

Contraindications

Cholecystitis is considered an absolute contraindication in the acute stage. After the underlying cause has been determined, medications may be prescribed to help deal with the formation of gallstones and infection, or the gallbladder may be removed completely. This will require a hospital stay, in which massage will not be performed.

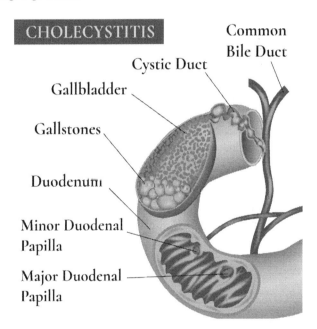

Cirrhosis
(Greek "kirrhos": yellowish; -osis: condition)

Cirrhosis is **scarring** the **liver**, due to other conditions such as Hepatitis(page 102). Each time the liver is damaged, it repairs itself. During this repair process, scar tissue is formed. As the liver is damaged over time, more scar tissue forms, which makes liver function difficult. Cirrhosis gives the liver a cobble-stone, yellow-orange appearance.

Causes

Most commonly, cirrhosis is the result of chronic hepatitis and/or alcohol abuse. Every time there is a flare-up of chronic hepatitis (HBV and HCV), it damages the liver, resulting in scar formation. Nonalcoholic fatty liver disease may also contribute to the development of cirrhosis.

Symptoms

Cirrhosis often does not present with symptoms until the damage caused is excessive. Symptoms may include nausea, weight loss, jaundice, bleeding and bruising easily, fatigue, edema in the legs, and an accumulation of fluid in the abdomen.

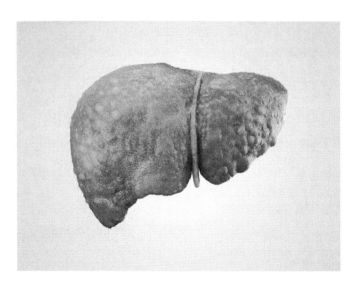

Treatments

Early stages of cirrhosis are treated by addressing the underlying cause, not the scarring itself, as the scarring is irreversible. A patient with early stages of cirrhosis may seek treatment for alcohol dependency to reduce the intake of alcohol, look into weight loss to reduce nonalcoholic fatty liver disease, and medications to help control HBV and HCV, which can substantially damage the liver.

Advanced stages of cirrhosis may require liver transplantation to provide the body with a liver that functions properly.

Contraindications

Massage should be avoided in a client with cirrhosis, due to increased waste products being filtered through the liver. This can overload the liver and cause more stress on the liver.

Crohn's Disease

Crohn's Disease is an inflammatory bowel disease, which causes **inflammation** ofthe **digestive tract**. Crohn's has periods of exacerbation and remission, where the disease is actively causing inflammation, then periods where it is not. Crohn's disease typically appears in younger people, people who are of East European Jewish descent, people who have relatives with the disease, and people who smoke cigarettes.

Causes

The exact cause of Crohn's disease is unknown. The leading theory is that heredity and an immune system that does not function properly are the main "causes" of Crohn's.

Symptoms

In acute stages of Crohn's, symptoms may include diarrhea, abdominal pain, cramping, fatigue, fever, and bloody stool. Damage to the digestive tract may include ulcerations and scarring. This may cause abscesses and constipation. Depending on the severity of these symptoms, a person may need to visit a doctor.

Treatments

A variety of medications may be prescribed for a patient with Crohn's, including anti-inflammatory drugs such as corticosteroids to reduce inflammation in the digestive tract, immunosuppresors to help regulate the effects of the immune system on the digestive tract, and antibiotics to reduce any abscesses that may result. Pain relievers may also be prescribed.

In serious cases, surgery may be required. During Crohn's, scarring in the ileum or large intestine may result. In this surgery, the damaged portion of the digestive tract may be removed. This does not cure Crohn's, but can make it easier to manage.

Changes in diet, especially in acute stages, may be beneficial.

Contraindications

Massage in the acute stage of Crohn's disease should be avoided, as the client will be in pain and experience symptoms such as diarrhea. In the stage of remission, massage is indicated for Crohn's disease.

Diverticulitis

(diverticula: tubular sac branching off a cavity; -itis: inflammation)

Diverticulitis is a condition affecting the large intestine, but may also affect other structures such as the abdomen, or the entire cardiovascular system. If a person is affected by diverticulosis, they have small pouches that develop in the large intestine. In certain cases, these pouches may become **inflamed** and/or **infected**, which then becomes diverticulitis.

Causes

Because diverticulitis puts strain on sections of the large intestine that are already weakened from diverticulosis, it may result in ulcerations, or open sores. These open sores may lead to infection, and leaking of feces into the abdomen, which results in peritonitis(inflammation of the peritoneum, a very serious condition that requires medical attention).

Symptoms

Symptoms of diverticulitis include fever, nausea, vomiting, pain in the lower left abdomen, and constipation. Tenderness in the abdomen may also be present.

Treatments

Diverticulitis may be treated in several different ways, depending on the severity. Pain medication may help with discomfort in less severe cases. In recurring diverticulitis, scarring may be present, which could lead to backing up of fecal content in the large intestine. Infections will require antibiotics.

If scarring is severe due to ulceration, surgery to remove the damaged part of the large intestine may be required.

Contraindications

Diverticulitis is considered an absolute contraindication to massage.

Diverticulosis

(diverticula: tubular sac branching off a cavity; -osis: condition)

Diverticulosis is a condition affecting the large intestine, which presents with **pouches** forming in the walls of the large intestine, typically in the descending and/or sigmoid colons. It is a common condition seen in roughly half of people over the age of 65.

Causes

During peristalsis, the smooth muscle located in the walls of the large intestine contract, forcing food to move further through the organ and eventually out of the body. If the large intestine does not contain enough fecal matter, as in the case of a low-fiber diet, the contractions may result in weakening of the wall of the large intestine. As a result, small pouches may develop.

If a person develops diverticulosis, small pieces of feces, nuts, seeds, etc, may become stuck inside the pouches. If feces becomes trapped in a pouch, the large intestine will absorb all of the water from it, and it will become very solid and extremely hard to remove. This may result in pain in the abdomen.

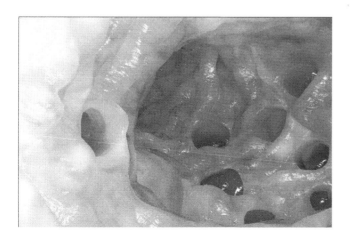

Symptoms

Typically, people with diverticulosis don't exhibit symptoms. When they do, however, symptoms may include diarrhea, abdominal cramping, or fever. These are typically the result of infection, which may lead to diverticulitis.

Treatments

Treatment primarily includes increasing intake of fiber via fruits and vegetables, and increasing fluid intake to make passing of stool easier to manage.

Contraindications

Diverticulosis is not contraindicated for massage. If pain is present, massage of the lower back and abdomen should be avoided, but may be performed elsewhere.

Gastritis
(gastr/o: stomach; -itis: inflammation)

Gastritis is **inflammation** of the **stomach**, specifically the lining of the stomach. Gastritis may occur suddenly or slowly over time.

Causes

Some primary causes of gastritis include infection by **H. pylori bacterium**, excessive use of alcohol, use of anti-inflammatory drugs, vomiting, and stress. Gastritis should be treated, as it may lead to more serious conditions such as stomach cancer.

Symptoms

Some people with gastritis actually don't exhibit any symptoms. Those that do, however, may present with nausea, vomiting, loss of appetite, pain and bloating in the abdomen.

Treatments

Treatment often consists of dietary changes, such as avoiding spicy food and dairy, taking antacids to reduce the amount of stomach acid present, and possibly even a round of antibiotics to combat infection by the H. pylori bacterium.

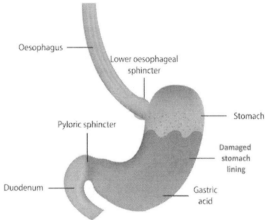

Contraindications

Massage on a client with gastritis is dependent on the cause and severity. If gastritis is causing nausea and vomiting, massage should not be performed.

Gastroesophageal Reflux Disease
(gastr/o: stomach; esophag/o: esophagus; reflux: flowing back)

Gastroesophageal Reflux Disease(GERD) is a condition in which **stomach acid**, or food from the stomach, comes back up into the **esophagus**, causing irritation and burning in the lining of the esophagus.

Causes

GERD is the result of acid flowing backwards into the esophagus. This is primarily caused by the lower gastroesophageal sphincter(also known as the cardiac sphincter) relaxing when it normally is contracted and tightened. This can happen abnormally, or be caused by the sphincter weakening over time.

Symptoms

Symptoms include burning in the chest, pain in the chest, a dry cough, a sour taste in the mouth, and a sore throat. It is advisable to seek medical attention if chest pain is present, because symptoms are very similar to those seen in myocardial infarction.

Treatments

Over-the-counter medications, such as antacids, are the primary treatment for GERD. Other medications may be prescribed by a doctor if the GERD is not helped by antacids, such as H-2-receptor blockers, which reduce stomach acid production, and proton pump inhibitors, which completely block the production of stomach acid and give the lining of the esophagus time to heal.

Contraindications

Unless chest pain is present, massage is indicated for Gastroesophageal Reflux Disease. Semi-reclined position may help reduce acid from moving into the esophagus.

Hepatitis
(hepat-: liver; -itis: inflammation)

Hepatitis is a condition that results in **inflammation** of the **liver**.

Causes

There are numerous causes of hepatitis, which affect numerous different organ systems. Most commonly, hepatitis is the result of a **viral** infection, but may also result from toxic substances entering into the body, such as alcohol. Short-term symptoms of hepatitis include jaundice(yellowing of the skin due to increased bilirubin in the blood stream), fever, and nausea. Long-term symptoms include cirrhosis(destruction of healthy liver cells), scarring of the liver, liver cancer, and liver failure.

There are five known hepatitis viruses: Hepatitis A, B, C, D, and E. Each varies in mode of contraction and severity in symptoms.

Hepatitis A is the most common form, and is typically transmitted through ingestion of fecal matter(most commonly seen in parts of the world with low sanitation standards). People infected with Hepatitis A most frequently make a full recovery, and develop an immunity to the virus.

Hepatitis B is typically transmitted through exposure to body fluids such as blood. The virus produces symptoms for a period greater than Hepatitis A, but most people will develop an immunity to it after about four weeks. A small percentage of people who contract Hepatitis B will become chronically affected by it. Vaccines for Hepatitis B are available.

Hepatitis C, much like Hepatitis B, is contracted through exposure to body fluids such as blood. Hepatitis C is a chronic condition which damages the liver even further each time the person's symptoms are in the acute stage. Hepatitis C is one of the leading causes of liver failure.

Hepatitis D is an infection that only results in symptoms if the person is also infected with the Hepatitis B virus. When this occurs, major complications may arise. Because Hepatitis D is only activated by the Hepatitis B virus, the Hepatitis B vaccine may contribute to the prevention of Hepatitis D.

Hepatitis E, like Hepatitis A, is contracted through exposure to fecal matter. It is most commonly seen in developing countries, where sanitation standards may not be high. Hepatitis E, if severe, may lead to liver failure, despite being an acute infection.

Symptoms

Hepatitis often results in no symptoms. More severe cases of hepatitis may result in a person presenting with nausea, fatigue, mild fever, loss of appetite, abdominal tenderness, and jaundice, among others.

Treatments

Treatments vary, depending on severity. Immunizations are available for Hepatitis B, and medications may help reduce the symptoms.

Contraindications

In the acute stage, massage is an absolute contraindication for hepatitis. In the period of remission, massage is indicated.

Hernia
(hernia: a rupture)

A hernia is a rupture in a muscle or connective tissue, allowing an organ or other tissue to **protrude** through its normal location. There are many different types of herniae in the digestive system, including hiatal, umbilical, and inguinal.

Causes

A hernia is caused by a weakness in the affected tissue, and/or straining of the tissue. When the tissue tears, the organ, usually the small intestine, protrudes through it. This can lead to many complications, such as organ strangulation, constipation, pain, or even trauma to other structures, such as the testes.

A hiatal hernia results from part of the stomach protruding upwards through the diaphragm, into the chest. Gastroesophageal Reflux Disease may result from this type of hernia, where stomach acids leak from the stomach backwards into the esophagus.

An umbilical hernia, most commonly seen in infants, is caused by the small intestine protruding through the abdominal wall and into the umbilicus. This condition usually resolves on its own.

An inguinal hernia, most commonly seen in men, is caused by the small intestine protruding through the wall of the abdomen, which typically descends into the scrotum. This may cause trauma to the testes. Sometimes, the small intestine may even drop farther down the body, into the thigh.

Symptoms

Symptoms vary depending on the type of hernia suffered. Examples include swelling beneath the skin in the abdomen or groin in an inguinal or umbilical hernia, and heart burn and pain in the upper abdomen in hiatal herniae.

Treatments

Treatments may include dietary changes in cases such as a hiatal hernia, weight loss, medication such as antacids, or even surgery to repair the hernia.

Contraindications

Massage of a hernia is locally contraindicated.

Umbilical hernia

Pancreatitis

(pancreat/o: pancreas; -itis: inflammation)

Pancreatitis is **inflammation** of the **pancreas**. Pancreatitis may be either acute or chronic, each presenting with differing levels of severity.

Causes

Pancreatitis results when enzymes produced by the pancreas, insulin and glucagon, and pancreatic juice, become active in the pancreas before entering into the blood stream or digestive tract. This causes the pancreas to become irritated and inflamed. Things that may contribute to pancreatitis include blockage of the bile duct by gallstones, alcoholism, pancreatic cancer, infection, and cystic fibrosis.

Symptoms

Acute pancreatitis presents with fever, nausea, vomiting, pain in the upper abdomen, abdominal tenderness, and pain radiating to the back. Chronic pancreatitis may also present with the same symptoms in the acute stage, but also weight loss.

Pancreatitis may lead to the development of other serious conditions such as diabetes, pancreatic cancer, and kidney failure.

ACUTE PANCREATITIS

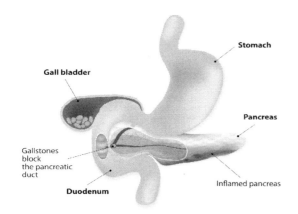

Treatments

Upon admission to a hospital, a patient with pancreatitis will be prescribed pain medication. Fasting reduces the production of insulin and glucagon, and is therefore beneficial to decrease irritation. Other treatments that treat the underlying causes of pancreatitis can include removal of the gallbladder or gallstones, and treatment for alcohol dependency.

Contraindications

In the acute stage, pancreatitis is considered an absolute contraindication. In a client with chronic pancreatitis, massage may be performed in the period of remission.

Peptic Ulcer
(peptic: digestion; ulcer: open sore)

An ulcer in the digestive tract is typically referred to as a stomach or peptic ulcer. These ulcers are **open sores** in the inner linings of the **stomach**, which can cause pain in the stomach.

Causes

Peptic ulcers are usually caused by stomach acid, such as pepsin, eating away the inner lining of the stomach and/or small intestine. Mucous lines the stomach, but when acid levels in the stomach rise and mucous production fails to match the rise in acid levels, the acid will eat through the mucous and the stomach lining. Reasons for increases in stomach acid can vary between prolonged use of things like aspirin, or a bacterial infection(H. pylori being the primary type of infection causing peptic ulcers). Excessive prolonged alcohol consumption may also contribute to the development of ulcers.

Symptoms

Peptic ulcers may cause painful burning sensations in the stomach, heartburn, nausea, and bloating. In less common cases, a person may also experience vomiting and have bloody stool.

Treatments

Treatment for peptic ulcers largely revolves around the cause of the ulcers. If H. pylori is the suspected cause, antibiotics will be prescribed to fight off the infection. Antacid medications may also be prescribed to lower the acid content of the stomach back to normal levels, giving the stomach lining a chance to heal and recover mucous.

Contraindications

Massage of a client with peptic ulcers often depends on the symptoms and their severity. If a client is nauseated, massage should be postponed.

Pharyngitis
(pharyng/o: pharynx; -itis: inflammation)

Pharyngitis is **inflammation** of the **pharynx**, or the throat. A sore throat is considered pharyngitis.

Causes

Pharyngitis is usually the result of a **viral infection** from the common cold or the flu. Bacterial infections may also result in pharyngitis, such as strep throat. Non-exudative pharyngitis, the kind usually caused by a virus, does not produce increased mucous, while exudative pharyngitis, the kind usually caused by bacteria, does produce mucous. Both types of pharyngitis are contagious.

Symptoms

Pain in the throat is one of the main symptoms of pharyngitis. Speaking and swallowing food may be painful. A person may develop a fever, and the tonsils and lymph nodes in the neck may enlarge. Excessive mucous may be produced if it is caused by bacterial infection.

Treatments

Antiviral medications may prevent the condition from worsening. If the condition is caused by bacterial infection, antibiotics can help combat the infection and improve the condition.

Contraindications

Pharyngitis is commonly considered an absolute contraindication to massage during the acute stage. After the infection has cleared, massage may be performed.

Strep Throat

Strep throat is a **bacterial infection**, resulting in sore throat. Typically, a throat culture is performed in order to diagnose strep throat.

Causes

Strep throat is caused by an infection of the streptococcal bacteria, which is contagious. Children are most at risk of contracting strep throat, but it can occur in people of all ages.

Symptoms

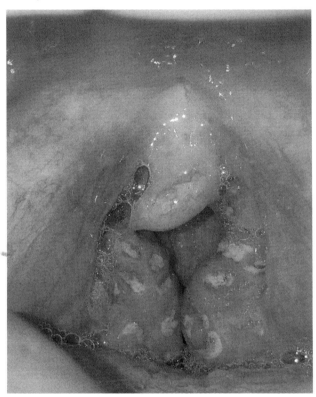

In addition to sore throat, a person with strep throat may develop red spots on the roof of the mouth, white patches on the tonsils, swollen lymph nodes in the neck, pain upon swallowing, and fever, amongst others. If left untreated, strep throat may contribute to the development of Rheumatic Fever, which can cause damage to heart valves.

Treatments

Because strep throat is caused by bacteria, antibiotics are the primary treatment. Acetaminophen is useful in treating any pain that may be present due to the infection. After starting a course of antibiotics, a person should begin feeling better within a couple days. Taking all the medication prescribed is required to prevent the infection from returning and becoming resistant to the antibiotics.

Contraindications

Because strep throat is highly contagious, it is considered an absolute contraindication until the condition has completely cleared.

Ulcerative Colitis
(ulcer: open sore; col/o: large intestine; -itis: inflammation)

Ulcerative colitis is an inflammatory disease of the digestive tract, specifically affecting the inner walls of the **large intestine** and rectum. Ulcerative colitis presents with **chronic inflammation and ulcers**, which can result in several symptoms. There are several different types of ulcerative colitis: Proctosigmoiditis(ulcers in the sigmoid colon and rectum), Ulcerative proctitis(ulcers in the rectum), Left-sided colitis(ulcers in the descending and sigmoid colons), and Pancolitis(ulcers throughout the entire large intestine). All forms of ulcerative colitis are chronic conditions, aside from acute severe ulcerative colitis, which is not common.

Causes

Direct causes of ulcerative colitis are unclear, but heredity may play a role. There is some belief that ulcerative colitis may be caused by an autoimmune disorder of some sort.

Symptoms

Symptoms of ulcerative colitis may include bloody diarrhea, weight loss, fever, fatigue, pain in the abdomen, difficulty defecating, pain in the rectum. Symptoms are usually mild, and a patient may go long periods without developing symptoms.

Treatments

There are several treatments available for ulcerative colitis, but there is no cure. Treatments include application of corticosteroids to reduce inflammation, antibiotics to combat any infections that may be present, acetaminophen to reduce pain, and possibly immunosuppresants to prevent inflammation.

Contraindications

Massage of a client with ulcerative colitis depends on the client's symptoms and how they are feeling that day. If a client presents with fever and body aches, massage should be postponed until the symptoms resolve. If symptoms are generally mild, massage may be performed.

Endocrine System Pathologies

Acromegaly

(acro-: extremity; -megaly: irregular enlargement)

Acromegaly is **abnormal growth** during adulthood, resulting from the release of excessive amounts of **growth hormone** by the pituitary gland. This can cause bones to keep growing, increasing a person's size and changing their appearance.

Acromegaly can result in numerous severe health issues, such as cardiovascular issues, hypertension, sleep apnea, and arthritis.

Causes

As previously discussed, acromegaly is caused by increased amounts of growth hormone being produced by the pituitary gland. The most common reason for this to occur is a **tumor** growing on the pituitary gland. The tumor produces growth hormone and secretes it into the blood stream, increasing the growth hormone levels in the body. Rarely, a tumor elsewhere in the body, such as the adrenal glands, may produce growth hormone. This can also increase growth hormone levels in the body.

Symptoms

Symptoms of acromegaly generally take some time to appear, as the disease slowly progresses. Enlarged hands and feet are an extremely common symptom. Enlargement of facial features, including the jaw and brow lines, can typically be seen in advanced stages. Skin can become thickened and the voice can deepen.

Treatments

If acromegaly is the result of a tumor, surgery may be performed to remove the tumor. Removing the tumor should stabilize the growth hormone levels in the body. After surgery, radiation therapy may be performed to destroy any remaining tumor cells in the body. This can help ensure the tumor does not return. Medications may help reduce the effects of growth hormone in the body.

Contraindications

Massage is indicated for acromegaly.

Addison's Disease

Addison's Disease is an autoimmune disorder affecting the adrenal glands, which results in a lack of cortisol and/or aldosterone production.

Causes

Addison's Disease is caused by damage to the **adrenal cortex** by the body's immune system. Damage to these glands results in an inability to produce cortisol and aldosterone. Cortisol regulates stress levels in the body by helping control blood sugar, blood pressure, and metabolism. Aldosterone aids in reabsorption of water and sodium back into the blood stream.

Symptoms

Addison's Disease may result in fatigue, weight loss, low blood pressure, hair loss, hyperpigmentation of the skin, and nausea. It may become life-threatening if not treated.

Acute adrenal failure, also known as Addisonian Crisis, may result in severe vomiting and diarrhea, dehydration, low blood pressure, and pain in the low back, abdomen, and/or legs.

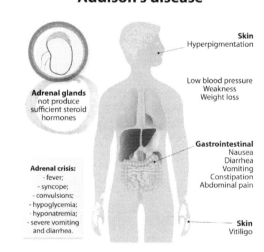

Addison's disease

Adrenal glands
not produce
sufficient steroid
hormones

Adrenal crisis:
- fever;
- syncope;
- convulsions;
- hypoglycemia;
- hyponatremia;
- severe vomiting
and diarrhea.

Skin
Hyperpigmentation

Low blood pressure
Weakness
Weight loss

Gastrointestinal
Nausea
Diarrhea
Vomiting
Constipation
Abdominal pain

Skin
Vitiligo

Treatments

Treatment primarily consists of hormone replacements, which may be taken orally or injected.

Contraindications

Massage is indicated for a client with Addison's Disease. However, the type and length of massage varies depending on how a client is feeling and their stamina. Clients with low stamina should receive shorter, lighter massages, while clients with increased stamina may receive longer and stimulating massages.

Cushing's Disease

Cushing's Disease is a disease of the pituitary gland, which results in **hyper-production** of **adrenocorticotropic hormone**(ACTH).

Causes

Cushing's Disease is the result of hyperplasia(excessive growth) of the pituitary gland, or development of a tumor. This causes too much ACTH to be released in the body, which stimulates hyper-production of **cortisol**.

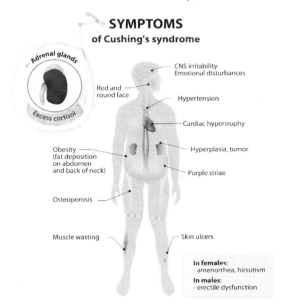

SYMPTOMS
of Cushing's syndrome

Symptoms

Cushing's Disease may result in weight gain around the face and torso, weakening of bone, thinning of skin, fatigue, and acne, amongst other complications.

Treatments

Treatments for Cushing's Disease include surgery to remove a tumor, and hormone therapy to reduce the production of cortisol.

Contraindications

Massage is indicated for Cushing's Disease, but precautions may be taken in clients with weakened bones. Lighter massage is recommended for these clients to prevent damaging bone.

Diabetes Mellitus
(diabetes: to pass through; mellitus: sweet)

Diabetes Mellitus is a condition of the endocrine system that affects **insulin** function in the body.

There are three types of diabetes: Diabetes Type I, Diabetes Type II, and Gestational Diabetes.

Causes

Diabetes Type I is often known as juvenile diabetes, as it begins in childhood. In Type I, the body's immune system attacks the pancreas, the organ that produces insulin. This results in the body **not producing enough insulin,** which the body needs in order to convert glucose to energy.

Diabetes Type II, the most common form of diabetes, is caused by the body having an **insulin resistance**. The insulin in the body is unable to break down glucose, which causes high levels of sugar in the blood stream. Obesity is a common cause of Diabetes Type II.

Gestational Diabetes is only present during pregnancy. Gestational Diabetes typically affects less than 10% of all pregnant women, and typically resolves after pregnancy ends.

Symptoms

Symptoms of diabetes include frequent urination, fatigue, weight loss, pain and/or numbness in the hands or feet, extreme thirst, and extreme hunger.

Treatments

Treatment for Diabetes Type I is primarily insulin injections. Treatment for Diabetes Type II includes medications, but exercise and dietary changes are most common. Treatment for Gestational Diabetes includes exercise, regulating weight gain during pregnancy, and possibly insulin medication depending on the severity.

Contraindications

Massage is indicated for a client with diabetes. If neuropathy is present, lighter massage in the affected area should be performed. If ulcers are present in areas afflicted with neuropathy, ulcers should be treated as local contraindications. If a client injects insulin, the injection site should also be avoided.

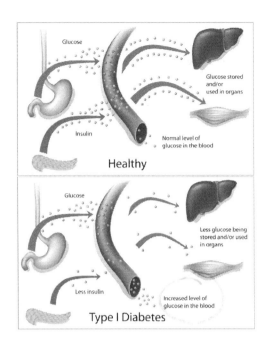

Goiter
(Latin "guttur": throat)

A goiter is an **enlargement** of the **thyroid** gland, located at the base of the neck.

Causes

The primary cause of a goiter is **a lack of iodine** in the diet. If a person does not consume enough iodine, the body is unable to produce sufficient thyroid hormones. Other conditions, such as Grave's disease or Hashimoto's disease, can affect the levels of thyroid hormone being produced. Too much thyroid hormone or too little thyroid hormone being produced can have negative effects on the thyroid and could produce a goiter.

Symptoms

Goiters produce a bulge in the throat, which may place pressure on other structures such as the esophagus or trachea, making it difficult to eat or breathe.

Treatments

Treatment of a goiter typically depends on the cause. If it is caused by low levels of thyroid hormones, thyroid hormone replacement medications may be prescribed. If the thyroid is producing too much thyroid hormones, medications may be prescribed to stabilize the levels of thyroid hormones in the body. Surgery to remove the thyroid may be an option if the goiter causes any difficulty in breathing or swallowing, or causes discomfort.

Increasing iodine consumption may be all it takes to reduce the goiter. Iodized salt may be added to the diet, along with other foods high in iodine such as seafood.

Contraindications

A goiter is considered a local contraindication.

Grave's Disease

Grave's Disease is an autoimmune disorder, in which the body's immune system attacks the thyroid gland, causing an increase in thyroid hormone production(**hyperthyroidism**).

Causes

The exact cause of Grave's disease is unknown.

Symptoms

Grave's Disease can affect numerous parts of the body, resulting in sensitivity to heat, weight loss, the development of a goiter(enlargement of the thyroid), bulging of the eyes, and irregular heart rhythm. Women are more likely to develop Grave's Disease, as well as people under the age of 40.

Treatments

Treatment for Grave's Disease include medications such as beta blockers and anti-thyroid medications. If medication isn't helpful, surgical removal of the thyroid may be an option.

Contraindications

Grave's Disease is generally considered not contraindicated. However, a client with Grave's Disease may be sensitive to heat, so anything that uses heat in the massage treatment should be avoided. A goiter may also be present, which would be considered a local contraindication.

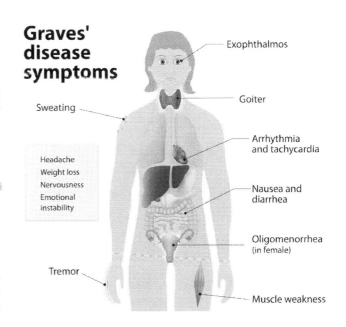

Hyperthyroidism

(hyper-: excessive; thyroid: thyroid gland; -ism: condition)

Hyperthyroidism is an increase in production of **thyroxine**, a hormone secreted by the thyroid gland. Thyroxine is primarily responsible for stimulating tissues to consume oxygen. Excessive amounts of thyroxine can significantly increase the body's metabolism, which can have numerous effects.

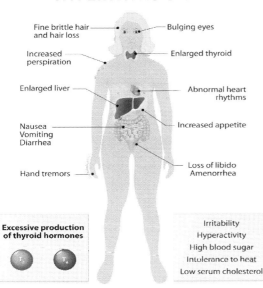

Causes

Hyperthyroidism is often caused by other conditions such as Grave's disease. Tumors may grow in or on the thyroid, which can increase production of thyroxine.

Symptoms

Symptoms of hyperthyroidism are vast, and may be confused with other medical conditions. The main symptom of hyperthyroidism is sudden, rapid weight loss due to an increased metabolism. This may even cause an increase in appetite, despite the lost weight. Arrhythmia, specifically tachycardia, may also result. Heat sensitivity and sweating are other symptoms to be aware of.

Treatments

Treatments are often the same as those seen with Grave's disease, including a prescription of oral radioactive iodine. Other medications may help lower the amount of hormones being produced by the thyroid. If a person has tachycardia as a result of hyperthyroidism, beta blockers may also be prescribed. In cases where these treatments aren't helpful, surgical removal of the thyroid may be performed.

Contraindications

Generally, hyperthyroidism is not contraindicated. However, conditions such as arrhythmia that can be caused by hyperthyroidism may be contraindicated if uncontrolled.

Integumentary System Pathologies

Acne

Acne is an infection of the skin, resulting from numerous factors. Acne may result in whiteheads, blackheads, or even cysts if left untreated.

Causes

Acne is caused by an increased production of sebum on the skin, which results in blocked pores. These blocked pores may become **infected**, which may develop into pustules. There are several contributing factors that lead to the development of acne, including **testosterone** production, stress, hormonal imbalances, and poor personal hygiene.

Symptoms

Acne may result in the development of whiteheads, blackheads, pimples, or even cystic lesions beneath the skin. These are often painful to the touch and may present with infection and inflammation.

Treatments

Treatment includes over the counter skin care products for mild acne, or in the case of severe acne, medications such as birth control pills to regulate hormone levels in women, and antibiotics to eliminate bacterial growth. Other treatments include light therapy and chemical peels.

Contraindications

Whiteheads are considered local contraindications. Any part of the body experiencing inflammation from acne should also be considered a local contraindication.

Athlete's Foot(Tinea Pedis)
(tinea: fungus; pedis: foot)

Athlete's Foot(also known as Tinea Pedis) is a **fungal** infection of the foot. Despite the name, anyone may develop Athlete's Foot, not just athletes. Athlete's Foot, like other fungal infections such as ringworm and jock itch, is highly contagious.

Causes

Athlete's Foot is caused by exposure to fungus on the foot. When a person wears tight-fitting shoes, it provides an environment for the fungus to thrive: a warm, humid, dark space. The fungus spreads, growing between the toes, then expands across the foot. The infection causes the skin to become dry and scaly, which may result in breaking of the skin and bacterial infection.

Symptoms

Symptoms of Athlete's Foot are typically the development of a red, scaly rash between the toes, which may spread proximally. Blisters and ulcers may be present in the area. Itching of the affected area is common.

Treatments

Treatment of Athlete's Foot primarily consists of over the counter medications, in addition to self-care, such as ensuring the foot and footwear are dry as much as possible, wearing shower shoes in public bathing areas, etc.

Contraindications

Because Athlete's Foot is contagious, it is considered a local contraindication. The feet should be avoided, and any linens the feet have come in contact with should be treated as contaminated.

Boil

A boil is a **bacterial** infection of a hair follicle, also known as a **furuncle**. A group of these infections together in one localized area is known as a carbuncle.

Causes

A boil typically results from small cuts in the skin(caused by things like shaving), allowing staphylococci bacterium to enter the body and reproduce. Boils can be red, inflamed, and painful to the touch. The lump initially produced by the infection begins to soften over a few days, and becomes much more painful. Pus develops on the affected area.

Symptoms

A boil may result in pain around the boil, the development of a fever, and swelling of lymph nodes. More boils may develop around the site of the original boil.

Treatments

Boils are treated by lancing(draining) the area with application of antibacterial soap and water, or in more severe cases, prescription of antibiotics to combat the bacterial infection.

Contraindications

A boil is considered a local contraindication for massage.

Burns

Burns are a skin condition in which the skin is damaged due to exposure to **heat, chemicals,** or other means. This may result in inflammation, blister formation, or necrosis, depending on the severity of the burn.

Burns of the skin can be categorized as first, second, third, or fourth degree, with first being the least severe.

A first degree burn only affects the epidermis. It may lead to pain and inflammation of the skin, but nothing more. A common first degree burn is a sun burn. The pain and inflammation subsides in a day or two, and the skin returns to normal.

A second degree burn is more severe. In a second degree burn, the burn moves through the epidermis and into the dermis. Because the burn goes deeper into the skin, it causes more damage, which can be seen by blistering. Blisters form to help repair the damage done by the burn. Second degree burns may result in scarring if they are too severe.

Third degree burns move even deeper into the skin, reaching the subcutaneous layer of the skin. Third degree burns often cause severe tissue damage and necrosis. Skin grafts may be needed to help repair an area affected by a third degree burn.

While first, second, and third degree burns are most common, a fourth degree burn moves completely through all layers of the skin, and goes deeper into tissues beneath the skin, such as tendons, ligaments, muscles, and bones.

Causes

As stated, burns may be caused by many different factors, including heat(thermal burns), chemicals, electricity, radiation(such as sunburns), friction(rug burns), and even extreme cold temperatures.

Symptoms

Burn symptoms vary based on severity. First degree burns often present with inflammation and pain. Second degree burns present with pain, blistering, and discoloration of the skin as the body repairs the damaged tissue. Third degree burns may present with blackened, charred tissue, with the skin having a waxy appearance. Because tissue is destroyed in third and fourth degree burns, loss of sensation may occur resulting from nerves being destroyed.

Treatments

Treatment for burns often depends on the severity of the burn. Application of aloe vera may help reduce the pain in first degree burns. Second degree burns may require bandages with topical antibiotic cream to prevent infection. Third degree burns may require surgery and skin grafts to repair the affected areas.

Contraindications

Burns are considered local contraindications for massage. Avoid any area experiencing inflammation, blistering, or has suffered necrosis.

Cellulitis
(cell: cell; -itis: inflammation)

Cellulitis is a bacterial infection of the skin, causing symptoms such as inflammation of the infected area, fever, pain, and blisters.

Causes

Cellulitis is caused by **staphylococci** bacterium entering the body through exposure to **wounds**, most commonly on the legs. The infection typically stays localized, but continues to spread to surrounding tissues as the bacteria grows. The infection can present with well-defined borders of infection. If the infection enters the blood stream, it may result in septicemia, a potentially life-threatening condition.

Spider or insect bites may also introduce the bacterium into the body. Any insect bite should be cleaned thoroughly to prevent infection.

Symptoms

Cellulitis may present with many symptoms, including a red area of skin that spreads and increases in size over time, swelling, pain, fever, and blisters on the infected area.

Treatments

Treatment for cellulitis includes antibiotic medication, taken orally. Cellulitis is not typically contagious.

Contraindications

Cellulitis is considered a local contraindication. Any open wounds should be avoided.

Decubitus Ulcer
(decubitus: the act of lying down; ulcer: open sore)

A decubitus ulcer is a condition affecting the skin, resulting in the development of open sores.

Causes

Decubitus ulcers are also known as **bed sores** or **pressure ulcers**. When the body is in a static position for an extended period of time, such as when lying down, the parts of the body coming in contact with the bed, floor, or chair experience **ischemia**, a reduction of blood flow to the tissues due to pressure. When ischemia is present for too long, the tissue experiences **necrosis** due to a lack of oxygen. The dead tissue becomes ulcerated, and bacterial infection may occur.

People who are prone to decubitus ulcers are the elderly, disabled people, and people confined to a bed or wheelchair.

Symptoms

Symptoms of decubitus ulcers include discoloration of the skin, tenderness in the affected area, temperature variation in the affected area, and swelling. In severe cases, infection may result after ulceration has occurred.

Treatments

Treatments for decubitus ulcers vary, depending on the severity of the ulceration. If an infection is present, antibiotics may be prescribed. If there is an abundance of necrotic tissue, cleaning of the area(debridement) may be performed. If there is ischemia, but no ulcer, massage and application of heat may help bring blood back into the area.

Contraindications

A decubitus ulcer is considered a local contraindication if the skin has developed into an ulcer. If the skin has not opened, massage in the area is indicated to increase blood flow into the affected tissue. If the sore is present, massage up to two inches around the area is indicated to increase circulation and prevent further necrosis.

Dermatitis
(dermat/o: skin; -itis: inflammation)

Dermatitis is **inflammation** of the **skin**. There are several types of dermatitis, including contact dermatitis, atopic dermatitis, and seborrheic dermatitis. Each has different causes, but each presents with some sort of inflammation of the skin.

Causes

Contact dermatitis results when the skin comes in to contact with some sort of **irritant or allergen,** causing the skin to become inflamed. Atopic dermatitis, also known as eczema, can be caused by numerous factors, including an improperly functioning immune system, bacteria, dry skin, and the environment. Eczema usually begins in infancy. Seborrheic dermatitis is typically the result of a fungus growing on the skin, usually in regions that are more oily than others such as the scalp.

Symptoms

Contact dermatitis presents with inflammation and possible blistering where the skin has come into contact with an irritant. This is usually an acute condition, and will improve after the irritant has been cleaned or removed from the body. Atopic dermatitis presents with red, itchy patches on the body, usually near joints that flex and extend. This can be a chronic condition, and the patches may go away and come back later depending on factors such as the weather. Seborrheic dermatitis can cause itchy patches around the face, cheeks, nose, back, and chest.

Treatments

Often times, application of an over-the-counter corticosteroid cream is all that's needed to alleviate dermatitis symptoms. If over-the-counter creams are ineffective, prescription strength corticosteroid creams may be administered, which usually take care of the dermatitis. Other treatments can even include exposure to sunlight.

Contraindications

Dermatitis is considered a local contraindication, as massage to the affected area will increase inflammation.

Herpes Simplex
(herpein: to creep; simplex: simple)

Herpes Simplex is a **viral** infection of the skin. There are two types of Herpes Simplex: Herpes Simplex I, which causes sores around the mouth, and Herpes Simplex II, which causes sores around the genitals.

Causes

Herpes Simplex is highly contagious, passing between people via direct contact. During an acute outbreak, a sore may appear on the skin, most commonly the mouth, face, or genitals. This sore disappears after a short time. Despite not having any sores present, a person may still be able to transmit the virus to another asymptomatically.

Symptoms

Symptoms vary depending on the type of Herpes Simplex a person has. Herpes Simplex I primarily presents with sores around the mouth, while Herpes Simplex II may cause painful urination. Both forms, however, may result in fever, headache, and swollen lymph nodes.

Treatments

While there is no cure for Herpes Simplex, medications may be prescribed to reduce the chance of spreading the infection to others.

Contraindications

In the acute stage, any sore caused by the herpes simplex virus is considered a local contraindication. In the period of remission, massage is indicated.

Impetigo
(impetere: to attack)

Impetigo is a **bacterial** infection of the skin, most commonly seen in children. Impetigo is often confused with Hand, Foot, and Mouth Disease, which is a viral infection.

Causes

Impetigo is a highly contagious infection, caused by staphylococci or streptococci, which most commonly enter the body through already damaged skin, but may affect healthy skin as well. When the bacteria enters the skin, it produces sores that blister and leak a yellow, crust-like fluid. These sores typically develop around the mouth, nose, and ears.

Symptoms

Symptoms of Impetigo include red sores that may pop and leave a yellowish crust, swollen lymph nodes, and fluid-filled blisters. The affected areas may also itch.

Treatments

Depending on the severity of the infection, impetigo may be treated with topical antibiotic cream for less severe cases, or with oral antibiotics for more severe cases. Recovery time is typically around one week with the use of medication.

Contraindications

Impetigo is a highly contagious bacterial infection, and therefore, is an absolute contraindication.

Lice

Lice are small **parasites** that live on the head that feed on human blood. They primarily live on the **scalp**. Children are most likely to contract a lice infestation, also known as pediculosis capitis.

Causes

Lice are spread via direct contact. Lice do not jump or fly, and therefore must physically come into contact with a person to transfer to them. After lice have attached to a new host, they lay eggs on hair shafts. Once the eggs hatch, more lice are present.

Symptoms

The main symptom of lice is itching, caused by an allergy to the saliva of the lice.

Treatments

Over-the-counter or prescription medications may be prescribed to help kill the lice. Shampoos specifically designed to eliminate lice are often used.

Contraindications

Lice is a highly contagious parasitic infection, and is therefore an absolute contraindication.

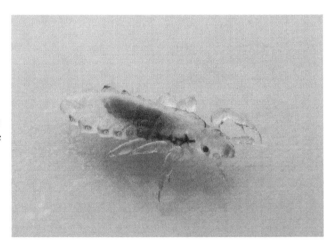

Onychomycosis
(onycho-: nails; myc-: fungus; -osis: condition)

Onychomycosis is a **fungal** infection of the **nails**, most commonly the result of an infection by the dermatophyte fungi.

Causes

Onychomycosis is caused by fungi entering a nail, typically more common in older people due to the natural drying and cracking of nails that happens with age. The fungus enters into these cracks and begins growing, infecting the nail. Athlete's foot may also spread in to the area and infect the nail.

Symptoms

Symptoms of onychomycosis include thickening of the infected nail, change in the nail shape, discoloration of the nail turning it yellow or brown, and the nail becoming brittle.

Treatments

If symptoms are mild, treatment may not be necessary. When treatment is required, however, antifungal medications are the main form of treatment. Oral antifungals are used more often than topical creams, as they can work quicker. If the infection is severe, the nail may need to be surgically removed to allow antifungal cream to be applied directly to the nail bed.

Contraindications

Onychomycosis is a contagious fungal infection, and is considered a local contraindication.

Psoriasis
(psora-; to itch; -iasis: condition)

Psoriasis is an **autoimmune** disorder of the skin, resulting in the production of thick, dry, scaly patches. Psoriasis has periods of exacerbation and remission, where the patches appear and then resolve themselves.

Causes

The exact cause of psoriasis is unknown. Certain triggers, such as stress, may cause the body's immune system to attack the skin. Normally, skin cells have a life span of 3-4 weeks, and ultimately flake off the body. When the immune system attacks the skin, the body responds by increasing production of epithelial cells at an extremely rapid pace, which is much faster than the cells are being destroyed. This rapid pace of cell production is what produces the patches on the skin.

Symptoms

Symptoms of psoriasis differ based on each person, but may include red, patchy skin covered in thick, silvery scales, dry skin that may crack and bleed, thickened finger and toe nails, and itchy skin.

Treatments

There is no cure for psoriasis, but treatments are available to help manage the condition. Treatments include topical creams(which may contain steroids), exposure to sunlight, and application of aloe vera.

Contraindications

Psoriasis is not contraindicated for massage. Massage may be altered if the patches are painful or are scabbing, but otherwise, the patches may be massaged.

Ringworm
(dermato-: skin, phyt-: plant; -osis: condition)

Ringworm(also known as dermatophytosis) is a **fungal** infection of the skin, similar to Athlete's Foot. Despite the name, it is not a parasitic infection. It results in a ring-like area of infection.

Causes

Fungus, like the kind found in ringworm, live on the dead cells of the body, such as the epidermis. When ringworm is contracted, it forms red blisters and a ring of infection begins to show, which then spreads as the infection grows through the skin.

Ringworm is contagious, and may be spread from person to person. It is especially common in athletes whose bodies come in close contact with one another, such as wrestlers.

Symptoms

Ringworm typically presents with well-defined circular patches of infection on the skin, usually more red on the outer edges than inside. These patches can be itchy and develop blisters.

Treatments

Treatment includes good personal hygiene, and most commonly application of antifungal ointment to the affected area. More severe cases may require oral antifungal medication.

Contraindications

Ringworm is a highly contagious fungal infection, and is considered a local contraindication. Linens should be treated as contaminated.

Scabies

Scabies is a **parasitic** infection caused by a **mite**, known as Sacroptes scabiei. This mite **burrows under the skin** and lays eggs, causing intense itching. The tunnels the mite creates are visible in the skin. Scratching due to a scabies infection may lead to an infection, and is not recommended.

Causes

Scabies are extremely contagious, transmitting easily from one person to the next via physical contact, or sharing clothing or other linens.

Symptoms

The main symptoms of a scabies infection are severe itching and visible burrows in the skin where the mite has worked its way in to the body.

Treatments

Topical creams that are specifically designed to kill mites are prescribed to treat scabies. They kill the mites quickly, but itching may persist for some time after treatment begins.

Contraindications

Scabies is a contagious parasitic infection, and is considered an absolute contraindication.

Sebaceous Cyst

A sebaceous cyst is a condition affecting the skin, but may affect other tissues as well.

Causes

A **sebaceous** gland produces oil, and secretes oil onto the surface of the skin. If a blockage of a sebaceous gland occurs, oil cannot escape the gland, and bacteria may infect the area. If too much bacteria is present, the body may develop connective tissue that surrounds the infected sebaceous gland, trapping it inside. This is a sebaceous cyst.

Sebaceous cysts may be large or small. They may be painful to the touch, or may lead to localized infections known as abscesses. Cysts may need to be removed surgically. If the entire cyst membrane is not removed, there may be a chance of the cyst returning in the future.

Symptoms

Some cysts show no symptoms, but symptoms are more likely to appear the larger the cyst is. Small cysts usually do not cause pain, but large cysts may cause pain and discomfort in the surrounding area.

Treatments

Treatment, if necessary, includes moist compresses on the area to help drain the cyst, or possible surgery if there is a risk of infection. Surgical removal may be required if the cyst is large, causes pain, or may be cancerous.

Contraindications

Sebaceous cysts are considered local contraindications, and should be avoided to prevent damaging the cyst and allowing the fluid inside to affect the body. The area may also be painful.

Urticaria

Urticaria, also known as **hives**, is a condition that results in welts, known as **wheals**, appearing on the skin. Wheals are raised areas that typically itch. Wheals can appear anywhere on the body.

Causes

Urticaria is caused by the release of **histamines** into the blood. The body may release histamines in response to the body coming in to contact with a substance it is allergic to, in response to insect or bug bites/stings, scratches, and even certain infections. Histamines dilate blood vessels, which bring leukocytes in to the area to help destroy any substance that may be causing the reaction.

Symptoms

Typically seen in the skin, wheals form that are usually itchy. These can be raised off the skin, discolored, and possibly painful.

Treatments

Over-the-counter histamines are likely the first treatment recommended. If the condition does not resolve, prescription antihistamines may be given. Immunosuppressants, anti-inflammatory medication, and even oral corticosteroids such as prednisone may also be given to help with the reaction.

Contraindications

In the acute stage, the cause of the hives should be determined before massage can be performed. Once cause is determined, massage on the area should be avoided, or if it's a more serious reason for hives, massage should be avoided completely.

Wart

Warts(also known as verrucae), are small benign growths on the skin, caused by the **human papilloma virus(HPV)**.

Causes

Warts are contagious, and may be spread by direct skin contact. The human papilloma virus stimulates the skin to produce more keratin, which causes a hard, thick overgrowth on a small localized area. This is a wart.

Warts may be located in numerous locations on the body, including the hands, feet(plantar warts), and genitals(genital warts).

Symptoms

Warts are typically rough, grainy bumps, which may be a range of colors, from the color of the person's skin to white, tan, or even pink. Often, warts may have black spots in them, which is nothing more than blood clots.

Depending on the location of the wart, such as plantar warts, the wart may be painful due to calluses forming over them, pushing them deeper into the skin.

Warts often go into remission on their own, and treatment is not necessary. Treatment options include cryotherapy to freeze the wart, excising(cutting out) the wart, or electrosurgery to burn the wart.

Contraindications

Warts are contagious, and should be treated as a local contraindication.

Wounds

Wounds are the result of a **breakage** in the skin, which exposes underlying tissues. There are several different types of open wounds. An **abrasion** is a scraping off of layers of the skin, such as a skinned knee from falling. An **incision**, such as produced during surgery, is a **clean cut** through tissue. A **laceration** is a cut that produces **jagged edges**. A **puncture** is caused by an object **piercing** the skin, producing a **hole**.

Causes

Wounds can be caused by many different factors. Ischemia may cause wounds in cases such as decubitus ulcers(page 115). Infections may cause wounds to appear in the skin as well. Damage to blood vessels, like those seen in diabetes mellitus(page 108) can result in wounds.

Trauma is usually the main cause of wounds, however. These include abrasions, lacerations, incisions, and punctures.

Symptoms

Wounds in the acute stage often present with bleeding, pain, and redness in the area. These symptoms usually resolve with the healing process. If a wound is not properly treated, infection may occur, along with fever if the infection becomes systemic. A wound that becomes infected and results in necrosis is known as gangrene, caused by a severe lack of blood flow in the area.

Treatments

Wounds should be cleansed with soap and water, and a sterile bandage should be applied to stop bleeding. If a wound is caused by a bite from an animal or insect, medical attention may(and probably should) be recommended.

Contraindications

Wounds should be treated as local contraindications until healed.

Abrasion

Laceration

Puncture

Lymphatic System Pathologies

Acquired Immunodeficiency Syndrome

Acquired Immunodeficiency Syndrome, also known as **AIDS**, is a chronic condition caused by **HIV** infection, the human immunodeficiency virus. Once in the body, HIV destroys the body's **T-cells**, which function to regulate the response of the body's immune system to antigens. When HIV destroys too many of the body's T-cells, the immune system is considered compromised, and a person is then diagnosed with AIDS. While most people who are infected with HIV in the United States are properly treated and don't develop AIDS, a small portion of people do gets AIDS after HIV infection, typically around ten years after initial infection.

Causes

HIV is spread though unprotected sex, through needles that have been shared by an infected person, as a result of a mother passing HIV on to their unborn child, or even through blood transfusions if the blood has not been properly screened beforehand. HIV cannot be spread through skin contact, water contact, through the bites of insects such as mosquitoes, or breathing in the air of an infected person.

Symptoms

Close after the initial infection has occurred, a person may experience fever, fatigue, body aches, headache, and swollen lymph nodes. As the infection spreads, symptoms emerge such as diarrhea and weight loss in conjunction with previously mentioned symptoms.

Complications caused by infection by HIV include being more prone to infection of other conditions, such as pneumonia. A type of cancer known as Kaposi's Sarcoma may develop. Severe wasting of the body may occur, in which a person loses at least ten percent of their total body weight.

Treatments

A person infected with HIV should be prescribed antiretroviral therapy to help prevent the virus from further replicating.

Contraindications

AIDS is not a contraindication to massage. Any open sores should be treated as a local contraindication. If the client isn't feeling well, massage should be rescheduled.

Allergy

An allergy is a reaction of the body's immune system in response to substances that normally **do not affect people**. Common substances people may be allergic to include dust, pollen, mold, certain foods, pet dander, and medication.

Causes

Allergies occur when a substance enters the body that the body's immune system thinks is dangerous. The body produces **antibodies** for that specific substance. When the substance enters the body, the body releases the antibodies and other substances such as **histamines** to attack the substance. The release of histamines is what gives people allergy symptoms.

Symptoms

Allergies may be mild, or may be severe and result in serious conditions such as anaphylactic shock. Anaphylactic shock requires the use of an epinephrine shot to reverse the effects of the allergen. Less severe allergies may result in a runny nose, itchy eyes or skin, and hives.

Treatments

Typical treatments of allergens include the use of antihistamines, decongestants, and steroid nasal sprays. Avoiding the allergen is advised.

Contraindications

Allergies should be determined prior to massage to avoid using any allergens in massage lubricant. If a client develops any signs of contact with an allergen during the massage, massage should be stopped. If essential oils are the cause of the allergic reaction, effects can be managed with the application of vegetable oil.

Lupus Erythematosus
(lupus: wolf; erythemat-: red skin; -osus: pertaining to)

Lupus Erythematosus is an autoimmune disorder affecting the **connective tissues** of the entire body, but can be physically seen in the skin by the formation of a **butterfly rash** that appears on the face during flare-ups. This rash is similar in shape to the markings found on the face of a wolf, which is where lupus gets its name.

Causes

The exact cause of lupus is unknown. Some experts believe it is a genetic disorder that affects the immune system's function. Lupus may also be triggered by smoking, sunlight, infections, and medications.

Symptoms

Symptoms of lupus erythematosus include fever, the formation of a butterfly rash, joint pain, discomfort, fatigue, and sensitivity to sunlight. It may also contribute to the development of other medical conditions, such as Raynaud's Syndrome.

Treatments

There is no cure for lupus erythematosus, but treatment is available to help manage the condition. Non-steroidal anti-inflammatory drugs may help with systemic inflammation in non-severe cases. Topical corticosteroid creams may help alleviate rashes. Blood thinners may also be used in more severe cases.

Contraindications

During flare-ups, lupus may cause extensive pain over the body, and massage would likely be postponed until the condition has gone into remission. If there are no symptoms, lupus is not contraindicated.

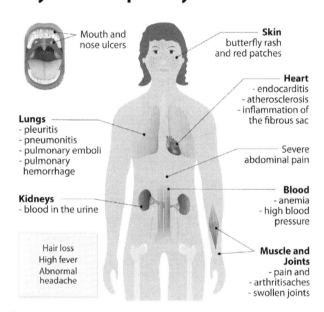

Systemic lupus erythematosus

Mouth and nose ulcers

Skin
butterfly rash and red patches

Heart
- endocarditis
- atherosclerosis
- inflammation of the fibrous sac

Lungs
- pleuritis
- pneumonitis
- pulmonary emboli
- pulmonary hemorrhage

Severe abdominal pain

Kidneys
- blood in the urine

Blood
- anemia
- high blood pressure

Hair loss
High fever
Abnormal headache

Muscle and Joints
- pain and
- arthritisaches
- swollen joints

Lymphedema
(lymph: lymph; -edema: swelling)

Lymphedema is a condition of the lymphatic system that results in increased **interstitial fluid** in a limb, which causes **swelling**.

Causes

Causes of lymphedema vary. Most commonly, it results from damage to the lymph nodes and vessels during treatment for cancer(such as a mastectomy, where breast tissue and lymph channels may be completely removed). This results in lymph not draining properly. Other causes include obesity and advanced age.

Symptoms

Symptoms of lymphedema include swelling in the limbs, restricted range-of-motion, discomfort in the affected area, and thickening of the skin.

Treatments

While there is no cure for lymphedema, treatments may help reduce the amount of fluid in the area by stimulating lymph circulation. Massage therapy is highly effective at increasing lymph circulation. Compression clothing may help move lymph. Exercise is also extremely helpful in increasing lymph flow.

Contraindications

Lymphedema is not contraindicated for massage. Lymphatic drainage may help move lymph out of the area. When performing lymphatic drainage, light strokes moving towards the trunk should be performed on the proximal end of the affected limb, then distal areas may be worked on, again with strokes moving towards the trunk.

Pitting Edema
(edema: swelling)

Pitting edema is a form of lymphedema that produces **pits** in the skin after pressure is applied and released. Lymphedema does not leave pits, and the skin rebounds immediately due to the amount of fluid in the area.

Causes

Pitting edema may be non-serious, or may have severe underlying causes. A common cause of pitting edema is pregnancy, due to the body creating much more fluid than it normally has. This increases fluid retention. Other more serious causes include heart failure, liver failure, or most commonly amongst these, **renal** failure. If these organs are not functioning properly, fluid is not properly drained from the body, which increases swelling.

Symptoms

Pitting edema results in pits left in the skin after applying pressure. Other symptoms may include swelling, pain, numbness, and cramping in the area. If the swelling is near a joint, movement of the joint may become difficult.

Treatments

For serious cases of pitting edema, it is recommended to visit a doctor to find the underlying cause. Once the cause is determined, a proper treatment plan may be developed. Typically, if a person is suffering from organ failure, diuretics may be prescribed to help drain excess fluid from the body. Keeping limbs such as the legs elevated may also help reduce swelling.

Contraindications

Massage on a client with pitting edema should not be performed until the cause of pitting edema is established. If the cause is something such as pregnancy and not organ failure, massage of the limb may be performed as it would be done with lymphedema.

Muscular System Pathologies

Adhesive Capsulitis
(capsul-: capsule; -itis: inflammation)

Adhesive capsulitis is a condition of the muscular system, which results in restricted range-of-motion at the shoulder joint. Another name for adhesive capsulitis is "Frozen Shoulder".

Causes

Surrounding the glenohumeral joint is connective tissue known as the joint capsule. This joint capsule holds everything in the joint in place, such as the bones themselves, synovial membrane, synovial fluid, etc. If there is irritation or over-use of the shoulder joint, **adhesions** may form between the joint capsule and the head of the humerus. These adhesions can decrease range-of-motion in the joint, and make movement in the joint uncomfortable.

The **subscapularis** muscle is often called the "Frozen Shoulder Muscle", due to its possible role in adhesive capsulitis. If the subscapularis is hypertonic, it may pull back on the humerus, which can restrict range-of-motion.

Symptoms

As adhesive capsulitis progresses, symptoms vary. In beginning stages, pain may be present, with a gradual decrease in the range-of-motion. As the condition advances, pain may subside, with a severely reduced range-of-motion.

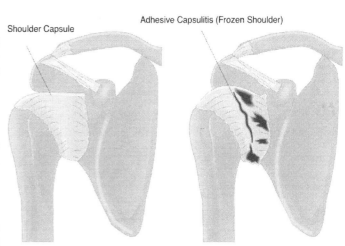

Shoulder Capsule

Adhesive Capsulitis (Frozen Shoulder)

Treatments

Treatments include stretching exercises and massage therapy to help break up the adhesions restricting range-of-motion, or to relax the subscapularis.

Contraindications

Adhesive capsulitis is not a contraindication. Massage may help loosen adhesions and increase range-of-motion. Stretching should be performed, as well as compression in the joint.

De Quervain's Tenosynovitis
(teno-: tendon; synov-: synovial; -itis: inflammation)

De Quervain's Tenosynovitis is a form of tenosynovitis(page 129) that specifically affects the **thumb**.

Causes

De Quervain's Tenosynovitis is caused by **over-use** of the thumb, which contributes to straining of the tendons around the thumb, and their protective sheaths. This may cause pain around the thumb, inflammation, and difficulty in moving the area.

Symptoms

Symptoms include pain and inflammation at the base of the thumb, loss of sensation in the posterior thumb, and difficulty moving the thumb and/or wrist while performing certain actions. Pain may gradually increase and radiate to other areas, such as the posterior forearm.

Treatments

Treatments primarily consist of rest and ice to reduce pain and inflammation in the area. Any repetitive actions that are causing the inflammation should be stopped to allow irritation to subside.

Contraindications

Massage is a local contraindication for De Quervain's Tenosynovitis, as it may increase inflammation and pain. Application of cold may be performed to decrease inflammation around the thumb.

Dupuytren's Contracture

Dupuytren's Contracture is a condition that results in **deformation of the hand** due to tissues under the skin hardening, thickening, and shortening. These tissues pull the fingers into **flexion**, and don't allow the fingers to completely straighten.

Causes

There are no known causes of Dupuytren's contracture. Men over the age of 50 are more likely to develop the condition, but exact reasons why are still not understood.

Symptoms

Deformity of the hand, specifically in the pinky finger, can occur. The skin on the palm of the hand can thicken, and the fascia under the skin thickens, pulling the pinky and ring finger towards the palm. This causes the affected fingers to lose the ability to fully extend, impairing function of the hand.

Treatments

Treatments include injecting enzymes into the cords to help soften them, a technique called needling in which needles are inserted in to the cords that help to break them, or surgery to partially or completely remove the cords from the hand. Each treatment has varying degrees of success, and the contracture may return.

Contraindications

Dupuytren's contracture is indicated for massage, although massage is unlikely to help loosen the tendon and help the finger return to its normal position.

Fibromyalgia
(fibro-: fibrous; my-: muscle; -algia: pain)

Fibromyalgia is a condition causing **pain** throughout the body, in conjunction with fatigue. Trouble with memory may also be present. Fibromyalgia may occur suddenly, or may worsen over time. Fibromyalgia typically affects women much more often than men. Diagnosis involves first ruling out other conditions that may be causing symptoms. If these other conditions are ruled out, then the duration of pain(over three months) and location of pain(using the Widespread Pain Index) are taken into account.

Causes

The exact cause of fibromyalgia is unknown. Many theories state the cause could range from hereditary to environmental factors, such as stress or trauma.

Symptoms

Symptoms of fibromyalgia primarily include widespread pain, usually a dull ache in specific regions of the body for longer than three months, general fatigue, and issues with memory.

Treatments

Medications are important in the treatment of fibromyalgia. Pain relievers help to reduce the pain a person may be experiencing, while antidepressants can help treat depression that may result due to the fatigue a person can experience.

Contraindications

✓ Fibromyalgia is indicated for massage, working within the client's pain tolerance.

Golfer's Elbow

Golfer's Elbow is a form of tendonitis that affects and weakens the **flexors** of the wrist. Golfer's Elbow is also known as Medial Epicondylitis, inflammation of the **medial epicondyle**.

Causes

Golfer's Elbow is caused by repetitive motions such as elbow flexion, which put strain on the tendons connecting the flexors of the wrist to the humerus, at the medial epicondyle.

Symptoms

Golfer's Elbow may present with pain and inflammation at the medial epicondyle of the humerus, weakness in the elbow joint, and numbness in digits four and five.

Treatments

Treatment typically involves rest and ice on the medial epicondyle to reduce inflammation. Any repetitive actions that are causing the inflammation should be stopped to allow irritation to subside.

Contraindications

Golfer's Elbow should be treated as a local contraindication. Application of cold may help reduce pain and inflammation at the medial epicondyle of the humerus.

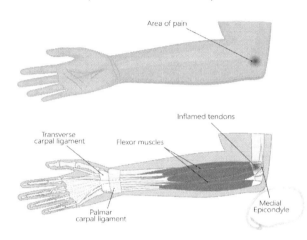

GOLFER'S ELBOW
(MEDIAL EPICONDYLITIS)

Strain

A strain is an injury to a **tendon** or **muscle**, usually caused by over-exertion or over-use.

Causes

Activities such as exercise are a common cause of strains. Much like burns, there are three grades of strains: grade 1, grade 2, and grade 3. The less severe the strain, the lower the grade.

A grade 1 strain results in slight tearing of a tendon or muscle. An example could be a person's muscles being sore after exercise. The muscles have experienced slight tears during exercise, but will heal after a day or two.

A grade 2 strain results in more tearing of a muscle or tendon. Grade 2 strains may require surgery to repair, or may heal on their own with rest. There may be accompanying bruising and inflammation around the strain.

A grade 3 strain results in complete tearing of a muscle, or more commonly, a tendon. Surgery is required to repair a grade 3 strain. The quadriceps and biceps brachii are two muscles prone to grade 3 strains more than others. Grade 3 strains will inhibit movement of the muscle involved, due to its inability to pull on the bone.

Symptoms

Strains may result in pain, inflammation, and an inability to move the injured muscle or tendon.

Treatments

Treatment varies depending on the severity of the strain. Grade 1 strains should be able to receive massage and heat therapy after 24-48 hours to increase circulation and promote healing. Grade 2 strains may need to rest longer before receiving treatment. Grade 3 strains would require surgery to repair.

Contraindications

Acute strains are considered a local contraindication, and should be avoided to prevent increasing pain and inflammation in the area. Contrast therapy, utilizing alternating cold and heat, ending with cold, may be performed to decrease inflammation and bring fresh blood and nutrients into the injured area.

Easy to Remember: To remember the difference between a strain and sprain, look for the "t" in "strain"! "T" for "tendon"!

Surgical repair of a grade 3 Achilles tendon rupture

Tendonitis
(tendon-: tendon; -itis: inflammation)

Tendonitis is an injury that results in **inflammation** of a **tendon**.

Causes

Tendonitis is a mostly repetitive strain injury, caused by repeated use of one specific muscle, which can over-exert the tendon. When the tendon is over-exerted, it may tear slightly, which causes pain and inflammation.

There are several different types of tendonitis, including Golfer's Elbow(inflammation of the tendon at the medial epicondyle of the humerus), Tennis Elbow(inflammation of the tendon at the lateral epicondyle of the humerus), and Jumper's Knee(inflammation of the patellar tendon). All these conditions are caused by repetitive movements.

Symptoms

Symptoms may include pain upon moving a muscle connected to an affected tendon, and inflammation.

Treatments

Treatment for tendonitis is primarily rest and application of ice to reduce any inflammation. Repetitive actions causing the inflammation should be stopped until the irritation subsides.

Contraindications

Tendonitis should be treated as a local contraindication. Alternating application of cold and heat, ending with cold, can assist in decreasing inflammation and associated pain.

Tennis Elbow

Tennis Elbow is a form of tendonitis that affects and weakens the **extensors** of the wrist. Tennis Elbow is also known as Lateral Epicondylitis, inflammation of the **lateral epicondyle**.

Causes

Tennis Elbow is caused by repetitive motions such as elbow extension, which put strain on the tendons connecting the extensors of the wrist to the humerus, at the lateral epicondyle.

Symptoms

Tennis Elbow commonly presents with pain that radiates distally to the posterior forearm. Weakness may result, especially when performing actions that require grasping.

Tennis Elbow
Right arm, lateral (outside) side

- Humerus
- Extensor muscles
- Lateral epicondyle
- Injured common extensor tendon

Treatments

Treatment typically involves rest and ice on the lateral epicondyle to reduce inflammation. Any repetitive actions that are causing the inflammation should be stopped to allow irritation to subside.

Contraindications

Tennis Elbow should be treated as a local contraindication. Alternating application of cold and heat, ending with cold, can assist in decreasing inflammation and associated pain at the lateral epicondyle of the humerus.

Tenosynovitis
(teno-: tendon; synov-: synovial; -itis: inflammation)

Tenosynovitis is a repetitive strain injury that results in **inflammation** of a **tendon** and its **protective sheath**.

Causes

Tenosynovitis primarily affects the hands, wrists, and feet due to the length of the tendons in these areas. The longer the tendon is, the easier it becomes to strain. Because there may be inflammation, pain may be present, and it may be difficult to move the affected area.

A common type of tenosynovitis is known as De Quervain's Tenosynovitis, which causes inflammation around the thumb due to overuse.

Symptoms

Tenosynovitis may produce pain and inflammation in affected joints, making it painful to move these joints. The area of the inflamed tendon may also be red.

Treatments

Tenosynovitis is typically treated the same as any strain, with rest and ice to reduce pain. Less commonly, tenosynovitis may be the result of bacterial infection, which may produce a fever. If a fever is present, medications such as antibiotics and antipyretics may be prescribed to combat bacterial growth and fever.

Contraindications

Massage is a local contraindication for tenosynovitis, as it may increase inflammation and pain. Application of cold may be performed to decrease inflammation in the tendon and reduce pain.

Torticollis
(torti-: twisted; collis: neck)

Torticollis, also known as **wry neck**, is a condition causing the neck to **twist to one side**, which tilts the head.

Causes

Trauma to the **cervical region** may cause torticollis, often an injury to the **sternocleidomastoid** the prime cause. Spasms of the sternocleidomastoid may cause a type of torticollis known as spasmodic torticollis, and is usually a chronic condition. An injury to the trochlear nerve may cause a separate type of torticollis known as trochlear torticollis, in which a person must adjust the position of their head to see properly due to the trochlear nerve, which provides stimulation to muscles controlling the eye, no longer functioning as effectively.

Symptoms

A person affected by torticollis will have their head tilted to one side. This can be uncomfortable or painful, especially when trying to move the neck or head back to a normal position. This can also lead to pain in the back and shoulders, and headaches.

Treatments

Because torticollis is the result of a spasm or contraction of neck muscles, treatments aim to relax the affected muscles. These treatments may include physical therapy, prescribing muscle relaxants, or possible surgery to correct any structural issues that may arise. Torticollis usually resolves itself within a few days, unless there is a more severe cause.

Contraindications

Torticollis is generally not considered a contraindication, but precautions should be taken if damage to a muscle or nerve is the cause.

SPASTIC TORTICOLLIS

Nervous System Pathologies

Alzheimer's Disease

Alzheimer's Disease, the most common form of **dementia** (page 165), is an over-arching term for **memory loss**, confusion, and a general loss of intellectual abilities. Alzheimer's is a result of brain tissue gradually dying over time. Increased age is a risk factor of developing Alzheimer's, and becomes much more common after the age of 65 in those affected.

Causes

While the exact cause of Alzheimer's is unknown, environmental factors are the most likely culprit. Few people with Alzheimer's disease develop the disease due to genetic factors.

Two factors strongly contribute to the death of nervous tissue: plaque and tangles. Plaque is the formation of deposits of a protein known as beta-amyloid, which develops in the space between nerves, restricting communication between nerve cells. Tangles are the development of another protein known as tau inside the nerve cells, which can cut off the natural flow of nutrients through cells.

Symptoms

Symptoms begin with difficulty remembering information, such as locations of items or things just learned. As the condition progresses, more brain tissue is lost, and a person may have difficulty making decisions, identifying people or places, and become more irritable or aggressive. Later stages of Alzheimer's may see the loss of the ability to read, write, dance, sing, and other activities learned early in life.

Treatments

There is no cure for Alzheimer's, but there are treatments available that can help manage the condition. Medications may be prescribed that can help with memory loss and other cognitive symptoms. In later stages, other medications may be prescribed that can help with memory, speech, and the ability to perform simpler tasks.

Contraindications

Alzheimer's Disease is not contraindicated, although precautions may be taken in advanced stages of the disease. A person the client knows and is familiar with may stay in the room to assist with the client if the client becomes forgetful regarding their location.

Normal   Alzheimer

Amyotrophic Lateral Sclerosis
(a-: without; my/o-: muscle; -trophic: nourishment)

Amyotrophic Lateral Sclerosis(ALS) is a **degenerative** disorder affecting **motor neurons**, which control muscles. The nerve degeneration causes loss of voluntary muscle control, and can eventually lead to death within five years of diagnosis due to respiratory failure. A small percentage of people diagnosed with ALS survive longer than five years.

Amyotrophic Lateral Sclerosis is also known as Lou Gehrig's Disease, named for the baseball player who was diagnosed with the condition in 1939.

Causes

The precise cause of ALS is unknown. Genetics seem to play a factor. Men are more likely to develop the condition than women, and it is much more common in people over the age of 50.

Symptoms

Symptoms of ALS begin subtly and may not be noticeable until they become more advanced. A person may experience muscle cramping and twitching, weakness in the muscles of the arms, legs, and neck, trouble chewing and swallowing, and slurred speech as the muscles responsible for vocalization are affected. As the disease progresses, muscle atrophy sets in and the person loses the ability to stand or walk.

Treatments

There is no cure for ALS, but treatment options may include medication to assist with muscle pain and cramping, physical therapy and speech therapy, and the use of ventilators as natural breathing support fails.

Contraindications

Massage is indicated for Amyotrophic Lateral Sclerosis. In advanced stages, the therapist may need to assist the client on and off the table. Because the muscles have atrophied, lighter pressure should be performed to avoid damaging tissue.

Bell's Palsy
(palsy: paralysis)

Bell's Palsy is a condition affecting the **facial nerve**, causing **paralysis** on one side of the **face.**

Causes

#7

The exact cause of Bell's Palsy is unknown, but is likely the result of an attack to the facial nerve (cranial nerve VII) by the (Herpes) Simplex virus. The inflammation damages the nerve, causing the muscles on the side of the face controlled by the facial nerve to become paralyzed or severely weakened. The side of the face affected may also become numb.

Bell's Palsy is mostly a temporary condition, and should resolve over the course of a month or two. In some cases, it can become permanent.

Symptoms

Symptoms, which are usually only present on one side of the face, include the inability to close the eye, difficulty chewing, twitching of muscles in the face, and watery eyes. These symptoms typically resolve within three weeks at the earliest, but may persist for several months, or even become permanent.

b/c inflamed
↓ damaged
nerve

Treatments

A person with Bell's Palsy may take corticosteroids to help treat the muscle weakness. Self care, including facial exercises, are recommended.

Contraindications

Bell's Palsy is indicated for massage. The side of the face that is paralyzed should be massaged lightly to avoid damaging any tissue. The client may not be able to tell the therapist if the massage is too deep around facial structures, so lighter massage on the affected area should be performed.

Carpal Tunnel Syndrome

Carpal Tunnel Syndrome is a condition caused by compression of the **median nerve** between the carpals and the **transverse carpal ligament**.

Causes

Several factors may contribute to the development of carpal tunnel syndrome, although the most common cause is repetitive movements. These repetitive movements can cause straining of the tendons that run through the carpal canal, which can place pressure on the median nerve. If the transverse carpal ligament tightens, it can also place pressure on the median nerve. When pressure is placed on the median nerve, numbness, pain, or tingling sensations may be experienced in the thumb, index, ring, and lateral side of the ring finger.

Symptoms

Carpal tunnel syndrome often results in pain, numbness, and tingling sensations in the hand and wrist. Atrophy of the hand muscles may result due to lack of use.

Treatments

Several treatments are available for carpal tunnel syndrome. Self-care is recommended, including stretching the forearm and wrist flexors, massaging the transverse carpal ligament and hand muscles, and icing the area. Because carpal tunnel syndrome is often caused by repetitive actions, ceasing these actions is recommended. Non-steroidal anti-inflammatory medications may be prescribed. Surgery to remove the transverse carpal ligament may also be an option if the condition is severe.

Contraindications

Massage is indicated for carpal tunnel syndrome. Cross-fiber and circular friction on the transverse carpal ligament should be performed to help loosen adhesions in the area. Application of heat can help soften the ligament, and allow more space in the carpal canal.

Exposure of the median nerve during carpal tunnel surgery

Encephalitis
(encephal-: brain; -itis: inflammation)

Encephalitis is primarily a **viral** infection that results in **inflammation** of the **brain**.

Causes

Causes of encephalitis vary, but may include mosquito-borne viruses, such as West Nile, the Herpes Simplex virus, and the Rabies virus. Symptoms of encephalitis are usually mild, with the infected person suffering no more than flu-like symptoms, but severe cases may result in brain damage or death.

Symptoms

Symptoms of encephalitis vary depending on severity. Mild cases result in flu-like symptoms, such as fever, headache, general body ache, and fatigue. More severe cases may result in unconsciousness, seizures, weakness, and difficulty speaking or hearing.

Treatments

Because most cases of encephalitis are mild, treatment often consists of bed rest, and letting the virus work through its course. Antiviral medications may also be administered via an IV if the infection is more severe.

Contraindications

Because encephalitis is contagious and a serious medical condition, it is an absolute contraindication. Massage may be performed after the condition has completely resolved.

Meningitis
(mening-: meninges; -itis: inflammation)

Meningitis is **inflammation** of the **meninges**, protective connective tissue surrounding the brain and spinal cord. In the US, meningitis is most commonly caused by **viral** infection. However, certain bacterial and fungal infections may also cause meningitis. Bacterial meningitis is the most severe form of meningitis, usually preceded by a sinus or ear infection.

Causes

Being exposed to a pathogen, such as streptococci bacterium, or West Nile virus, are the causes of meningitis. Exposure to these may differ, and contracting them does not necessarily mean a person will develop meningitis. West Nile virus, which also may cause encephalitis, is often transmitted by mosquitoes.

Rarely, meningitis may be caused by things that are not infectious, such as medications or allergies to certain chemicals.

Symptoms

Symptoms vary depending on the underlying cause. Viral meningitis may present with symptoms extremely similar to influenza, and will likely clear up on their own within a couple weeks. Fever, headache, nausea, vomiting, and an unusually stiff neck are symptoms to watch for. Meningitis is considered a medical emergency, and a person with suspected meningitis should be seen by a medical professional right away.

Treatments

Bacterial meningitis is treated with intravenous antibiotics to combat the infection, and a course of corticosteroids to prevent inflammation in the brain. Draining the infection from the sinuses may be helpful. Viral meningitis, however, is far less serious, and often clears up after a couple weeks. Treatment for viral meningitis is simply rest and increasing fluid intake. Pain relievers may also help if a person has general body aches or is suffering from mild fever.

Contraindications

Because meningitis is a contagious condition, it is an absolute contraindication to massage. Massage may be performed after the condition has completely resolved.

Meningitis

- Severe headache
- Photophobia and phonophobia
- **Neck** Muscle tone and stiffness
- Red or purple rash
- Cold hands and feet
- **Gastric** Nausea and vomiting

Neisseria meningitidis

Classic triad of diagnostic signs:
- nuchal rigidity;
- sudden high fever;
- altered mental status.

Multiple Sclerosis
(scler-: hard; -osis: condition)

Multiple Sclerosis is an **autoimmune** disorder, affecting the **myelin sheaths** that protect the axons of the nervous system.

Causes

The cause of Multiple Sclerosis is unknown, but may be hereditary, and even environmental factors have been linked to the development of the disease. The disease begins with the body's immune system attacking the myelin sheaths, the protective fatty layers surrounding axons. These sheaths help to insulate the axons and prevent damage to the axons. When the myelin sheath is attacked and destroyed, it exposes the axons, which can have many different effects. Impulses traveling along an axon may terminate at the site of myelin degeneration, which may cause loss of functions. Scar tissue may form over the axons, which leads to extreme pain.

Symptoms

Symptoms of Multiple Sclerosis in acute stages include pain, weakness, fatigue, numbness(usually in the face), tingling sensations, blurry vision, and difficulty walking.

MULTIPLE SCLEROSIS

Healthy

Nerve affected by MS

Damaged myelin

Node of Ranvier

Exposed fiber

Schwann cells

Nerve fiber

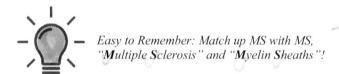

*Easy to Remember: Match up MS with MS, "**M**ultiple **S**clerosis" and "**M**yelin **S**heaths"!*

Treatments

There is no cure for Multiple Sclerosis. People may be prescribed disease-altering drugs, that may suppress the functions of the immune system. People may seek other means of managing Multiple Sclerosis and the accompanying pain and fatigue, including massage therapy, yoga, and meditation.

Contraindications

Massage in the acute stage of Multiple Sclerosis may be performed, but it is highly unlikely a client will seek massage because of the pain involved. Modalities that do not involve touching, such as Reiki, may be recommended and performed in these instances. In periods of remission, massage may be performed.

Paralysis
(paraleyin: disable)

Paralysis is a loss of **function** of a part of the body. This condition can affect a small area, or a large portion of the body.

Causes

Paralysis is caused by **damage** to a nerve that innervates a muscle or muscles. When a nerve is damaged, it can cause weakness (partial paralysis) in a muscle, making it extremely difficult to use, or even result in complete loss of function. The three main types of paralysis that result in complete loss of function are paraplegia, quadriplegia, and hemiplegia.

Paraplegia is paralysis affecting the lower limbs. This is typically caused by an injury to the spinal cord, but may also be caused by conditions such as spina bifida.

Quadriplegia(also known as tetraplegia) is paralysis affecting all four limbs and the trunk. This is typically caused by an injury to the spinal cord around the C4 vertebrae, which eliminates nerve supply to the limbs.

Hemiplegia is paralysis that affects one side(hemisphere) of the body. This is typically caused by a stroke, transient ischemic attack, or even Multiple Sclerosis.

Symptoms

Primarily, paralysis results in loss of sensation. Depending on which type of paralysis, different parts of the body may lose sensation. In the initial acute stage of paralysis, a person may experience weakness, extreme pain in the back, head, or neck, difficulty walking or standing, difficulty breathing, and loss of control over the bladder or bowels. In the acute stage, a person needs medical attention immediately.

Treatments

Treatment for paralysis may be helpful in cases of partial paralysis, where there is still some function. Physical and occupational therapy may also help the nervous tissue regenerate.

Contraindications

Massage may be performed on an area that is paralyzed. Because the muscles involved will be atrophied, massage should be light to avoid damaging underlying tissue. Stretching and range-of-motion exercises may be performed to help with muscle elasticity.

Parkinson's Disease

Parkinson's Disease is a motor disease that results in **trembling** due to a loss of the neurotransmitter **dopamine**.

Causes

There is no known cause of Parkinson's Disease. Neurons in the brain that produce dopamine are gradually destroyed. Dopamine is the neurotransmitter that stabilizes the body during motor movements, especially fine movements like writing. When dopamine levels in the body drop, trembling and shaking increases. As dopamine continues to drop, larger movements become affected, like walking and talking.

Symptoms

Symptoms of Parkinson's Disease include tremors, which usually begin in the hands and fingers and advance to larger body areas, difficulty writing, slower movement, difficulty in speech, and the loss of movements such as blinking.

Treatments

While there is no cure for Parkinson's Disease, treatments are available to help manage the condition, including dopamine replacement medications.

Contraindications

Massage is indicated for clients with Parkinson's Disease. In advanced stages, when a client is unable to lie on a table without the entire body trembling, a doctor's note may be requested. In these advanced stages, the therapist may need to help the client on and off the table.

Sciatica

Sciatica is a condition causing pain radiating down the buttocks, posterior thigh, and leg.

Causes

Sciatica is most commonly caused by a **herniated disc** in the lumbar vertebrae, which puts compression on the nerves that comprise the **sciatic nerve**. Bone spurs may also place pressure on the nerves.

Piriformis Syndrome is often confused with sciatica. Piriformis Syndrome is caused by tightness in the piriformis muscle, which may place substantial pressure on the sciatic nerve.

Symptoms

The primary symptom of sciatica is pain in the posterior leg, thigh, and glutes, usually only on one side of the body. There may also be numbness and tingling in the affected area.

Treatments

Treatment for sciatica may include physical therapy, anti-inflammatory medications, or surgery if the condition is severe enough.

Contraindications

Massage is indicated for sciatica. However, if sciatica is the result of a herniated disc, the site of disc herniation should be considered a local contraindication. Stretching techniques, especially in the glutes, may help ease some pain associated with sciatica.

Thoracic Outlet Syndrome

Thoracic Outlet Syndrome is a condition caused by **compression** of **nerves** and **blood vessels** passing through the **thoracic outlet**.

Causes

Thoracic Outlet Syndrome may be caused by tight muscles, including **pectoralis minor** and **scalenes**, obesity, and tumors in the neck, such as those seen in Non-Hodgkin's Lymphoma.

Symptoms

Pressure placed on the nerves and blood vessels may cause pain, numbness, and weakness in the upper limb. If a blood vessel is compressed, it may cause your hand to become a bluish color due to lack of circulation, cause pain and fatigue in the arm, and coldness in the hands and fingers. If a nerve is compressed, numbness in the limb and atrophy of the muscles innervated by the nerve may result.

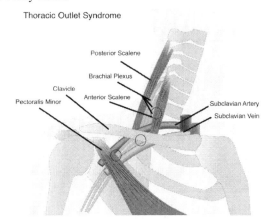

Thoracic Outlet Syndrome

Posterior Scalene
Brachial Plexus
Clavicle
Anterior Scalene
Pectoralis Minor
Subclavian Artery
Subclavian Vein

Treatments

Treatments primarily consist of stretching of the tight muscles to release pressure on the nerves and blood vessels. In the case of a tumor, surgery to remove the tumor may be required.

Contraindications

Massage is generally indicated for Thoracic Outlet Syndrome. Massaging the scalenes and pectoralis minor may assist in releasing pressure on the area, returning sufficient blood supply to the area. Sensation may return to the upper limb as a result. If Thoracic Outlet Syndrome is the result of tumors, the area should be avoided, and massage would be a local contraindication.

Trigeminal Neuralgia
(neur-: nerve; -algia: pain)

Trigeminal Neuralgia is a chronic condition causing extreme **pain in the face**.

Causes

The **trigeminal nerve**(cranial nerve V) sends sensory information from the face to the brain. When a blood vessel comes into contact with the trigeminal nerve at the brain stem, it results in dysfunction of the trigeminal nerve. This dysfunction results in hyper-sensitivity of the face, making even light touch extremely painful.

Symptoms

Extreme pain in the face, which may last from days to weeks, is the primary symptom of trigeminal neuralgia. This pain is typically only felt in one side of the face, but may worsen over time.

Treatments

Treatments for trigeminal neuralgia include medications to reduce pain, botox injections, or possible surgery to reduce pressure on the trigeminal nerve caused by blood vessels.

Contraindications

Massage for trigeminal neuralgia is generally not contraindicated, but everything is dependent on the severity of pain experienced by the client. If pain is severe, massage may be considered a local contraindication, or the client may not want to be massaged at all and the appointment would need to be rescheduled. If massage is able to be performed, the therapist should not use a face rest, instead opting to use a pillow for the client to rest their head upon while prone.

Respiratory System Pathologies

Apnea
(a-: without; -pnea: breathing)

Apnea, commonly referred to as sleep apnea, is a temporary **cessation of breathing** during **sleep**. Apnea may be a serious condition, depending on the patient. There are three types of sleep apnea: Central sleep apnea, Obstructive sleep apnea, and Complex sleep apnea syndrome.

People who are overweight have a much higher rate of occurrence than others. Advanced age and being male are also common demographics for the development of sleep apnea.

Causes

Central sleep apnea is the result of the brain not stimulating muscles responsible for breathing. A patient may experience shortness of breath due to lack of oxygen intake. This form of sleep apnea is not common.

Obstructive sleep apnea is the result of throat muscles relaxing, which causes the air passages to narrow or completely close upon inhalation. This reduces the amount of oxygen getting into the body. As a result, the brain may force the patient awake momentarily to unblock the airways. People with obstructive sleep apnea often snore, and may even sound as if they are choking.

Complex sleep apnea syndrome is diagnosed when a person experiences both common and obstructive sleep apnea.

Symptoms

Symptoms of apnea include snoring, shortness of breath upon waking, fatigue, and briefly waking at night. Another person may see the cessation of breathing and report it to the patient.

Treatments

Less severe forms of apnea may require less drastic forms of treatment, such as losing weight. In more severe forms, a person may be instructed to wear a CPAP(continuous positive airway pressure) machine during sleep, which increases air pressure in the airway, keeping the airways open enough for adequate oxygen intake to occur.

If other treatments are ineffective, surgery may be performed to remove tissue in and around the airway, which can increase the passageway for air to travel through.

Contraindications

Apnea is not contraindicated for massage.

Patient utilizing a CPAP machine

Asthma

Asthma is a chronic respiratory disease that causes **constriction** of the **airways**, restricting oxygen intake.

Causes

Asthma affects the **smooth** muscle in the walls of the bronchial tubes. Typically, when a person inhales an irritant(such as dust or smoke), the smooth muscle spasms and constricts in an effort to reduce the irritant moving further into the lungs. The bronchi will also produce an excessive amount of **mucous,** which further restricts the flow of oxygen into the lungs.

Symptoms

Symptoms include wheezing, chest tightness, and shortness of breath. Treatment varies depending on the severity in acute stages. If it is mild, medication may not be required. If symptoms are more severe, bronchodilators may be required to calm and open the airways. In extreme cases, where regular bronchodilators do not work, medical attention should be sought. A nebulizer, with inhalable steroids, should be used with asthma attacks.

Asthma usually begins in childhood, but may disappear with age. Other times, it remains a chronic condition. Other factors such as smoking or obesity may lead to the development of asthma.

Treatments

Treatment for asthma primarily consists of the use of steroids and bronchodilators administered directly to the lungs via inhalers If a person suffers from an asthma attack or has more severe forms of asthma, a nebulizer(which turns medication into a mist) may be required. Corticosteroids may also be used to lessen the chances of having an asthma attack.

Contraindications

In the acute stage, asthma is considered an absolute contraindication. Once breathing has returned to normal, massage may be performed. Tapotement may be performed on the back and chest to help loosen any excess phlegm that may be present.

Bronchitis
(bronch-: bronchi; -itis: inflammation)

Bronchitis is an inflammatory disease of the respiratory system, restricting oxygen intake.

Causes

There are two different types of bronchitis: acute bronchitis and chronic bronchitis. Acute bronchitis is the result of a **primary** infection of the respiratory system, such as influenza or pneumonia. These diseases affect the bronchial tubes, causing them to become irritated and inflamed. When these diseases resolve, the bronchitis will also resolve. Chronic bronchitis is the result of **constant irritation** to the bronchial tubes, caused by things such as **cigarette smoking** or exposure to things like dust. When exposure to the irritant ceases, the bronchitis will also cease.

Symptoms

With both forms of bronchitis, there is an increased amount of mucous produced in the lungs, which makes breathing difficult. Increased coughing may be a side effect of the increase in mucous.

Treatments

Treatments vary depending on which type of bronchitis is involved. Acute bronchitis may require nothing more than a bronchodilator or cough suppressant. Because acute bronchitis is usually caused by a viral infection, antivirals may be prescribed to stop the advancement of the virus. Chronic bronchitis often requires the use of a bronchodilator, but not much else.

Contraindications

Acute bronchitis is considered an absolute contraindication, because it only appears as a secondary condition with another infection that is an absolute contraindication, such as influenza or pneumonia. Once these conditions resolve, the bronchitis will also resolve, and massage may be performed. Chronic bronchitis is indicated for massage. Tapotement may help loosen any excess phlegm as a result of the bronchitis, which can help breathing.

Emphysema
(emphyso: inflate)

Emphysema is a chronic condition of the lungs, resulting in difficulty bringing oxygen into the body and eliminating carbon dioxide from the body.

Causes

Emphysema is caused by over-exposure to substances such as **cigarette smoke**. Constant irritation of the lungs by smoke can lead to degeneration of the **alveoli**, air sacs at the end of bronchial tubes where gas exchange takes place. When the alveoli degenerate, they lose surface area, which is what capillaries move across to eliminate carbon dioxide from the body and bring oxygen into the body. Lack of enough alveoli surface area makes gas exchange extremely difficult.

Symptoms

Emphysema causes shortness of breath. A person with emphysema may be much more likely to develop a collapsed lung due to damage to the lungs.

Treatments

Breathing exercises and oxygen supplementation may help control emphysema. If needed, bronchodilators can help relax the airways. If infections such as pneumonia occur, antibiotics may help.

Contraindications

Massage is indicated for emphysema.

Influenza
(Italian "influenza": influence)

Influenza is a highly contagious **viral** infection that primarily affects the lungs. *flu virus*

Causes

There are many different strains of the flu virus. It is constantly mutating, so treatment can be difficult. **Vaccinations** are the primary form of prevention for influenza.

Influenza, during acute stages, results in fever, general malaise, body aches, runny nose, and cough. Symptoms generally last no more than a week. Depending on the person involved, it can be a moderate infection, or can be life-threatening. Children and the elderly are much more likely to have serious cases of influenza than the general population.

Symptoms

Influenza typically has a sudden onset of symptoms, including fever, body ache, fatigue, sore throat, nasal congestion, body chills, and sweating.

Treatments

Treatment for influenza is usually nothing more than rest and increased fluid intake. Antiviral medication may be prescribed, and may help reduce the length of the infection. Influenza usually clears up on its own.

Contraindications

Influenza is highly contagious, and is considered an absolute contraindication.

Laryngitis
(laryng-: larynx; -itis: inflammation)

Laryngitis is **inflammation** of the larynx, also known as the **voice box**. Laryngitis may affect one's ability to speak due to the presence of the vocal cords inside the larynx.

Causes

There are many different causes of laryngitis. There are two main types of laryngitis: acute and chronic. Acute laryngitis is commonly the result of **trauma** to the larynx caused by yelling, or caused by an **acute infection**. Once the larynx has had time to heal, or the infection goes away, the inflammation should dissipate and the voice should return to normal. In chronic laryngitis, common causes include smoking and acid reflux.

Symptoms

Symptoms include difficulty speaking, pain in the throat, and dry coughing. In some cases, the voice may completely be lost, and in others, the voice is only hoarse.

Treatments

If laryngitis is not caused by an infection, resting the voice is extremely helpful. If bacterial infection is the cause, antibiotics may aid in destroying bacteria causing the inflammation. Most cases of infectious laryngitis are viral, however, and won't be helped by antibiotics.

Lozenges may aid in soothing the throat, as well as using humidifiers.

Contraindications

Massage on a client with laryngitis depends on the cause. If the cause of laryngitis is an infection, massage should be considered an absolute contraindication. If the cause of Laryngitis is trauma, such as shouting, massage is indicated.

Pneumonia
(pneumo: lung)

Pneumonia is a highly contagious infection of the lungs, resulting in a buildup of **fluid** in the **alveoli**.

Causes

The primary cause of pneumonia is **bacterial** infection(staphylococci), but may also be caused by a virus or fungi. The bacterium enters the body through breathing, which then infects the lungs.

Symptoms

Mild cases of pneumonia usually present with symptoms similar to those of influenza. Other symptoms may include pain in the chest upon breathing, coughing which may produce phlegm, fever, nausea, and shortness of breath. Symptoms can range from mild to severe, and even life threatening, based on the overall health and age of the person infected.

Treatments

Pneumonia is typically treated with antibiotics. Cough medicine and antipyretics may be prescribed to aid with coughing and to lower fever.

Contraindications

Pneumonia is a highly contagious condition, and is therefore an absolute contraindication.

Sinusitis
(sinus: sinus; -itis: inflammation)

Sinusitis is an acute condition causing inflammation and swelling in the nasal sinuses, which can result in excessive mucous production. It can also prevent mucous from properly draining from the sinuses, causing a person to feel a lot of pressure in the face around the nose and eyes. Bacterial infection may result, which can increase the amount of fluid present in the sinuses.

Causes

The most common cause of sinusitis is an acute viral infection, such as the common cold, which may in turn cause bacterial infection to take place.

Symptoms

A person with sinusitis may experience pressure in the face around the nose, eyes, and ears, headache, a thick mucous produced by the nose usually presenting with a yellow or green color, and congestion in the nasal cavity.

Treatments

Decongestants are effective at helping to drain the nasal cavities, which can help ease pressure in the area. Nasal sprays can help alleviate inflammation and clean out the nasal cavity, further helping to reduce pressure. If bacterial infection is present, antibiotics may be prescribed.

Contraindications

During the acute stage, and due to being caused by a contagious viral infection, sinusitis is considered an absolute contraindication. Once the condition has resolved, a client may receive massage.

Healthy sinus

Nasal mucus

Skeletal System Pathologies

enclosing spno

Ankylosing Spondylitis

(ankyl/o: crooked; spondyl-: spine; -itis: inflammation)

Ankylosing Spondylitis is an autoimmune disorder, similar to Rheumatoid Arthritis(page 151), in which the body's immune system attacks and destroys the **annulus fibrosus** of the intervertebral discs. Over time, the curvature in the vertebrae is lost. Because the intervertebral discs are destroyed, the space between vertebral bodies lessens, eventually allowing the vertebral bones to sit directly atop one another. Movement between these bones is severely reduced, and eventually the bones can **fuse together**, which eliminates any movement between the bones at all.

A person with ankylosing spondylitis may appear to be hunched forward, and may present with Kyphosis(page 147) as a result. Another name for ankylosing spondylitis is "Bamboo Spine" due to its appearance after the vertebrae fuse together, which resembles bamboo.

Causes

Ankylosing spondylitis is caused by the body's immune system attacking the intervertebral discs for unknown reasons.

Symptoms

Pain is an extremely common symptom of ankylosing spondylitis, especially in the neck, base of the skull, and lumbar region. Lack of mobility is a secondary symptom, usually the result of pain.

Treatments

Non-steroidal anti-inflammatory medications may be prescribed to help reduce pain and inflammation in affected areas. Physical therapy, massage therapy, stretching, and range-of-motion exercises are all helpful in maintaining mobility in the vertebral joints and preventing bones from fusing together.

If the condition is severe, surgery may be performed to remove fused bone, or to insert metal rods to correct posture.

Healthy spine   Ankylosing spondylitis

Body of vertebra

Disc

Inflammation of joints   Fusion of bones "Bamboo spine"

Contraindications

Massage is indicated for ankylosing spondylitis. Stretching and range-of-motion exercises should be performed within the client's pain tolerance. If the client has difficulty lying supine due to kyphosis, side-lying position may be needed.

Baker's Cyst

A Baker's Cyst is a small sac filled with synovial fluid that forms on the **back of the knee**. Another name for this is **Popliteal Cyst**. A Baker's Cyst is usually the result of an **injury** in the knee joint.

Causes

Tearing of the meniscus or ligaments in the knee can cause an overproduction of synovial fluid in the joint. If too much synovial fluid is produced, a sac can form around it on the back of the knee.

Symptoms

Pain and stiffness in the knee are common symptoms experienced. The popliteal region can feel swollen and bulge out due to the cyst being present.

Baker's cyst

Treatments

Typically, a Baker's Cyst goes away on its own without treatment. However, if the cyst causes pain or discomfort, treatments are available. Medications may be prescribed to reduce inflammation, the fluid may physically be drained by a doctor, or ice may be applied to reduce inflammation. If the cause of the cyst is known, such as torn cartilage, an arthroscopic surgery may be performed to repair or clean up the tissue, which may aid in the cyst draining.

Contraindications

A Baker's Cyst is considered a local contraindication. Massage may be performed, but massaging the cyst itself should be avoided.

Bunion

A bunion is a **subluxation** of the **big toe**, the result of the toe pushing back against the first metatarsal. Excessive force against this bone causes the big toe to subluxate medially, creating a **large bump**.

Causes

Tight fitting shoes may contribute to the development of bunions. Rheumatoid Arthritis(page 151) may also contribute. Foot injuries may also play a role.

Symptoms

Pain and swelling may present in the area of the bunion. With bunions, the big toe may cross under the second toe. This may cause calluses or corns to form on the area where these toes rub together. Movement in the big toe may reduce.

Treatments

How severe the bunion is determines the treatment. Less severe bunions may require only changing shoes or applying a splint to help reset the toe. More severe forms of a bunion may require surgery to correct the placement of the toe.

Contraindications

Massage is generally not contraindicated for a bunion. However, if the client is experiencing pain as a result of the bunion, massage in the area should be avoided.

Bursitis
(burs-: bursa; -itis: inflammation)

Bursitis is a condition that results in **inflammation** of a **bursa**, a small sac filled with synovial fluid.

Causes

Bursae are located all over the body, typically between a tendon and bone to prevent friction and irritation. When there is repeated stress placed on the bursa, it can become inflamed. Bursitis may affect many different joints, including the knee, shoulder, elbow, hip, and ankle.

Bursitis is most often caused by repetitive motions in the affected joint, which may irritate the bursa. Trauma may also result in bursitis, such as fractures or tendonitis.

Symptoms

Typically, a joint affected with bursitis will be inflamed and painful to move. The inflammation may be moderate or severe.

Treatments

Bursitis is easily treatable, primarily with rest and ice. Depending on the severity, the bursa may also need to be surgically drained or removed, or injected with corticosteroids to reduce the inflammation.

Contraindications

Bursitis is considered a local contraindication for massage. Cold packs may be used to help decrease inflammation in the area.

Dislocation

A dislocation is when a bone at an articulation becomes **displaced** from its normal location. A dislocation, in the acute stage, results in immobilization of the joint and temporary deformation. It may also be painful and result in inflammation around the joint.

Causes

Dislocations are most commonly the result of trauma to the joint, which pushes a bone out of place. The most common areas for dislocations are the fingers and shoulder, but dislocations may occur in many other joints as well, such as the knee or hip.

Dislocations may result in tearing of tendons, ligaments, muscles, or in the case of the shoulder or hip, the labrum(circular cartilage surrounding the joint). The dislocated joint, while most commonly returns to normal strength and function after being relocated, may become prone to dislocations in the future. This may cause arthritis to develop.

Symptoms

Dislocations are extremely painful, and often present with deformity of the joint and an inability to move the joint. Inflammation may be present in some cases.

Treatments

Treatment of a dislocation in the acute stage primarily involves trying to get the bone back to its normal position, known as reduction. After the joint has returned to its normal position, it is typically immobilized for a number of weeks to reduce recurrence of dislocation and to help the tissues around the joint to heal. If the dislocation is severe and unable to be returned to position, surgery may be required.

Contraindications

In the acute stage, a dislocation is considered a local contraindication. If the joint has healed, massage may be performed on the area with caution. Stretching and range-of-motion should be avoided because the joint is much weaker after a dislocation.

Fracture

A fracture is a **break** in a bone. There are several different types of fractures, including transverse, greenstick, oblique, and spiral.

Causes

Fractures are the result of trauma to a bone. Despite many different types of fractures, every fracture is categorized as one of the following: Simple or Compound. A **simple** fracture is a fracture that **does not break through** the skin, and does not damage any surrounding tissue. A **compound** fracture, which is much more severe, **breaks through** the skin and damages surrounding tissues. Compound fractures are much more prone to infection due to exposure to the outside environment.

Surgical repair of fracture located at C1-C2 vertebrae

Symptoms

Fractures result in deformity of the affected bone, pain, immobilization of the area, and inflammation. In the case of compound fractures, external bleeding may also occur.

Despite most fractures being the result of blunt trauma, certain diseases that weaken the bones may also cause fractures, such as osteoporosis.

Treatments

Fractures should be treated immediately. A cast or splint may be applied, depending on which bone is fractured. Other fractures, such as vertebrae fractures, may need more extensive treatment, including metal plates or bone grafts.

Contraindications

In the acute stage, a fracture should be considered a local contraindication. After the fracture has healed, massage may be performed on the area. If metal plates, rods, screws, or pins have been placed in the bone, caution should be taken in the area, but massage may still be performed.

Gout

Gout is a form of arthritis, mostly seen around the base of the **big toe**, but may also affect other joints in the body, such as the hands and fingers.

Causes

Gout is the result of an over-abundance of **uric acid** crystals in the body. Gravity pulls the uric acid crystals down the body, where they collect in the most distal points in the limbs, the big toes, hands and fingers. Gout is typically the result of the kidneys not excreting enough uric acid, or the body producing too much uric acid.

Symptoms

Gout may be extremely painful in the acute stage as the crystals collect in the joints. Inflammation may set in, which can increase the pressure and pain in the joint. Loss of range-of-motion may also occur. Untreated, gout may result in kidney stones.

Treatments

Treatments for gout include non-steroidal anti-inflammatory drugs and/or corticosteroids to reduce pain and inflammation. Gout may also require the use of certain medications that prevent the creation of uric acid in the body.

Contraindications

Gout is considered a local contraindication.

Herniated Disc

A herniated disc is a condition affecting the vertebral column, which may cause intense pain and numbness.

Causes

An intervertebral disc, located between two vertebrae, is made of two parts: the nucleus pulposus, and the annulus fibrosus. The nucleus pulposus is a gelatinous substance located in the center of the disc. The annulus fibrosus is the part of the disc made of thick cartilage. If a tear occurs in the **annulus fibrosus**, the **nucleus pulposus** may **protrude** through the torn section, which may place pressure on spinal nerves emerging from the spinal cord. This is a herniated disc.

A herniated disc is primarily caused by degeneration of a disc, which takes place gradually. This makes injury of the disc much easier in actions such as lifting and twisting. Other times, trauma may cause a herniated disc, such as in car accidents.

Symptoms

Herniated discs may result in pain and/or numbness due to the disc placing pressure on the spinal nerves. Because numbness may occur, weakness in the muscles innervated by the nerves may also set in due to impaired function.

Treatments

Treatment for a herniated disc varies depending on the severity. Pain medication may help control pain. Muscle relaxers may help take pressure off the area of the herniation. Physical therapy may also contribute to lessening the effects of the herniated disc. Very rarely, surgery may be required.

Contraindications

Herniated discs are considered local contraindications. The area around the hernia may be massaged, but the disc itself should be avoided.

Spinal disc herniation

Compressed spinal nerve

Normal disc   Herniated disc

Kyphosis
(kyph-: hill; -osis: condition)

Kyphosis is a condition affecting the **thoracic** vertebrae, resulting in **hyper-curvature**. Another name for kyphosis is "Dowager's Hump".

Causes

A kyphotic curvature in the vertebrae is a curvature that moves posteriorly. If the curvature is exaggerated, it is known as kyphosis. Kyphosis has many different causes. Kyphosis may be caused by extremely tight muscles(such as **pectoralis minor** and **serratus anterior**) pulling the scapulae anteriorly, which rounds the back. Kyphosis may also be the result of bone degeneration (osteoporosis), disc degeneration(ankylosing spondylitis), or even birth defects.

Symptoms

Kyphosis may cause pain in the back, and difficulty in movement and breathing as a result. It may also result in the lumbar vertebrae losing its curvature, a condition known as **flat back**.

Treatments

Kyphosis may vary from mild to severe, depending on the cause. Treatments include exercises that strengthen the muscles of the back, stretching of tight muscles that may contribute to kyphosis, braces to keep the vertebrae properly aligned, and possibly even surgery if it's warranted.

Contraindications

Kyphosis is not contraindicated for massage. A person with kyphosis may be uncomfortable lying supine, and may need to be placed into side-lying position for comfort. Massage of the pectoralis minor and serratus anterior muscles may help the scapulae return to their normal locations, which can help straighten the vertebrae.

Lordosis
(lord-: curve; -osis: condition)

Lordosis is a condition affecting the **lumbar** vertebrae, resulting in **hyper-curvature**. Another name for lordosis is "Swayback".

Causes

A lordotic curvature in the vertebrae is a curvature that moves anteriorly. If the curvature is exaggerated, it is known as lordosis. Lordosis has many different causes. Lordosis may be caused by tight muscles(such as **psoas major**, **iliacus**, **quadratus lumborum**, and **rectus femoris**), weak muscles(such as **rectus abdominis** and the **hamstrings**), obesity, or bone diseases(such as osteoporosis). Pregnancy is also a common cause of lordosis, but the condition typically subsides post-pregnancy.

Symptoms

Lordosis may place excessive pressure on the vertebrae, and alter a person's stance and gait. Lordosis may result in pain in the back, and cause difficulty moving.

Treatments

Treatment primarily includes strengthening weak muscles, stretching tight muscles, and lifestyle changes, such as adjusting posture, diet, and exercise.

Contraindications

Lordosis is not contraindicated for massage. Stretching exercises on the psoas major, iliacus, and quadratus lumborum muscles may help return the lumbar spine back to its normal curvature.

Lyme Disease

Lyme Disease is a **bacterial** infection spread by **deer ticks**, and contracting the infection is much more common in grassy or wooded areas where deer ticks are found. The condition may affect a person for months, and lead to symptoms that may last for years afterwards.

Causes

The bacteria responsible for Lyme Disease is spread through a bite from deer ticks. The bacteria is usually only transmitted if the bite lasts longer than 36 hours.

Symptoms

Symptoms of Lyme Disease vary depending on the stage of infection. In the early stages, a bump may appear where the person has been bitten. Sometime later, within 30 days, a rash may appear that forms a **bullseye pattern**. It may spread outward from that area over a few days. A person may experience flu-like symptoms when the rash appears. In advanced stages, conditions may begin occurring such as pain and inflammation in joints, meningitis, and paralysis in different parts of the body such as the face.

Treatments

Lyme Disease is a bacterial infection, and therefore is treated with antibiotics. Advanced stages of Lyme Disease, where there may be some sort of paralysis, require the use of intravenous antibiotics. Otherwise, oral antibiotics may be taken. The course of treatment usually lasts up to three weeks to completely destroy all bacteria.

Contraindications

Massage largely depends on the symptoms a client is experiencing. Lesser symptoms such as aches and joint inflammation may allow for massage while avoiding general local contraindications. If a client is experiencing flu-like symptoms, the massage should be postponed until the client is feeling better.

Osgood-Schlatter Disease

Osgood-Schlatter Disease is a repetitive strain injury, caused by over-use of the **patellar** tendon.

Causes

Osgood-Schlatter Disease primarily affects adolescents, particularly those involved in sports. Over-use of the **quadriceps** during activities such as running and jumping can cause tightness in the patellar tendon. When the patellar tendon tightens, it pulls proximally on the tibial tuberosity. Because the bone is still growing, the force of the patellar tendon on the tibial tuberosity can cause an **over-growth of bone**, resulting in a bony lump. Males are more likely to develop this condition than females, but instances in females are increasing as participation in sports by females increases.

Symptoms

Osgood-Schlatter Disease may cause pain, but it varies from person to person. The pain may be mild, or it may be more intense, making movement of the knee difficult.

Despite complications from Osgood-Schlatter Disease being rare, inflammation of the area may persist over time. The bony lump produced by increased bone production may also remain.

Treatments

Treatment is mild, usually nothing more than pain relievers, rest, and ice. Exercises that stretch the quadriceps are recommended.

Contraindications

In the acute stage, massage of the tibial tuberosity is a local contraindication. If the client is beyond the age of 21, and bone is no longer being produced at the tibial tuberosity, massage on the area may be performed.

In the acute stage, massage and stretching techniques should be performed on the quadriceps to loosen the muscles and take pressure off the patellar tendon, which can reduce the excessive development of bone at the tibial tuberosity.

Osteoarthritis
(osteo-: bone; arthr-: joint; -itis: inflammation)

Osteoarthritis is the most common form of arthritis, which is **inflammation** of a **joint**.

Causes

Osteoarthritis, also known as "wear-and-tear arthritis", is caused by damage to the **hyaline cartilage** separating one bone from another. The cartilage between bones reduces friction between the bones, and absorbs shock in the joint. Over time, the articular cartilage may begin to break down and wear away. This causes irritation in the joint and increases friction between the bones, which causes inflammation. As this persists, damage to the bone may take place. The most common location of osteoarthritis is the knee, but in massage therapists, it may also affect the metacarpophalangeal joint of the thumb(saddle joint).

Symptoms

Osteoarthritis may cause pain, difficulty moving the affected joint, and bone spurs in the joint due to increased friction between the bones. When the condition advances to the point of the joint being mostly unusable, joint replacement surgery may be recommended.

NORMAL JOINT

DESTRUCTION OF CARTILAGE

BONE

CARTILAGE

BONE ENDS RUB TOGETHER

THINNING CARTILAGE

BONE SPUR

THINNED CARTILAGE

Treatments

Treatment includes non-steroidal anti-inflammatory drugs, lifestyle and dietary changes if caused by obesity, and alternative methods such as yoga.

Contraindications

In the acute stage, massage is considered a local contraindication for any form of arthritis because it can bring more blood into the area and increase inflammation. In the remission stage, massage should be performed on the area usually affected to bring fresh blood and nutrients into the area, and to increase production of synovial fluid in the joint. This can help reduce irritation in the joint and lessen the effects of arthritis.

Osteoporosis
(osteo-: bone; por-: porous; -osis: condition)

Osteoporosis is a condition that causes weakness and **degeneration** in the **bones**.

Causes

Osteoporosis mainly affects post-menopausal women. After menopause, a woman's body produces less **estrogen.** Estrogen, during growth stages of a person's life, help the bones grow and mature. When estrogen levels drop post-menopause, osteoclast levels increase, and more bone is destroyed than is created. When this occurs, the bones become brittle, weak, and prone to fracture.

Osteoporosis, in addition to making bones brittle, may also contribute to the development of kyphosis and back pain. One of the most common places for fracture to occur is in the neck of the femur. The femur, which is normally the strongest bone in the body, should be able to support roughly 2,000 pounds of pressure per square inch. When the femur becomes weakened, it makes it incredibly easy to break. If a fracture takes place around the hip joint, joint replacement surgery is often required.

Symptoms

In the early stages of osteoporosis, there are usually no symptoms. As bone loss increases over time, a person may experience back pain, hunched posture(kyphosis), and bones that fracture easier than usual. These symptoms often become worse as the disease progresses and more bone tissue is lost.

NORMAL BONE

OSTEOPOROSIS

Treatments

Treatments for osteoporosis include estrogen replacement therapy, and weight-bearing exercise earlier in life before any symptoms of osteoporosis surface. Weight-bearing exercise, such as squats and dead-lifts, helps to strengthen the bones, which substantially reduces the risk of developing osteoporosis in older age.

Contraindications

Massage is indicated for osteoporosis. However, precautions should be taken, such as performing a lighter massage, and not performing techniques such as tapotement to avoid damaging bone.

Plantarfasciitis
(plantar-: sole of the feet; fasci-: fascia; -itis: inflammation)

Plantarfasciitis is inflammation of the fascia on the plantar surface of the foot. It is usually the result of over-stretching of the plantarfascia, connecting the calcaneus to the toes, which results in tearing. The tearing is usually small, but constant injury to the plantarfascia may cause pain. It is a common injury in athletes, people who are flat-footed, and people who are obese.

Causes

Plantarfasciitis is the result of the plantarfascia being stretched further than it normally does, causing small tears.

Symptoms

Stabbing pain in the foot is a common symptom, occurring near the calcaneus. The pain usually subsides when the foot is not in use.

Treatments

PRICE(protect, rest, ice, compression, elevation) is extremely useful in aiding the healing of plantarfasciitis. Splints may be used to return the foot back to its normal position, taking pressure off the plantarfascia. Pain relievers may be taken to aid with any discomfort and pain a person may be experiencing.

Contraindications

Plantarfasciitis is considered a local contraindication in the acute stage.

PLANTAR FASCIITIS

plantar fascia

area of microtears

Rheumatoid Arthritis

Rheumatoid Arthritis is an **autoimmune** disorder, resulting in inflammation, pain, and deformity of the joints around the hands and wrists.

Causes

Around synovial joints, there is a membrane called the synovial membrane, which supplies joints with synovial fluid. In rheumatoid arthritis, the body's immune systems attacks the **synovial membranes**, destroying them. This is especially common in the metacarpophalangeal joints. After the synovial membranes have been destroyed, extremely thick, fibrous material replaces them, which not only makes movement painful and difficult, but can also cause deformity, turning the fingers into an adducted position.

Symptoms

Rheumatoid arthritis can produce pain and discomfort in the affected joints, as well as cause pain and stiffness after long periods of inactivity in the joints. Fever and fatigue may also be symptoms of general rheumatoid arthritis. Less commonly, some people may experience symptoms in structures completely unrelated to the affected joints, such as the eyes, heart, lungs, and kidneys.

Treatments

There is no cure for rheumatoid arthritis, but treatments include non-steroidal anti-inflammatory drugs, corticosteroids, and physical therapy.

Contraindications

In the acute stage, rheumatoid arthritis is considered a local contraindication, as the pain may be too intense for the client to receive massage on the affected area. In general, however, a client with rheumatoid arthritis may receive massage to help ease pain associated with inflammation if the body can tolerate a light-to-medium pressured massage.

Scoliosis
(scoli-: crooked; -osis: condition)

Scoliosis is a condition causing the vertebral column, usually in the thoracic region, to be pulled into a **lateral** position.

Causes

The causes of scoliosis are unknown, but there may be a hereditary link. Scoliosis typically develops around the beginning stages of puberty. Scoliosis is mostly mild in severity, but can become much more prominent, which can put incredible strain on the ribs, vertebrae, and hips. With scoliosis, one hip may be higher than the other, which causes a discrepancy in gait. Tight muscles may also contribute to the development of scoliosis, as seen in cases such as a hypertonic rhomboid major and minor unilaterally, which pulls the vertebrae to one side.

Symptoms

If scoliosis is severe, damage to the heart or lungs may occur, due to the deformity of the rib cage. Back pain may also persist.

Treatments

Treatment, while commonly unnecessary, may include the use of braces to correct posture, the use of chiropractic therapy, massage therapy, or in severe cases, surgery with metal rod implantation.

Contraindications

Scoliosis is indicated for massage. In instances where scoliosis is caused by hypertonic muscles, such as the rhomboids unilaterally, massage may help loosen the muscles and allow the bones to realign themselves. If surgery has been performed and metal rods have been placed in the back, massage should be performed lighter on the area, and the use of cold packs should be avoided.

Sprain

A sprain is an injury to a **ligament**.

Causes

Sprains are much less likely to be caused by repetitive motions, unlike strains. Sprains typically occur quickly, causing tears in a ligament. Like strains, sprains may be broken down in severity by using grades: grade 1, grade 2, and grade 3.

A grade 1 sprain is caused by stretching of a ligament, but does not cause major tearing. Common grade 1 sprains may be caused by activities such as running. After 24/48 hours, the ligament should return to normal, and any pain and/or inflammation should subside.

A grade 2 sprain, such as a high ankle sprain, causes tearing of a ligament and presents with bruising and inflammation. Grade 2 sprains may require surgery to repair, or they may heal on their own, depending on the severity of the tear.

A grade 3 sprain is a complete rupture of a ligament, and much like a grade 3 strain, does require surgery to repair. The most common form of grade 3 sprain is a torn anterior cruciate ligament(ACL, the ligament holding the femur and tibia together), most commonly caused by sports, or automobile accidents.

Symptoms

Symptoms of sprains are very similar to symptoms of strains, including inflammation, pain, and potential bruising depending on the grade of sprain. If the sprain is severe, a pop in the joint may be heard or felt at the time of injury.

Treatments

Sprains take much longer to heal than strains, due to ligaments being avascular, compared to muscles and tendons, which have a rich blood supply. Treatment for sprains vary depending on the severity of the sprain. The less severe, the more likely it is that rest, ice, and elevation will suffice. Surgery is only required when there is no chance of the ligament repairing itself.

Contraindications

In the acute stage, sprains are local contraindications. If inflammation has subsided from a first degree sprain, gentle massage in the area may be performed to bring fresh blood and nutrients into the area and speed healing. Contrast therapy may be performed in addition to gentle massage to reduce any inflammation that may occur due to the massage.

Temporomandibular Joint Dysfunction

Temporomandibular Joint Dysfunction(TMJD) is a condition affecting the mandible, causing simple tasks such as **chewing** to become **painful** and **difficult**.

Causes

The temporomandibular joint is the joint that connects the mandible to the temporal bone. Between the bones, there is a small disc of cartilage, used to prevent friction between the bones and to make movement smooth. If there is arthritis in the joint, or the disc is damaged, it can result in Temporomandibular Joint Dysfunction. This can cause pain, difficulty in moving the jaw, and produce a clicking sensation when the jaw opens. Often times, the muscles that connect to the mandible(temporalis, lateral pterygoid) may tighten and pull the mandible out of place.

Symptoms

Temporomandibular Joint Dysfunction can produce pain in the face, a clicking or popping sound when closing the mouth, and difficulty in opening the mouth. The jaw may become locked while open.

Treatments

Treatments vary depending on the primary cause, ranging from prescription muscle relaxants and pain relievers, to physical and massage therapy.

Contraindications

Massage is indicated for Temporomandibular Joint Dysfunction. Massage of the temporalis may help the jaw realign and reduce the pain and clicking.

Whiplash

Whiplash is an injury to the neck, resulting from a **quick**, forceful movement of the head **forward and back**. This results in the tendons and ligaments in the neck to become stretched further than normal, damaging the tissue and making the neck much less stable than normal.

Causes

The most common cause of whiplash is a car accident. Injuries during sport or physical abuse may also cause whiplash. Shaking a baby may result in whiplash, and is one of the reasons shaking a baby should never happen.

Symptoms

The neck can become stiff and painful, especially upon movement. Headaches may occur. Pain may radiate to the shoulders, and range-of-motion may be restricted. Numbness may be experienced in the upper limbs due to possible injury to nerves emerging from the brachial plexus.

Treatments

Rest and ice are effective treatments for whiplash. The use of pain relievers can help eliminate pain associated with the condition. Inflammation in the area may be present, and contrast therapy on the neck may be performed to assist with reduction of inflammation. Physical therapy may also be performed to help strengthen the tendons and ligaments affected.

Contraindications

In the acute stage, massage is considered a local contraindication for a client with whiplash. Once the symptoms have subsided, gentle massage in the area may be performed. Stretching of the neck should be avoided to prevent injuring the tissue.

Whiplash   Hyperflexion   Hyperextension

Urinary System Pathologies

Cystitis
(cyst-: bladder; -itis: inflammation)

Cystitis is a **bacterial** infection, resulting in **inflammation** of the **bladder**. Often, it can involve the entire urinary system, and is then known as a Urinary Tract Infection(UTI). Cystitis is most common in women, as the female urethra is shorter than the male urethra, giving bacteria a shorter passage to the bladder.

Causes

Cystitis is caused most commonly by E. Coli entering the urethra, then reproducing. The increased amount of bacterium in the urethra causes the infection to spread upwards, into the bladder. Cystitis can cause numerous symptoms, including blood in the urine, burning sensations while urinating, and a frequent urge to urinate. If untreated, the infection may spread to the kidneys. When this happens, it is known as pyelonephritis.

Symptoms

Symptoms of cystitis include a frequent urge to urinate, a painful burning sensation upon urination, urinating small amounts at a time, fever, and blood in the urine.

Treatments

Cystitis, because it is a bacterial infection, is treated with antibiotics.

Contraindications

In the acute stage of infection, massage is contraindication for cystitis. Once the infection has cleared, massage may be performed.

Kidney Stones

Kidney Stones, also known as Nephroliathiasis, are **deposits of salts and minerals** created inside the kidney, which are hard and rough. They vary in size, and may cause many differing health complications.

Kidney stones are more common in people who are obese or have a family history of kidney stone development. Diet may play a role as well.

Causes

Kidney stones may be caused by numerous factors. Most commonly, they are caused by increased amounts of calcium oxalate, which is found in many types of food. Excessive amounts of calcium oxalate can cause stones to develop. Uric acid may also produce stones if a person does not drink enough fluids. A high protein diet may contribute to the development of uric acid stones.

Less commonly, struvite stones may form, which are the result of bacterial infections of the urinary tract.

Symptoms

Kidney stones are largely asymptomatic, until they leave the kidney and enter the ureter. When this occurs, pain may be felt around the abdomen, groin, back, and sides. Painful urination may take place as the stone blocks the ureter. The urine may have a pink or brown appearance due to blood in the urine. An inadequate amount of urine may be produced due to blockages.

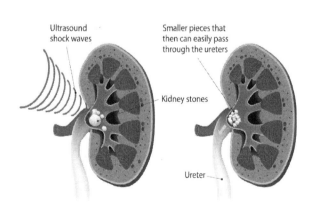

LITHOTRIPSY

Ultrasound shock waves

Smaller pieces that then can easily pass through the ureters

Kidney stones

Ureter

Treatments

Many treatment options are available. In less severe cases, increasing water intake can help flush the kidneys of the increased calcium, and help move the stones out of the body. To aid in moving the stone out of the body, a doctor may prescribe medications that help to relax the smooth muscle in the ureter, known as alpha blockers.

In more severe cases, stones may be destroyed while still inside the body using a treatment known as extracorporeal shock wave lithotripsy. The stones are broken down using sound waves, and then are able to be passed out of the body easier. If the stones are too big to be destroyed using sound waves, they may be removed surgically.

Contraindications

Kidney stones are not considered a contraindication for massage therapy.

Pyelonephritis
(pyel/o: renal pelvis; nephr/o: kidney; -itis: inflammation)

Pyelonephritis is a bacterial infection of the kidney, usually beginning in the urethra or bladder. The infection spreads upwards through the ureters and into the kidneys. Pyelonephritis is considered a serious condition, and if suspected, should be seen by a doctor immediately for treatment.

Causes

Bacteria enters the urethra. Usually, urinating cleans out the urethra. Rarely, it does not, and bacteria can reproduce in the urethra. The bacteria can then spread upwards into the bladder, then move further up into the ureters and kidneys. Women are more likely than men to develop urinary tract infections due to a shorter urethra.

Symptoms

Symptoms of an acute infection in the kidneys include pain in the back, groin, or abdomen, nausea, vomiting, fever, blood in the urine, burning during urination, and an urge to constantly urinate. Cloudy urine may also be a sign of an infection, especially if there is a foul odor.

Treatments

Antibiotics are used to combat pyelonephritis. Typically they are administered orally, but in more severe cases that require hospitalization, they may be administered via IV. Pain relievers may be used to aid with associated pain.

Contraindications

Pyelonephritis is considered an absolute contraindication. A client who suspects a kidney infection should seek medical treatment.

Renal Failure

Renal Failure is **kidney failure**, where the kidneys stop functioning properly. This can lead to the body being **unable to eliminate waste**, electrolytes, and excessive fluid. This can lead to dangerous, even fatal levels of these substances in the body.

Causes

Renal failure is commonly the result of another condition damaging the kidney enough to impair function. Examples are hypertension, glomerulonephritis, pyelonephritis, diabetes, and polycystic kidney disease.

Symptoms

Usually, renal failure occurs gradually, and symptoms become more known as the kidney begins to lose function. Fatigue, nausea, vomiting, hypertension, increased fluid accumulation in the lower limbs, and loss of appetite are common symptoms.

Treatments

As the kidneys begin failing, treatment usually revolves around treating the symptoms to try and slow the disease. Once the kidneys have experienced too much damage and the body is unable to eliminate waste and fluid effectively, dialysis may be performed to remove these substances, either through the blood or through the peritoneum.

Kidney transplants may be performed. Instead of removing the damaged kidneys, a doctor will leave the damaged kidneys in the body and attach another kidney. Despite not functioning optimally, the damaged kidneys can still assist the new kidney in filtering waste and fluid, even though it may only be a small amount.

Contraindications

Because massage may increase the load on kidneys by helping rid the body of waste, massage is considered an absolute contraindication in clients with renal failure. There is debate amongst kidney specialists on this matter, though, and some believe massage therapy does not do harm in people with renal failure.

Urethritis
(urethr/o: urethra; -itis: inflammation)

Urethritis is **inflammation** of the **urethra**, usually caused by a **bacterial** infection. It is extremely treatable.

Causes

Urethritis is caused by a bacterial infection. Bacteria enters the urethra and reproduces, resulting in an infection. The infection may spread up the urinary tract, and may lead to Cystitis or Pyelonephritis if left untreated.

Less commonly, urethritis may be caused by Herpes Simplex.

Symptoms

Pain upon urination is the primary symptom of urethritis. A less common symptom is inability to effectively urinate, known as dysuria. Discharge from the vagina may present, and the urine may contain blood.

Treatments

Because urethritis is most commonly caused by bacterial infection, antibiotics are prescribed to destroy the bacteria and prevent the infection from moving further into the urinary system.

Contraindications

Massage is indicated for clients with urethritis.

Cancers

Basal Cell Carcinoma
(carcin-: cancer; -oma: tumor)

Basal Cell Carcinoma is a type of **skin** cancer typically seen around the face, head, neck, and arms.

Causes

Basal Cell Carcinoma is the most common form of skin cancer, caused by exposure to ultraviolet light. The tumor grows extremely slowly, which makes basal cell carcinoma much more treatable than other types of skin cancer. Because it is much more treatable, it is considered the least serious form of skin cancer.

Basal cell carcinoma is considered a malignant form of cancer, due to its ability to spread to the tissues immediately surrounding it. It will very rarely spread to other organs, however.

Symptoms

Basal cell carcinoma tumors may appear to have blood vessels in them, and vary in color from black to brown to pink. These growths may bleed easily.

Treatments

Treatment for Basal Cell Carcinoma includes surgical excision of the tumor, freezing the tumor, or in more serious cases, medications that prevent the cancerous cells from spreading to other tissues.

Contraindications

Massage is indicated for a client with basal cell carcinoma. However, the tumor is a local contraindication, and massage around the area should be avoided to prevent spreading of cancerous tissue through increased blood and lymph flow.

Breast Cancer

Breast cancer is cancer of **breast tissue**, including lymph nodes and vessels in the breast and axillary region. Breast cancer is the second most common form of cancer diagnosed in women, behind skin cancer. Breast cancer is much more common in women, but it can also occur in men.

Breast cancer can spread throughout the breast and to other regions of the body, and is considered a malignant form of cancer.

Causes

Breast cancer occurs when breast tissue begins growing abnormally, forming a tumor that feels like a lump under the skin. Breast cancer may be a genetic disorder, or may be the cause of unspecified environmental factors. Women who are older in age tend to develop breast cancer more often than younger women.

Symptoms

Symptoms include a lump in the breast that does not feel the same as tissue surrounding it, a nipple that has recently become inverted, change in size or appearance of the breast, dimpling of the skin of the breast, the skin of the breast and/or areola becoming scaly or flaky, and the skin of the breast becoming red. If any of these symptoms occur, a person should be seen by a medical professional.

Treatments

Treatment is based on the severity of the tumor growth. Surgery to remove the tumor will likely be performed after locating it via mammogram and ultrasound. If a large amount of breast tissue is involved, the breast may be completely removed, known as a mastectomy. Lymph nodes may also be removed to prevent any cancerous tissue from spreading to other parts of the body. Chemotherapy and radiation therapy are performed to kill the remaining cancerous cells.

Contraindications

A massage therapist should obtain a doctor's note approving massage. Afterwards, massage may be performed, avoiding any tumors, lymph nodes, or other areas affected.

Hodgkin's Lymphoma
(lymph-: lymph; -oma: tumor)

Hodgkin's Lymphoma is a malignant cancer affecting the lymphatic system, specifically the **lymph nodes** in the **upper limb, chest, and neck**. Hodgkin's Lymphoma usually follows lymph channels in a predictable manner, moving from one lymph node to the next.

Causes

Hodgkin's Lymphoma is caused by an excessive amount of B cells being produced. These cells, known as Reed-Sternberg cells, are larger than normal and contain multiple nuclei, as opposed to non-cancerous B cells, which are smaller and only contain one nucleus.

Symptoms

Symptoms of Hodgkin's Lymphoma include swelling of lymph nodes in the neck, upper limb, axilla, and neck that may be painless, weight loss, fever, and fatigue. A person may also experience sensitivity to alcohol.

Treatments

Surgery isn't usually performed for a patient with Hodgkin's Lymphoma. Instead, chemotherapy and radiation therapy are used to destroy the cancerous lymphocytes. Bone marrow transplants may also be performed to stimulate the production of non-cancerous cells.

Contraindications

A massage therapist should obtain a doctor's note approving massage. Afterwards, massage may be performed, avoiding any tumors, lymph nodes, or other areas affected.

Leukemia
(leuk/o: white; -emia: blood condition)

Leukemia is a cancer of the **bone** and **lymph** involving **excessive** production of **non-functioning leukocytes**. These leukocytes do not function the way normal leukocytes should, leaving the body with a compromised immune system. These cancerous cells may spread to other parts of the body such as the liver and brain.

Causes

There is no known cause for the development of leukemia.

Symptoms

Common symptoms of leukemia include pain in the bone, swollen lymph nodes, fatigue, fever, chills, increased likelihood of developing infections, the appearance of small red spots in the skin, and bruising or bleeding easily. A doctor should be seen if any of these symptoms persist.

Treatments

Treatment for leukemia largely depends on the advancement of the condition. If the cancer has metastasized to other parts of the body, treatment would be performed on those areas in conjunction with treating the leukemia. Chemotherapy and radiation therapy are used to target and destroy cancerous cells throughout the body. After chemotherapy and/or radiation therapy, stem cell transplant may be performed to supply the bone with stem cells that grow healthy marrow, which produces functioning leukocytes. Bone marrow itself may also be transplanted into the patient to accomplish the same goal.

Contraindications

A massage therapist should obtain a doctor's note approving massage. Afterwards, massage may be performed, avoiding any tumors, lymph nodes, or other areas affected.

Symptoms of leukemia

Chronic fatigue (weakness and low energy)

Lungs (shortness breath)

Lymph node (swelling)

Skin (tiny red spots)

Liver and spleen (swelling)

Bone and joints (pain or tenderness)

Muscle aches

Lung Cancer

Lung cancer is the development of tumors in the **lung.** People who **smoke** are at a much higher risk to develop lung cancer than anyone else. Lung cancer is the leading cause of cancerous death in the United States.

Causes

Lung cancer is primarily caused by exposure to **carcinogens** being **inhaled**. Carcinogens that cause lung cancer may be found in cigarette smoke. Other carcinogens may include radon and asbestos. These substances damage the tissue of the lungs, which in turn may begin reproducing unnaturally, causing cancer.

Lung cancer may spread to other areas and organs of the body, including the liver and brain.

Symptoms

Lung cancer is usually asymptomatic in early stages. As the condition progresses, however, symptoms may begin to appear and worsen over time. Symptoms include coughing that may produce blood, shortness of breath, and chest pain. Hoarseness may occur due to excessive coughing.

Treatments

Treatment largely depends on the stage of the cancer. The earlier stages of cancer may only require surgical removal of a small portion of the lung to take out the tumor. Advanced stages involving larger tumors may require an entire lobe of a lung to be removed, or in extreme cases, having the entire lung removed.

After the tumor is removed, radiation and chemotherapy may be performed to destroy any remaining cancerous cells.

Contraindications

A massage therapist should obtain a doctor's note approving massage. Afterwards, massage may be performed, avoiding any tumors, lymph nodes, or other areas affected.

Malignant Melanoma
(melan-: black; -oma: tumor)

Malignant Melanoma is a type of **skin** cancer that may affect any part of the skin, and can also affect other tissues such as the eyes and internal organs.

Causes

Malignant melanoma is the **least common** form of skin cancer, but it is the **most serious**. It is caused by exposure to ultraviolet light. The cells in your body that produce skin pigment, **melanocytes**, become stimulated by exposure to ultraviolet light, and reproduce, causing darker skin. In malignant melanoma, the melanocytes reproduce uncontrolled. This uncontrolled reproduction results in a tumor, and these cancerous cells can easily spread throughout the body and damage other organs and tissues.

Dermatologists use the ABCDE method to diagnose Malignant Melanoma:

- A: Asymmetrical; moles are typically symmetrical, but melanoma tumors have an unusual shape, and the sides don't match.

- B: Borders; the borders of the growth change over time. This is a sign of significantly increased melanin production.

- C: Color; moles are typically some shade of brown. If there are multiple shades or colors, or if the tumor is black, this may be a sign of increased melanin production.

- D: Diameter; if a growth is 6mm or greater in diameter(the distance through it), this may be a sign of melanoma.

- E: Evolving; moles typically look the same over time. If a mole or growth begins to evolve or change in any way, this may be a sign of melanoma.

Malignant melanoma most commonly begins to appear on a part of the body that doesn't have any prior lesions, like moles. If a new growth appears where there was nothing prior, this may be a sign of melanoma. Less commonly, moles may become cancerous.

Symptoms

Symptoms of melanoma are all included in the ABCDE's.

Treatments

Malignant melanoma, if caught early enough, is easily treatable. Later stages, where it has metastasized into other areas, need more advanced treatments, including surgery to remove any tumors or cancerous lymph nodes, chemotherapy, and radiation therapy.

Contraindications

A client with malignant melanoma should obtain permission from a doctor before proceeding with any type of massage, because the cancerous cells are easily spread throughout the body via the blood and lymph. The site of tumor growth should be avoided.

Non-Hodgkin's Lymphoma
(lymph-: lymph; -oma: tumor)

Non-Hodgkin's Lymphoma is a type of cancer of the **lymphatic** system, caused by the development of tumors by lymphocytes.

Causes

In the body, lymphocytes, like every cell, go through their normal life cycle and die when they are supposed to. In Non-Hodgkin's Lymphoma, the lymphocytes don't die, but continue reproducing. This causes an **excessive amount** of **lymphocytes** to build up in the lymph nodes.

Symptoms

People with Non-Hodgkin's Lymphoma may experience swollen lymph nodes around the neck, groin, and axilla, fatigue, weight loss, and fever.

Treatments

Often times, Non-Hodgkin's Lymphoma isn't serious, and treatment is only required when it becomes advanced. Advanced Non-Hodgkin's Lymphoma is treated with chemotherapy and radiation therapy to destroy the cancerous cells.

Contraindications

A massage therapist should obtain a doctor's note approving massage. Afterwards, massage may be performed, avoiding any tumors, lymph nodes, or other areas affected.

Squamous Cell Carcinoma

Squamous Cell Carcinoma is a form of **skin** cancer that in many cases is not serious, but has the ability to spread to other parts of the body. Squamous cell carcinoma is **more serious** and **less common** than **basal cell carcinoma**, but **not as serious** and **more common** than **malignant melanoma**.

Causes

Squamous cell carcinoma, much like basal cell carcinoma and malignant melanoma, is most often caused by exposure to ultraviolet light. Tumors most commonly develop on areas of the body constantly exposed to sunlight, such as the head, neck, arms, and hands. Tumors may be flat, scaly, and firm, and appear around the mouth, in the mouth, and on the lips.

Symptoms

Squamous cell carcinoma tumors are typically shaped like a dome, and tend to bleed easily. They appear red and scaly, with a rough texture. If the tumor is large, pain may be present around the area.

Treatments

Much like basal cell carcinoma, treatment for squamous cell carcinoma is relatively easy, with several different methods, from surgical excision and freezing of the tumor, to radiation therapy for more advanced tumors.

Contraindications

A client with squamous cell carcinoma may receive massage, but the site of the tumor should be avoided due to possible spreading of cancerous tissue.

Psychological Disorders

Anorexia Nervosa

Anorexia nervosa is a condition marked by **severe weight loss** resulting from an unhealthy **restricting of caloric intake**. In conjunction with eating an inadequate amount of food, a person with anorexia may also try losing weight by taking diuretics, laxatives, and vomiting after eating. This can cause a severe lack of nutrition, resulting in the body thinning far beyond a healthy level.

Causes

Anorexia is a psychological disorder in which a person's **perception** of their weight is **distorted**. Contributing factors towards the development of anorexia include environmental influences that put an overemphasis on being thin, and psychological issues such as obsessive compulsive disorder that make it easier to not eat by sticking to set goals.

Symptoms

Symptoms are wide-ranging, from severe thinness and weight loss, to problems with tooth decay from excessive vomiting. A lack of proper nutrition can lead to fatigue, weakness, thinning hair, and dehydration. A person with anorexia may develop anemia, osteoporosis, abnormalities in hormone production and regulation, issues with kidney function, and muscle atrophy.

Psychologically, a person may withdraw socially, and try to hide their anorexia by wearing clothing to hide their weight loss. A person may become irritable and skip meals. When confronted, a person may deny skipping meals or lie about how much food they have eaten.

Treatments

Treatment for anorexia may include hospitalization in severe cases, where the body is not receiving adequate nutrition over a long period of time. While in the hospital, a person will be given fluids to balance hydration and electrolyte levels, and be treated for issues possibly relating to the heart, liver, and kidneys. A feeding tube may be inserted to ensure a person is receiving enough nutrients.

Aside from a stay in the hospital, a person may be seen by a mental health professional to deal with underlying causes of anorexia. A person may work closely with a dietician to maintain a healthy diet.

Contraindications

Massage therapy is not contraindicated in clients with anorexia. A lighter massage should be performed to prevent damage to bones and other structures in the body.

Anxiety Disorders

Anxiety disorders are a group of disorders in where a person experiences an increased amount of **anxiety**, often at a level where the person feels they are in a **life-or-death situation**. These anxious moments can adversely affect a person's daily life and relationships. Different types of anxiety disorders include panic disorder, social anxiety disorder, and general anxiety disorder.

A person with an anxiety disorder may also suffer from addiction, depression, chronic pain, or even attempt suicide.

Causes

Often times, underlying medical issues may be the cause of anxiety disorders. Some examples include cardiovascular diseases, substance withdrawal, asthma, and hyperthyroidism. Medications may also induce anxiety.

Symptoms

Symptoms vary depending on the type of anxiety a person suffers from. General symptoms include nervousness, increased breathing and heart rate, shaking, trembling, digestive issues, and the inability to stop thinking about whatever it is that is putting a person into a state of anxiety.

Panic anxiety may leave a person with a feeling of fear or terror, and lead to chest pain, shortness of breath, and a rapid heart beat. Social anxiety may lead a person to avoid contact with others as a means to protect themselves from situations they might find themselves being embarrassed or self-conscious in.

Treatments

Psychotherapy is the primary treatment for anxiety disorders. Cognitive Behavioral Therapy is used to help treat social anxiety by exposing a person to situations they may experience in real life, helping them learn how to cope with the situation when it arises. Medications may be prescribed, such as antidepressants, that can help a person from feeling anxious.

Contraindications

Anxiety disorders are not contraindicated for massage therapy.

Bulimia
(Greek "boulimia": ravenous hunger)

Bulimia is a psychological disorder in which a person ingests abnormally large portions of food, followed by **purging** of the food ingested. Purging of food can be caused by self-induced **vomiting**, by consuming **laxatives** or **diuretics**, and/or **excessive exercise**. This is all done in an effort to avoid weight gain.

The use of self-induced vomiting and laxatives/diuretics is known as Purging Bulimia. These involve ridding the body of the ingested food in some way that doesn't allow it to be properly digested. The use of excessive exercise is known as Non-Purging Bulimia.

Causes

The exact cause of bulimia is unknown, although there are several contributing factors that may lead to the development of the condition. Stress, history of abuse, trauma, low self-esteem, and having a negative image of one's body can all be contributing factors.

Symptoms

Common symptoms may include dehydration, imbalances in electrolyte levels, fluctuating weight, lesions in the mouth due to excessive vomiting, chronic heart burn, and infertility.

People with bulimia may exhibit some of the following traits and behaviors: frequent bathroom usage after eating, eating privately, smelling of vomit, and lacking control when eating.

Treatments

Bulimia is most commonly caused by low self-esteem and negative body image. Therefore, the primary treatment is therapy to help the patient overcome these psychological issues.

Contraindications

Bulimia is not contraindicated for massage. Massage may help psychologically and improve self esteem and body image. A lighter massage may be indicated, as the client may have atrophied muscles and a weakened body due to lack of nutrients.

Dementia

Dementia is a general term for symptoms that involve **loss of memory, social skills**, and **critical thinking skills**. These skills may be impaired to the point where it affects a person's ability to function effectively on a daily basis. Dementia is caused by **damage to neurons in the brain**. There are numerous reasons for neurons to be damaged that can contribute to dementia.

Causes

Dementia may be permanent, or may be reversed, depending on the cause. Causes of dementia that involve permanent damage to the brain include progressive disorders such as Alzheimer's disease. Strokes may permanently damage the brain. Similar to strokes, injuries to the brain, such as concussions, may lead to brain damage.

Cases where dementia may be reversed include certain infections that cause high fever, autoimmune disorders such as multiple sclerosis, tumors in the brain, hypoxia, inadequate fluid intake, and hormonal problems such as having too much calcium in the body. As these conditions are treated, the dementia should go away.

Symptoms

Dementia is most commonly associated with memory loss. This can lead to problems communicating, focusing, using the body properly, and problem solving. A person may become depressed, develop anxiety or paranoia, and become easily irritated.

Treatments

Dementia itself can't be cured. Treating the underlying cause is the best way to treat dementia. This can include medications to help brain function, and physical therapy to help with any motor skills that may be affected.

Contraindications

Dementia is not contraindicated for massage therapy.

Depression

Depression is a disorder affecting **mood**, causing a person to feel **sad**, usually over a **prolonged** period of time. A person may become disinterested in normal daily activities, and become more distant.

Depression usually develops during teenage years, but may occur at any time. If a person is experiencing depression, they should seek help from a mental health professional.

Causes

There are many different causes for depression, and no one person is the same as another. Causes include a change in the body's hormone levels, such as during and after pregnancy, changes in the function of neurotransmitters in the brain, and even may be genetically passed down in the genes.

Symptoms

Symptoms are wide-ranging, and people experience depression differently. Symptoms may include a feeling of sadness, fatigue, disinterest in eating, anxiety, insomnia, irritability, and constantly thinking about death and suicide. A person with depression may attempt suicide.

Treatments

Is a person is diagnosed with depression, antidepressants known as selective serotonin reuptake inhibitors, or SSRIs, are usually prescribed to help manage hormone levels and increase serotonin levels in the blood. Talking with a mental health professional may help a person feel better. Exercise and a healthy diet may help with hormone imbalances and increase a person's self esteem, which can aid in lowering depression. Other relaxation techniques, such as massage therapy and yoga, may be sought.

Contraindications

Depression is not contraindicated for massage therapy. Massage may help relax a person with depression, increase self-esteem and body image, and help manage hormone levels in the body.

The National Suicide Prevention Lifeline is 1-800-273-8255

Insomnia
(in-: not; somnus: sleep)

Insomnia is a disorder causing a **lack of sufficient sleep**. This may be the result of a person having difficulty falling asleep, staying asleep, or waking too early. This can lead to many health complications.

Causes

There are many reasons a person's sleep may be affected. **Stress** is the most common cause of insomnia, making it difficult to "turn off" thoughts when it's time to sleep. Having an irregular sleep schedule may make it difficult for the body to adjust when it's time to sleep. Jet lag may also cause insomnia.

Certain medications may interfere with normal sleep. Pain associated with medical conditions may also keep a person from sleeping.

Symptoms

Common symptoms include trouble falling asleep, trouble staying asleep, waking too early, general fatigue, irritability, increased stress and anxiety, and depression. A person with insomnia may develop other health conditions as a result of not getting enough sleep, such as hypertension.

Treatments

Determining the root cause of the insomnia and treating that is the primary treatment for insomnia. Reducing stress, getting a person on a set sleep schedule, increasing exercise, meditation, yoga, and massage therapy can all aid in eliminating insomnia. If these methods do not accomplish the goal, medications to help a person sleep may be prescribed. Over-the-counter sleep aids may help a person sleep, but should not be used long-term as a person may develop a dependency for them.

Contraindications

Insomnia is not a contraindication for massage. Massage therapy may aid a person in reducing stress and helping them obtain a normal sleep cycle.

Vertigo

Vertigo is the sensation that a person's surroundings are moving or spinning, which may cause **dizziness**. This can be especially prevalent if a person is looking down from a tall height.

Causes

Commonly, vertigo is the result of a problem with the inner ear. Meniere's disease, which causes fluid buildup that changes pressure inside the ear, is a common cause. A buildup a calcium deposits in the inner ear can affect balance. Viral infections, such as vestibular neuritis, may also cause vertigo. Less commonly, tumors in the ear may cause vertigo.

Symptoms

Vertigo presents with a feeling of the environment around a person spinning, moving, swaying, or tilting. A person may become unbalanced, become nauseated, vomit, or develop headaches.

Treatments

Treatment for vertigo is usually dependent on the cause. If calcium is present in the inner ear, certain head and neck movements may be performed to aid the calcium in leaving the inner ear, allowing it to be broken down by the body. Medications may be prescribed to aid with nausea and fluid build up associated with Meniere's disease. Surgery may be performed if there is a tumor present.

Often times, no treatment is necessary, as the brain comes acclimated to vertigo and the symptoms lessen or disappear.

Contraindications

Vertigo is not contraindicated for massage. The massage therapist may need to help the client on and off the table to avoid accidental falls due to dizziness.

CPR and First Aid

CPR

CPR, which stands for **Cardiopulmonary Resuscitation**, is extremely important to know and understand how to perform. Refer to REMSA guidelines for appropriate instruction. CPR consists of alternating **chest** compressions and **breathing** support in cases where cardiac arrest has occurred. Refer to REMSA for up-to-date CPR techniques and requirements.

First Aid

There are many different ways to care for a person with a medical emergency, depending on the type of injury and the severity. When using first aid, **universal precautions** should be administered. Universal precautions are treating every person and fluid as if they are **contaminated** or **infectious**. Universal precautions are extremely important in containing blood-borne pathogens. Any time there is exposure to any type of bodily fluid, **gloves** and other **personal protective equipment** should be worn, and contact with blood should be avoided at all costs.

Heat Injuries

There are three main types of heat injuries, that don't involve burns: heat exhaustion, heat cramps, and heat stroke. **Heat exhaustion** is caused by a person having a **high body temperature** with **excessive sweating**. Sweating is a product of homeostasis, which is trying to cool the body. If the person continues to sweat, it means the body isn't properly cooling down. This can lead to **heat cramps**, which cause tightening and involuntary **spasms of the muscles** due to dehydration and loss of electrolytes, such as sodium and potassium. **Heat stroke** is when a person has an **extremely high body temperature**, with a **lack of sweating**. This occurs when a person is severely dehydrated, and has no more fluid to use as sweat to try cooling the body down. This can be potentially fatal.

Cold Injuries

There are two main types of cold injuries: hypothermia and frostbite. **Hypothermia** is caused by the body temperature dropping **below 90 degrees**. This can be potentially fatal. **Frostbite** is caused by a formation of **ice crystals** in **soft tissues**, typically the fingers, toes, and parts of the face such as the nose and ears. If the tissues are frozen for too long, they experience **necrosis**.

Frostbite

The Rule of 9's

The **Rule of 9's** is used to determine the extent of **burns** by the total body area involved. Each percentage represents the percentage of the body damaged by burns:

- Head and Neck: 9%
- Right Arm : 9%
- Left Arm: 9%
- Right Leg: 18%
- Left Leg: 18%
- Thorax: 18%
- Abdomen: 9%
- Lower Back: 9%
- Groin: 1%

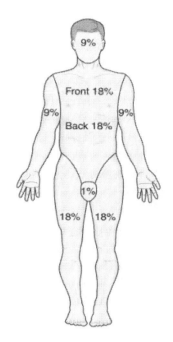

Orthopedic Injuries

As previously discussed, strains, sprains, and fractures are all forms of **orthopedic injuries**. Strains and sprains are primarily treated with the use of **PRICE: Protect, Rest, Ice, Compression, Elevation**. The damaged area should be protected from further injury, rested to allow proper healing, iced to reduce inflammation, compression to help further reduce inflammation, and elevated to assist in proper circulation and reduce inflammation.

Poisoning

Poisoning may occur in several different ways. Poisoning via **inhalation**, such as carbon monoxide poisoning, may require the person be given an **antidote**, or require breathing support by way of an **oxygen mask**.

Injection poisoning introduces harmful substances into the body via **needles**, **insect stings**, **sharp objects**, or **bites.** The poison usually requires the use of an **antidote** to treat.

Absorption of poison typically includes exposure to substances such as **pesticides**. The area affected should be cleansed thoroughly with water.

Ingestion is introducing harmful substances through **swallowing.** Depending on the substance ingested, the person may be required to induce **vomiting**, or need to drink milk or water.

Pathology Matching

__D__ : Hyper-curvature of the thoracic vertebrae caused by tight pectoralis minor and serratus anterior

__P__ : Protrusion of the nucleus pulposus through the annulus fibrosus

__G__ : Inflammation of the liver

__O__ : Erosion of the articular cartilage, causing inflammation in a joint

__A__ : Swelling of veins due to malfunctioning valves

__N__ : Injury to a ligament caused by over-stretching

__T__ : Lack of cortisol production caused by damage to the adrenal cortex

__J__ : Epidermal growth caused by the human papilloma virus

__S__ : Fungal infection of the skin causing a circular rash

__E__ : Autoimmune disorder causing dry, scaly patches to form on the skin

__R__ : Swelling of a limb due to excessive interstitial fluid in an area

__B__ : Degeneration of alveoli, reducing gas exchange

__I__ : Constriction of blood vessels in the hands and feet, reducing blood flow

__M__ : Bacterial infection causing inflammation of the bladder

__L__ : Paralysis of one side of the face due to damage to the facial nerve

__H__ : Necrosis of heart tissue

__C__ : Compression of the brachial plexus and blood vessels caused by tight scalenes and pectoralis minor

__F__ : Bacterial infection of a hair follicle, also known as a furuncle

__K__ : Form of tendonitis causing inflammation at the lateral epicondyle of the humerus

__Q__ : Highly contagious viral infection of the respiratory tract

A: Varicose Veins

B: Emphysema

C: Thoracic Outlet Syndrome

D: Kyphosis

E: Psoriasis

F: Boil

G: Hepatitis

H: Myocardial Infarction

I: Raynaud's Syndrome

J: Wart

K: Tennis Elbow

L: Bell's Palsy

M: Cystitis

N: Sprain

O: Osteoarthritis

P: Herniated Disc

Q: Influenza

R: Lymphedema

S: Ringworm

T: Addison's Disease

Answer Key on Page 271

Pathology

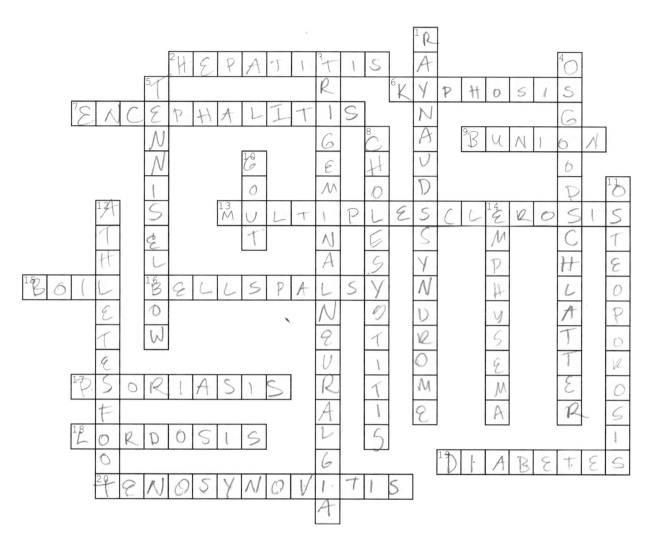

Across

2. Inflammation of the liver
6. Hyper-curvature of the thoracic vertebrae
7. Inflammation of the brain
9. Subluxation of the big toe
13. Autoimmune disorder damaging myelin sheaths
15. Bacterial infection of a hair follicle
16. Paralysis of one side of the face
17. Autoimmune disorder resulting in increased skin buildup
18. Hyper-curvature of the lumbar vertebrae
19. Insulin resistance in the blood
20. Inflammation of a tendon and its protective sheath

Down

1. Constriction of blood vessels in fingers and toes
3. Compression of cranial nerve V causing intense pain in the face
4. Excessive bone production at the tibial tuberosity
5. Tendonitis affecting the extensors of the wrist
8. Inflammation of the gallbladder
10. Excessive uric acid crystal buildup
11. Gradual decalcification of bone
12. Fungal infection of the foot
14. Destruction of alveoli due to agents such as cigarette smoke

Answer Key on Page 276

Medications

Find the medications based on what they're used for!

```
W  J  A  P  K  D  H  D  W  E  A  N  T  I  F  U  N  G  A  L
V  S  M  C  I  Q  T  N  J  Q  W  W  B  Y  E  Y  X  F  J  X
C  B  L  X  A  E  N  I  M  A  T  S  I  H  I  T  N  A  U  N
M  I  A  Z  N  A  N  T  I  B  I  O  T  I  C  L  H  S  B  Q
N  A  Q  W  T  K  T  F  U  K  C  D  L  O  L  B  V  R  R  G
A  N  T  I  I  N  F  L  A  M  M  A  T  O  R  Y  O  P  X  Z
T  D  R  U  V  Z  U  J  Z  S  L  H  C  G  O  N  A  B  V  J
H  B  Q  E  I  I  N  M  X  J  R  A  H  X  C  N  E  L  W  O
P  Y  R  F  R  U  N  Z  I  C  L  F  O  H  T  K  V  V  X  E
B  R  M  B  A  I  N  B  V  A  U  G  O  I  N  I  I  O  D  X
P  Y  A  I  L  S  D  X  N  I  T  D  P  P  A  M  T  N  W  C
K  A  Z  U  G  Y  S  E  A  F  I  Y  Z  S  T  X  A  Z  R  X
B  G  S  X  Z  F  S  N  D  L  R  J  R  G  S  V  D  S  Z  N
S  N  J  X  U  T  T  N  A  E  B  T  P  G  E  D  E  G  I  W
I  Z  Y  B  H  A  N  T  T  A  N  A  L  G  E  S  I  C  P
O  S  Q  E  C  A  O  I  F  T  K  P  I  P  N  U  E  N  J  O
G  T  T  I  R  R  C  I  S  V  Z  I  Z  L  O  M  M  B  H  S
E  I  D  J  S  N  G  K  W  S  L  K  W  U  C  C  B  Y  A  Y
C  T  N  A  L  U  G  A  O  C  I  T  N  A  E  H  G  S  M  J
C  I  T  E  R  U  I  D  E  F  L  B  Y  R  D  V  I  K  O  M
```

Numbs a localized area	Pain reliever	Reduces activity of acid in stomach
Combats growth of bacteria	Prevents blood clots	Destroys fungus
Reduces effects of histamines on the body	Reduces inflammation	Reduces fever
Combats virus reproduction	Dilates bronchial tubes	Reduces inflammation in the nasal cavity
Increases production of urine	Helps control diabetes	Calms and relaxes the body

(handwritten annotations:)

ANTIPYRETIC

Insulin
ANTIHISTAMINE.

ANTIINFLAMMATORY

BRONCHODILATORS

ANTIBIOTIC
ANTIFUNGAL
ANESTHETIC
ANTICOAGULANT
ANTIPYRETIC

ANALGESIC
ANTIVIRAL
DIURETIC

Answer Key on Page 276

Pathology Practice Exam

1. Most common form of arthritis
A. Rheumatoid arthritis
B. Gouty arthritis
C. Osteoarthritis
D. Periostitis

2. Loss of density in bone, caused by a decrease in the hormone estrogen in the body
A. Osteomyelitis
B. Menopause
C. Osteoporosis
D. Scoliosis

3. Cellulitis
A. Bacterial infection resulting in yellow scabs around the nose
B. Viral infection resulting in yellow scabs around the mouth
C. Bacterial infection involving the skin and surrounding tissues
D. Viral infection causing cold sores to appear around the mouth

4. Aneurysm
A. Bulge in an artery wall, usually caused by a weakened artery due to a condition such as hypertension
B. Inflammation of a vein due to trauma, resulting in blood clot formation
C. Blood clot in the blood stream becoming lodged in the heart, lungs, or brain, resulting in death of tissue
D. Ischemia in the myocardium due to a blockage in the coronary arteries, resulting in myocardial infarction

5. Pain felt at the medial epicondyle of the humerus is associated with
A. Tennis elbow
B. Golfer's elbow
C. Carpal tunnel syndrome
D. Synovitis

6. Bradycardia is a form of
A. Aneurysm
B. Heart murmur
C. Infarction
D. Arrhythmia

7. Bacterial infection resulting in honeycomb sores around the mouth and nose
A. Boil
B. Impetigo
C. Psoriasis
D. Meningitis

8. Lordosis is also known as
A. Swayback
B. Dowager's hump
C. Scoliosis
D. Bamboo spine

9. Decrease in oxygen traveling throughout the body
A. Hypoplasia
B. Hypoglycemia
C. Hypoxia
D. Hyperplasia

10. Achilles tendonitis can be caused by a strain to the
A. Pes anserinus
B. Patellar tendon
C. Calcaneal tendon
D. Ischial tuberosity tendon

11. While at work, Chris falls and lands on his back, injuring it. The next day, he calls to make a massage appointment, hoping the massage will help with his pain. The appropriate response would be
A. Reschedule the massage and refer the client to a physician
B. Perform the massage and do compression onto the back
C. Perform the massage and apply heat to the affected area
D. Perform the massage and do passive joint mobilization on the vertebrae

12. The most common site of sprain
A. Shoulder
B. Knee
C. Elbow
D. Ankle

13. Nausea, vomiting, and fatigue with yellowing of the skin may be the result of
A. Hepatitis
B. Food poisoning
C. Diarrhea
D. Meningitis

14. Spasm of capillaries in the fingers and toes, restricting circulation
A. Cyanosis
B. Raynaud's syndrome
C. Emphysema
D. Diabetes mellitus

15. Signs of inflammation include
A. Heat, pain, redness, coldness
B. Pain, edema, swelling, redness
C. Swelling, heat, redness, pain
D. Redness, pain, heat, dehydration

16. Squamous cell carcinoma is what type of tumor
A. Benign
B. Malignant
C. Idiopathic
D. Lymphatic

17. A client who suffers from pitting edema would be referred to which doctor
A. Dermatologist
B. Nephrologist
C. Cardiologist
D. Gastroenterologist

18. Ischemia may ultimately result in
A. Phlebitis
B. Arteriosclerosis
C. Necrosis
D. Varicose veins

19. Anticoagulants are medications that prevent
A. Blood vessel dilation
B. Inflammation
C. Mucous production
D. Blood clotting

20. All of the following are contagious conditions except
A. Mononucleosis
B. Herpes Simplex
C. Psoriasis
D. Tinea Pedis

21. Encephalitis
A. Inflammation of the brain caused by a viral infection
B. Aneurysm in the cerebrum causing brain damage
C. Blockage of a coronary artery, resulting in necrosis of myocardium
D. Inflammation of the meninges, leading to migraine headaches

22. Inflammation of a bursa sac, usually present due to trauma
A. Synovitis
B. Bursitis
C. Osteoarthritis
D. Bruxism

23. Medication prescribed to fight off bacterial infections
A. Anti-inflammatory Agents
B. Antivenoms
C. Antipyretics
D. Antibiotics

24. Pacemakers are commonly implanted in patients who suffer from
A. Arrhythmia
B. Emphysema
C. Angina pectoris
D. Heart murmur

25. Virus resulting in the development of warts
A. Herpes simplex
B. Human papilloma virus
C. Epstein-Barr virus
D. Urticaria

26. Excessive death of myocardium results in
A. Arrhythmia
B. Stroke
C. Myocardial infarction
D. Heart murmur

27. Grade 3 sprain
A. Complete rupture of a ligament
B. Partial tearing of a tendon
C. Complete rupture of a tendon
D. Partial tearing of a ligament

protein O₂

28. A lack of hemoglobin in erythrocytes may result in
A. Decreased immune response
B. Raynaud's syndrome
C. Myocardial infarction
D. Anemia

29. Due to having a shorter urethra, women are more prone to developing the following condition than men
A. Prostatitis
B. Nephritis
C. Cystitis
D. Cholecystitis

30. In a client with lordosis, the following muscle might be weakened, resulting in an exaggerated anterior tilt of the pelvis
A. Psoas major
B. Latissimus dorsi
C. Quadratus lumborum
D. Rectus abdominis

31. Viral or bacterial infection resulting in severe increases of fluids in the lungs
A. Pneumonia
B. Asthma
C. Bronchitis
D. Emphysema

32. Dopamine is a neurotransmitter which helps to stabilize the body in specific movements. A lack of dopamine in the body would result in
A. Anemia
B. Alzheimer's disease
C. Parkinson's disease
D. Sleep apnea

33. A cardiologist is a doctor who specializes in the
A. Lungs
B. Heart
C. Liver
D. Bladder

34. A blood pressure reading of 140/90 results in a person being diagnosed with
A. Hypertension
B. Hypotension
C. Hyperemia
D. Myocardial infarction

35. The most common type of diabetes
A. Insulin-dependent diabetes
B. Diabetes type I
C. Juvenile diabetes
D. Diabetes type II

36. Emphysema
A. Spasm of smooth muscle surrounding bronchial tubes, reducing inhalation
B. Inflammation of bronchial tubes due to inhalation of smoke from cigarette smoking
C. Destruction of alveoli, resulting in decreased oxygen intake
D. Bacterial infection of the lungs, reducing carbon dioxide output

37. Paralysis of one half of the face, caused by stimulation of the Herpes Simplex virus, which affects the Facial nerve
A. Graves disease
B. Cerebral palsy
C. Trigeminal neuralgia
D. Bell's palsy

38. Chronic inflammation located at the tibial tuberosity, caused by overuse of the quadriceps
A. Osgood-Schlatter disease
B. Grave's disease
C. Raynaud's disease
D. Knock-knee

39. Viral infection resulting in inflammation of the liver
A. Nephritis
B. Hepatitis
C. Mononucleosis
D. Encephalitis

40. Varicose veins most often occur in
A. Legs
B. Arms
C. Thighs
D. Ankles

41. Portion of an intervertebral disc that protrudes through the annulus fibrosus during a disc herniation
A. Spinal cord
B. Annulus pulposus
C. Facet cartilage
D. Nucleus pulposus

42. Autoimmune disorder affecting myelin sheaths in the central nervous system
A. Multiple sclerosis
B. Myasthenia gravis
C. Parkinson's disease
D. Alzheimer's disease

43. Paralysis of the lower limbs
A. Quadriplegia
B. Hemiplegia
C. Paraplegia
D. Triplegia

44. Fungal infection affecting the epidermis, resulting in a circular rash
A. Cordyceps
B. Athlete's foot
C. Ringworm
D. Whitlow

45. A common treatment for bursitis
A. Lymphatic drainage
B. Heat and compression
C. Rest and ice
D. Cold compress and friction

46. Chris has recently recovered from a severe pneumonia infection. A massage technique that may aid in lung decongestion would be
A. Vibration
B. Effleurage
C. Tapotement
D. Friction

47. Analgesics are used to combat
A. Pain
B. Obesity
C. Inflammation
D. Gout

48. Benign tumors
A. Spread to other parts of the body through lymph
B. Do not spread to other locations in the body
C. Spread to other parts of the body through blood
D. Spread to other parts of the body through interstitial fluid

49. Overproduction in melanocytes results in a tumor known as
A. Sarcoma
B. Carcinoma
C. Melanoma
D. Lymphoma

50. Lice, scabies, and ticks are all types of
A. Parasites
B. Bacterium
C. Fungi
D. Viruses

Answer Key on Page 280

174

Kinesiology

A large portion of a massage therapist's knowledge should be about muscles, bones, attachment sites, and actions. All of this information may be seen on the MBLEx.

In this section, we will discuss many subjects, covering a wide range of information.

Information covered in this section includes:

Muscle Actions
Bony Landmarks
Muscles of the Head
Muscles of the Neck
Muscles of the Back
Muscles of the Chest
Muscles of the Abdomen
Muscles of the Arm
Muscles of the Forearm
Muscles of the Pelvis
Muscles of the Thigh
Muscles of the Leg

This information is followed by four assignments:

Kinesiology Matching
Kinesiology Crossword
Muscle Labeling
Bone Labeling

The end of the section has a 50 question practice exam on Kinesiology. These questions ARE NOT the exact same questions you will see on the MBLEx. They are meant to test information that MAY be seen on the MBLEx.

While taking the practice exam, make sure to utilize your test-taking strategies(page 4) to optimize your test scores.

Muscle Actions

Eyebrow Elevation

Eyelid Depression

Jaw Depression

Jaw Elevation

Smiling

Lips Puckering

Jaw Protraction

Jaw Retraction

Jaw Lateral Deviation

Neck Rotation

Neck Flexion

Neck Extension

Neck Lateral Flexion

Scapula Protraction/Abduction

Scapula Retraction/Adduction

Scapula Elevation

Scapula Depression

Shoulder Flexion

Shoulder Extension

Shoulder Abduction

Shoulder Adduction

Shoulder Medial Rotation

Shoulder Lateral Rotation

Shoulder Horizontal Adduction

Shoulder Horizontal Abduction

Circumduction

Elbow Flexion

Elbow Extension

Forearm Supination

Forearm Pronation

Wrist Flexion

Wrist Extension

Wrist Abduction

Wrist Adduction

Digit Flexion

Digit Extension

Digit Abduction

Digit Adduction

Opposition

Thumb Adduction

Thumb Abduction

Trunk Flexion

Trunk Extension

Trunk Rotation

Trunk Lateral Flexion

Hip Flexion

Hip Extension

Hip Abduction

Hip Adduction

Hip Medial Rotation

Hip Lateral Rotation

Knee Flexion

Knee Extension

Dorsiflexion

Plantarflexion

Foot Inversion/Supination

Foot Eversion/Pronation

Digit Flexion

Digit Extension

Bony Landmarks

Bony landmarks are specific locations on bones where muscles attach. There are many different kinds of landmarks, from tubercles and tuberosities, to condyles and epicondyles.

A condyle is a rounded projection coming off a bone at an articulation.
An epicondyle is the part of the bone located superior to the condyle.
A crest is a thin ridge of a bone.
A facet is a smooth articular surface of a bone.
•A fissure is a narrow opening, resembling a crack.
A foramina(foramen) is a hole or opening in a bone.
A fossa is a shallow depression in a bone.
A linea is a narrow ridge, less pronounced than a crest.
A meatus is a canal-like passage.
A process is a prominent structure on a bone.
•A ramus is an elongated, seemingly stretched-out part of a bone.
A sinus is a cavity created by bones.
•A suture is a type of synarthrotic joint that doesn't allow movement.
A trochanter is a very large process, only found on the femur.
A tubercle is a small, rounded projection.
A tuberosity is a large, rounded, often rough projection.

Bones have numerous different types of landmarks. Landmarks are not only named after their type (above), but often times what they look like(example, "coracoid" means "resembling a crow's beak"), what muscles attach to them(example, deltoid tuberosity), or even where they're located in the body (example, anterior superior iliac spine).

Head

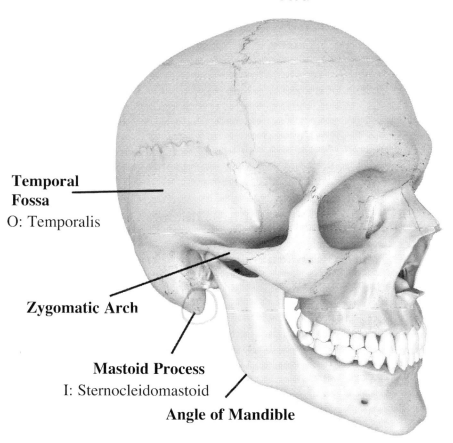

Temporal Fossa
O: Temporalis

Zygomatic Arch

Mastoid Process
I: Sternocleidomastoid

Angle of Mandible

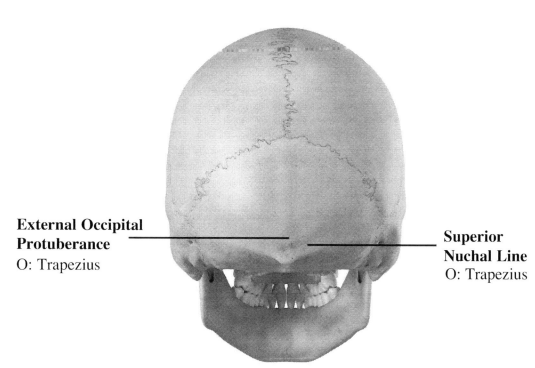

External Occipital Protuberance
O: Trapezius

Superior Nuchal Line
O: Trapezius

Vertebrae

Spinous Process

Superior Articular Process

Vertebral Body

Transverse Process

Inferior Articular Process

Back

Anterior Scapula

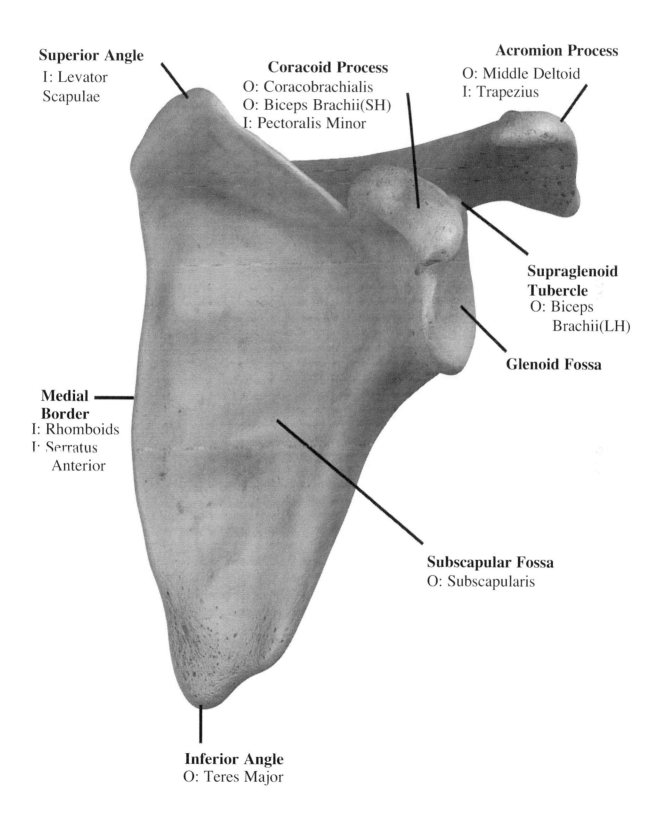

Superior Angle
I: Levator
Scapulae

Coracoid Process
O: Coracobrachialis
O: Biceps Brachii(SH)
I: Pectoralis Minor

Acromion Process
O: Middle Deltoid
I: Trapezius

**Supraglenoid
Tubercle**
O: Biceps
   Brachii(LH)

Glenoid Fossa

**Medial
Border**
I: Rhomboids
I: Serratus
   Anterior

Subscapular Fossa
O: Subscapularis

Inferior Angle
O: Teres Major

Posterior Scapula

Spine of Scapula
O: Posterior Deltoid
I: Trapezius

Supraspinous Fossa
O: Supraspinatus

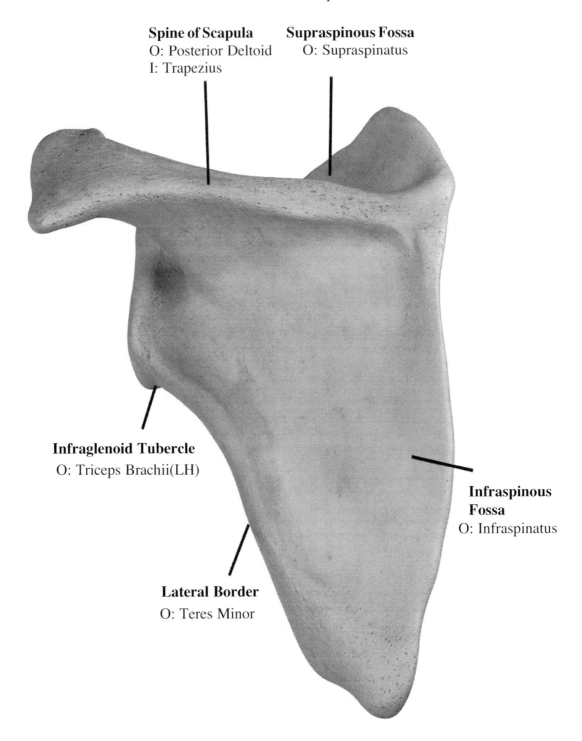

Infraglenoid Tubercle
O: Triceps Brachii(LH)

Infraspinous Fossa
O: Infraspinatus

Lateral Border
O: Teres Minor

Chest

Clavicle

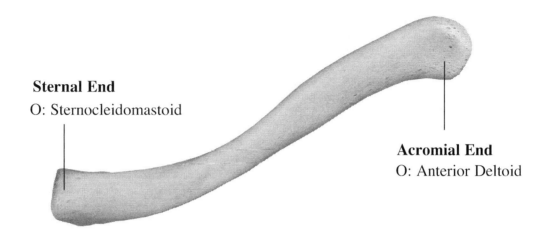

Sternal End
O: Sternocleidomastoid

Acromial End
O: Anterior Deltoid

Sternum

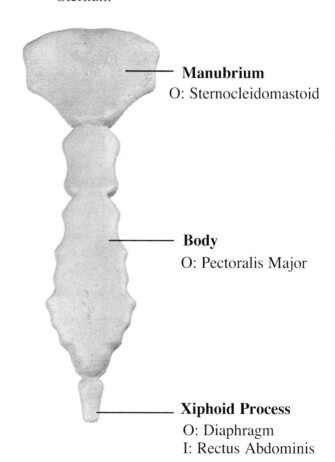

Manubrium
O: Sternocleidomastoid

Body
O: Pectoralis Major

Xiphoid Process
O: Diaphragm
I: Rectus Abdominis

Arm

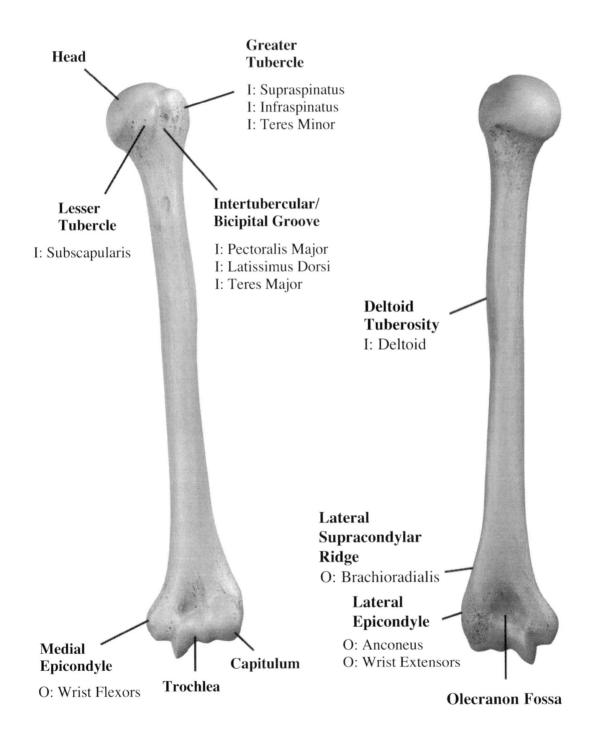

Anterior Humerus

Head

Greater Tubercle

I: Supraspinatus
I: Infraspinatus
I: Teres Minor

Lesser Tubercle

I: Subscapularis

Intertubercular/ Bicipital Groove

I: Pectoralis Major
I: Latissimus Dorsi
I: Teres Major

Medial Epicondyle

O: Wrist Flexors

Trochlea

Capitulum

Posterior Humerus

Deltoid Tuberosity
I: Deltoid

Lateral Supracondylar Ridge
O: Brachioradialis

Lateral Epicondyle

O: Anconeus
O: Wrist Extensors

Olecranon Fossa

193

Forearm

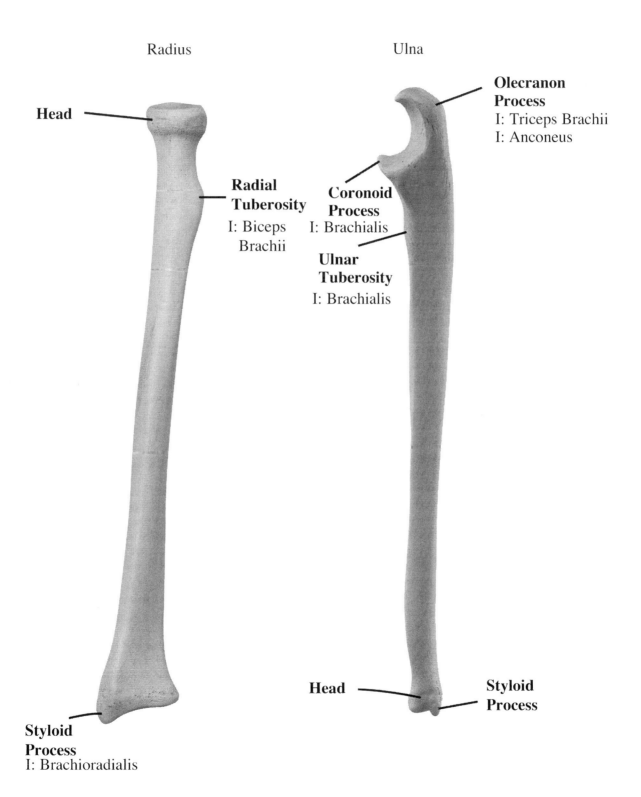

Radius

Head

**Radial
Tuberosity**
I: Biceps
Brachii

**Styloid
Process**
I: Brachioradialis

Ulna

**Olecranon
Process**
I: Triceps Brachii
I: Anconeus

**Coronoid
Process**
I: Brachialis

**Ulnar
Tuberosity**
I: Brachialis

Head

**Styloid
Process**

Wrist

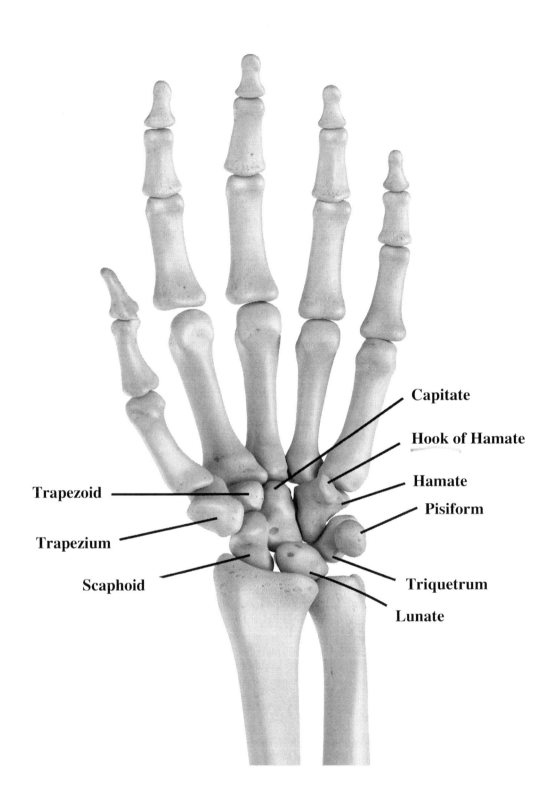

Capitate

Hook of Hamate

Hamate

Pisiform

Triquetrum

Lunate

Trapezoid

Trapezium

Scaphoid

Pelvis

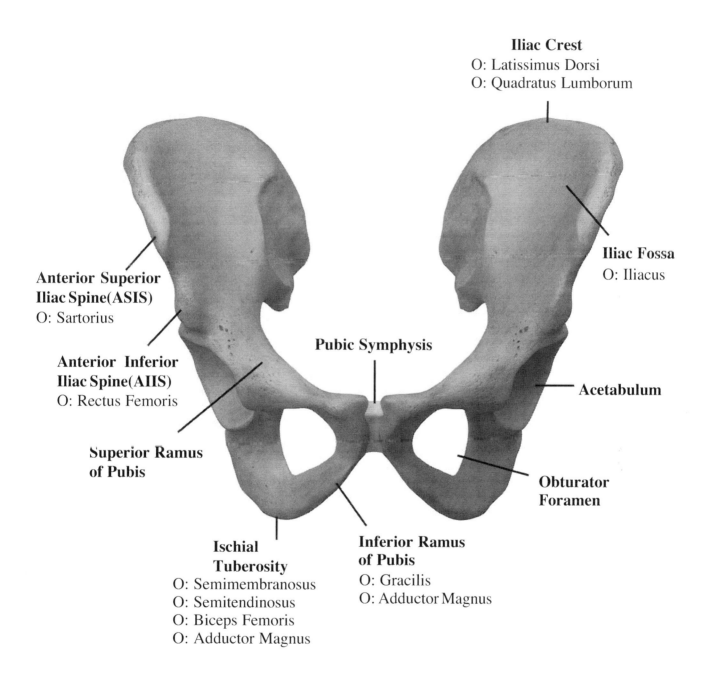

Iliac Crest
O: Latissimus Dorsi
O: Quadratus Lumborum

Iliac Fossa
O: Iliacus

Anterior Superior Iliac Spine(ASIS)
O: Sartorius

Anterior Inferior Iliac Spine(AIIS)
O: Rectus Femoris

Pubic Symphysis

Acetabulum

Superior Ramus of Pubis

Obturator Foramen

Ischial Tuberosity
O: Semimembranosus
O: Semitendinosus
O: Biceps Femoris
O: Adductor Magnus

Inferior Ramus of Pubis
O: Gracilis
O: Adductor Magnus

Thigh

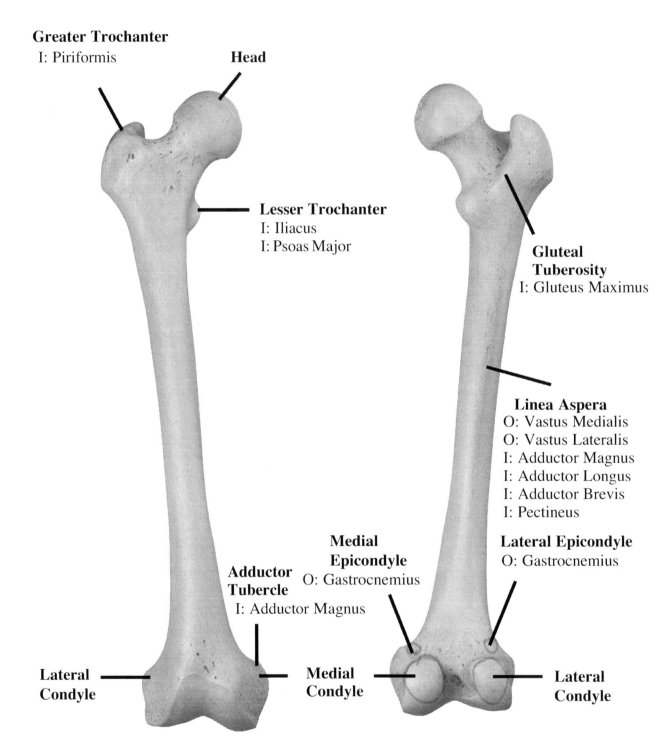

Anterior Femur

Greater Trochanter
I: Piriformis

Head

Lesser Trochanter
I: Iliacus
I: Psoas Major

Adductor Tubercle
I: Adductor Magnus

Lateral Condyle

Medial Condyle

Posterior Femur

Gluteal Tuberosity
I: Gluteus Maximus

Linea Aspera
O: Vastus Medialis
O: Vastus Lateralis
I: Adductor Magnus
I: Adductor Longus
I: Adductor Brevis
I: Pectineus

Medial Epicondyle
O: Gastrocnemius

Lateral Epicondyle
O: Gastrocnemius

Lateral Condyle

Leg

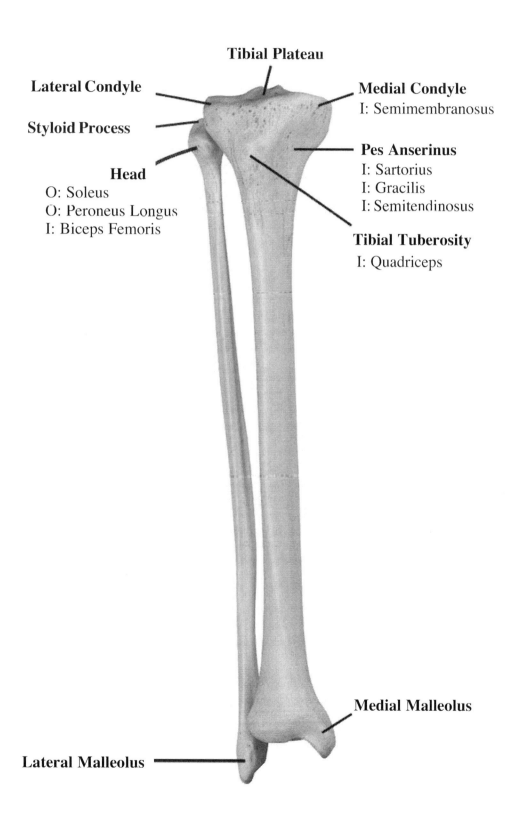

Tibial Plateau

Lateral Condyle

Medial Condyle
I: Semimembranosus

Styloid Process

Pes Anserinus
I: Sartorius
I: Gracilis
I: Semitendinosus

Head
O: Soleus
O: Peroneus Longus
I: Biceps Femoris

Tibial Tuberosity
I: Quadriceps

Medial Malleolus

Lateral Malleolus

Ankle

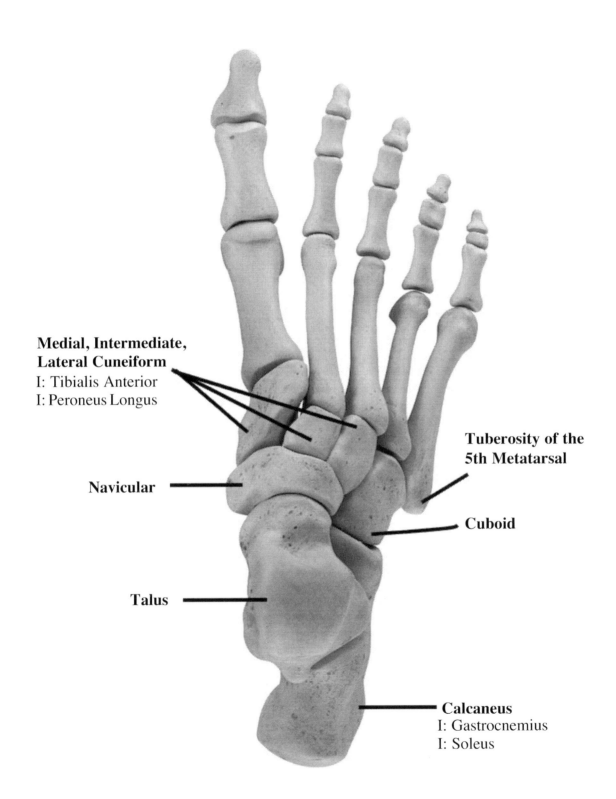

Medial, Intermediate, Lateral Cuneiform
I: Tibialis Anterior
I: Peroneus Longus

Tuberosity of the 5th Metatarsal

Navicular

Cuboid

Talus

Calcaneus
I: Gastrocnemius
I: Soleus

Muscles of the Head

Muscles to Know:
Buccinator
Masseter
Temporalis

Terms to Know:
Bucc/o: Cheek

Buccinator

Buccinator is a muscle of the face located in the area of the cheek, also known as the "buccal" region. The term"bucc/o" means "cheek".

Buccinator originates on the Alveolar Processes of the Mandible and Maxilla, and inserts onto the angle of the mouth and the Orbicularis Oris muscle.

Buccinator primarily assists in chewing by squeezing the cheeks closer together while the jaw is depressed. This forces the food back in towards the teeth, allowing proper mastication to take place upon elevation of the mandible. Buccinator is also the muscle primarily used for whistling, again by squeezing the cheeks together.

If a person is affected by Bell's Palsy, the Buccinator becomes paralyzed, which produces slurred speech.

Origin: Alveolar Processes of Mandible and Maxilla
Insertion: Angle of the Mouth, Orbicularis Oris
Action(s): Elevation of Mandible, Compresses Cheeks against Teeth
Innervation: Buccal Branch of Facial Nerve
Synergist: Masseter
Antagonist: Lateral Pterygoid

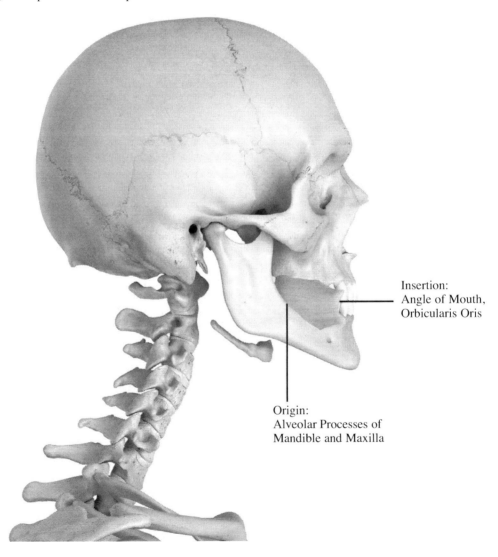

Insertion:
Angle of Mouth,
Orbicularis Oris

Origin:
Alveolar Processes of
Mandible and Maxilla

Masseter

Masseter, named after its primary action of mastication, is a muscle of the face that attaches to the mandible. When it contracts, it allows for chewing to take place. It works with other muscles, such as Buccinator, to perform mastication.

Masseter originates on the zygomatic arch and maxilla, and inserts onto the coronoid process and ramus of the mandible.

Masseter is one muscle primarily involved in TMJ (Temporomandibular Joint) Dysfunction, along with Temporalis and Pterygoid.

Origin: Zygomatic Arch, Maxilla
Insertion: Coronoid Process and Ramus of Mandible
Action(s): Elevation, Protraction of Mandible
Innervation: Mandibular Nerve
Synergist: Buccinator
Antagonist: Lateral Pterygoid

DID YOU KNOW?

*Masseter is the **strongest** muscle in the body by proportional size!*

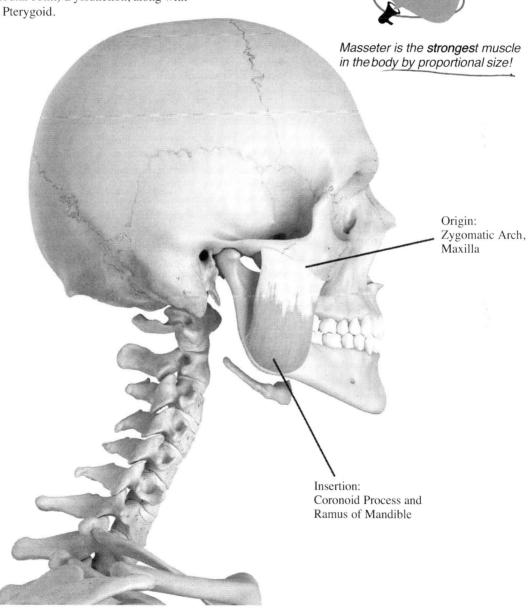

Origin:
Zygomatic Arch,
Maxilla

Insertion:
Coronoid Process and
Ramus of Mandible

Temporalis

Temporalis is a muscle of the cranium, named after the Temporal bone, which is its origin.

Temporalis inserts onto the Coronoid Process of the Mandible. "Coronoid" means "resembling a crown". Inserting onto the Mandible allows the Temporalis to assist in mastication, along with Masseter.

If a person is affected by TMJ(Temporomandibular Joint) Dysfunction, Temporalis may be involved.

Origin: Temporal Fossa
Insertion: Coronoid Process of Mandible
Action(s): Elevation, Retraction of Mandible
Innervation: Facial Nerve
Synergist: Masseter
Antagonist: Lateral Pterygoid

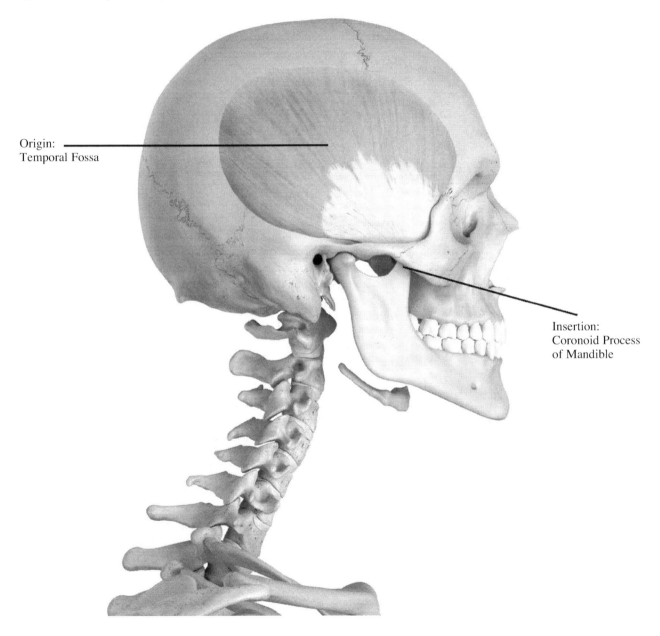

Origin:
Temporal Fossa

Insertion:
Coronoid Process
of Mandible

Muscles of the Neck

Muscles to Know:
Levator Scapulae
Scalenes
Sternocleidomastoid

Terms to Know:
Skalenos: Uneven
Stern/o: Sternum
Cleid/o: Clavicle
Mast/o: Breast
-oid: Resembling

Levator Scapulae

Levator Scapulae is a muscle of the posterior neck, named after its action(elevation), and insertion(scapula).

Levator Scapulae originates on the Transverse Processes of C1-C4, and inserts onto the Superior Angle of the Scapula.

Levator Scapulae is one of the prime movers of scapular elevation, such as shrugging the shoulders. It also may slightly downwardly rotate the scapula.

Origin: Transverse Processes of C1-C4
Insertion: Superior Angle of Scapula
Action(s): Elevation of Scapula
Innervation: Dorsal Scapular Nerve
Synergist: Upper Trapezius
Antagonist: Lower Trapezius, Serratus Anterior

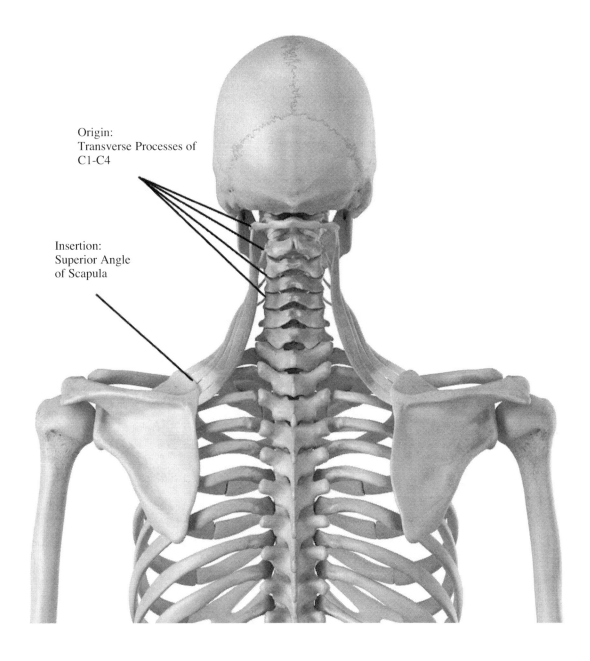

Origin:
Transverse Processes of
C1-C4

Insertion:
Superior Angle
of Scapula

Scalenes

The Scalenes are muscles of the anterior neck. The Scalenes are split into three parts: Anterior Scalene, Middle Scalene, and Posterior Scalene. The name "Scalene" comes from the Greek word "skalenos", which means uneven. All three Scalene muscles are a different size.

The Scalenes originate on the Transverse Processes of C1-C7, and insert onto Ribs 1 and 2.

The Scalenes, unilaterally, laterally flex the cervical vertebrae, bringing the ear to the shoulder. The Scalenes also elevate the ribs.

The Scalenes are neurovascular entrappers. Conditions such asThoracic Outlet Syndrome, where the Brachial plexus, Subclavianartery, and Subclavian vein are compressed, can be caused byhypertonic Scalenes. This condition may result in loss of sensationin the upper limb and reduced blood flow.

Origin: Transverse Processes of C1-C7
Insertion: Ribs 1 and 2
Action(s): Unilaterally: Lateral Flexion of Cervical Vertebrae; Elevation of Ribs
Innervation: Branches of Cervical Plexus and Brachial Plexus
Synergist: Sternocleidomastoid
Antagonist: Spinalis Cervicis, Splenius Capitis

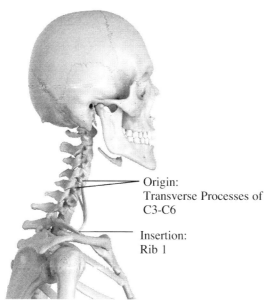

Origin:
Transverse Processes of
C3-C6

Insertion:
Rib 1

Anterior Scalene

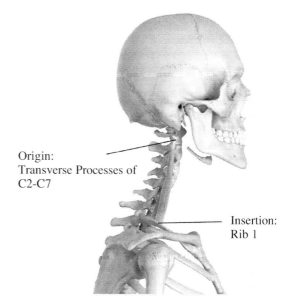

Origin:
Transverse Processes of
C2-C7

Insertion:
Rib 1

Middle Scalene

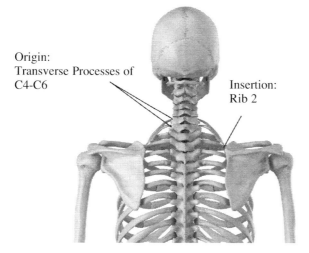

Origin:
Transverse Processes of
C4-C6

Insertion:
Rib 2

Posterior Scalene

Sternocleidomastoid

Sternocleidomastoid is a muscle of the anterior neck, named after its origins(Sternum, Clavicle) and insertion (Mastoid Process). This muscle may also be known as "Sternomastoid".

Sternocleidomastoid has numerous actions. Unilaterally, it rotates the cervical vertebrae to the opposite side of the contracting muscle. It also laterally flexes the cervical vertebrae to the same side of the contracting muscle. Bilaterally, it flexes the cervical vertebrae, allowing the chin to come to the chest.

Sternocleidomastoid establishes the borders of the anterior triangle of the neck, creating a V shape.

Origin: Manubrium, Medial Third of Clavicle
Insertion: Mastoid Process of Temporal bone
Action(s): Unilaterally: Rotation of Cervical Vertebrae to opposite side, Lateral Flexion of Cervical Vertebrae to same side; Bilaterally: Flexion of Cervical Vertebrae
Innervation: Accessory Nerve
Synergist: Scalenes
Antagonist: Splenius Capitis, Trapezius

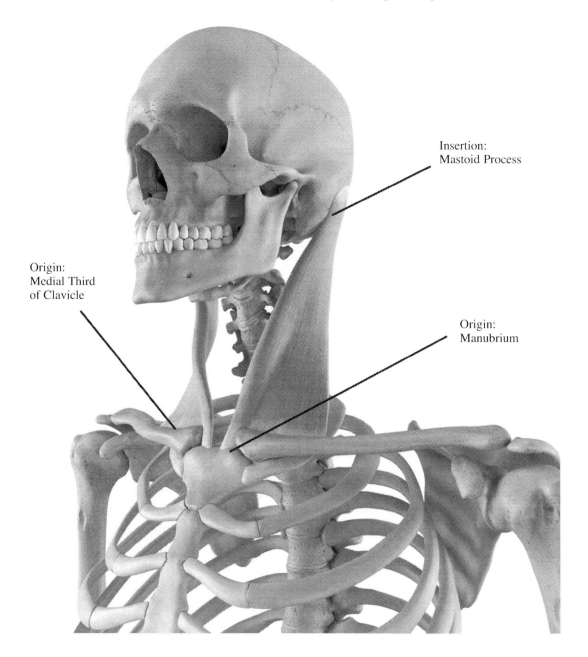

Insertion:
Mastoid Process

Origin:
Medial Third
of Clavicle

Origin:
Manubrium

Muscles of the Back

Muscles to Know:
Infraspinatus
Latissimus Dorsi
Longissimus
Multifidus
Quadratus Lumborum
Rhomboids
Rotatores
Spinalis
Subscapularis
Supraspinatus
Teres Major
Teres Minor
Trapezius

Terms to Know:
Infra-: Below
Latissimus: Wide
Dorsi: Back
Quadr/o: Four
Lumb/o: Lumbar
Sub-: Under
Supra-: Above
Teres: Round and Long

Infraspinatus

Infraspinatus is a muscle of the back, named after its location (inferior to the Spine of Scapula).

Infraspinatus is a member of the rotator cuff muscle group, along with Supraspinatus, Teres Minor, and Subscapularis. Infraspinatus originates on the Infraspinous Fossa, located on the posterior surface of the Scapula. Infraspinatus inserts onto the Greater Tubercle (sometimes also known as the Greater Tuberosity) of the Humerus.

Infraspinatus is primarily responsible for lateral rotation, extension, and horizontal abduction of the shoulder. Infraspinatus and Teres Minor have the same actions.

Origin: Infraspinous Fossa
Insertion: Greater Tubercle of Humerus
Action(s): Lateral Rotation, Horizontal Abduction of Shoulder
Innervation: Suprascapular Nerve
Synergist: Teres Minor, Latissimus Dorsi, Posterior Deltoid
Antagonist: Anterior Deltoid, Subscapularis, Pectoralis Major

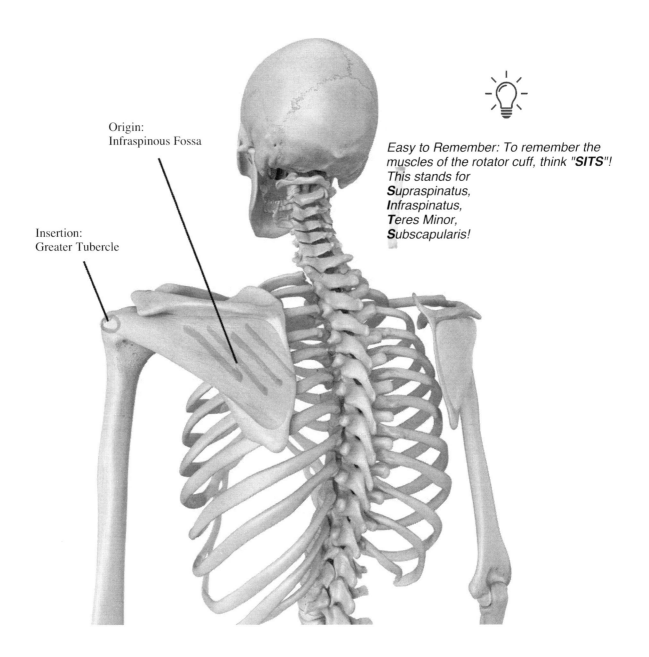

Origin:
Infraspinous Fossa

Insertion:
Greater Tubercle

*Easy to Remember: To remember the muscles of the rotator cuff, think "**SITS**"! This stands for **S**upraspinatus, **I**nfraspinatus, **T**eres Minor, **S**ubscapularis!*

Latissimus Dorsi

Latissimus Dorsi is a muscle of the back, named after its size ("Latissimus" means "wide") and location("Dorsi" refers to the back). Latissimus Dorsi is the widest muscle in the body.

Latissimus Dorsi originates on the Iliac Crest, Thoracolumbar Aponeurosis, and the Spinous Processes of T7-T12. Latissimus Dorsi inserts onto the Medial Lip of the Intertubercular Groove(also may be known as the Bicipital Groove).

Latissimus Dorsi is the muscle primarily responsible for performing adduction of the shoulder. If a person were to perform pull-up exercises, it would be Latissimus Dorsi contracting strongest. Latissimus Dorsi also medially rotates and extends the shoulder. Latissimus Dorsi, Teres Major, and Subscapularis all perform the same actions. When the insertion is fixed in place, Latissimus Dorsi may elevate the hip.

Latissimus Dorsi is often referred to as the "Swimmer's Muscle" due to its actions, which are used when swimming.

Origin: Iliac Crest, Thoracolumbar Aponeurosis, Spinous Processes of T7-T12
Insertion: Medial Lip of Intertubercular Groove
Action(s): Extension, Adduction, Medial Rotation of Shoulder
Innervation: Thoracodorsal Nerve
Synergist: Teres Major, Subscapularis
Antagonist: Pectoralis Major, Coracobrachialis

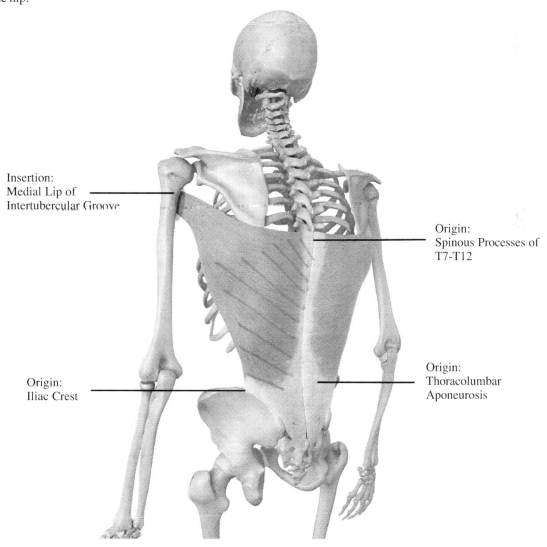

Insertion:
Medial Lip of
Intertubercular Groove

Origin:
Spinous Processes of
T7-T12

Origin:
Iliac Crest

Origin:
Thoracolumbar
Aponeurosis

Longissimus

Longissimus is a group of three muscles, Longissimus Cervicis, Longissimus Capitis, and Longissimus Thoracis, which are all part of the Erector Spinae muscle group. Each muscle is named after the region of the body it is located on or attaches to.

Longissimus Thoracis originates on the Transverse Processes of L1-L5, the Iliac Crest, and the Sacrum. Longissimus Cervicis originates on the Transverse Processes of T1-T5. Longissimus Capitis originates on the Articular Surfaces of C4-C7.

Longissimus Thoracis inserts onto the Transverse Processes of T1-T12. Longissimus Cervicis inserts onto the Transverse Processes of C2-C6. Longissimus Capitis inserts onto the Mastoid Process.

Unilaterally, the Longissimus laterally flexes the trunk. Bilaterally, Longissimus extends the trunk.

Origin: Transverse and Spinous Processes of L1-L5, Iliac Crest, Sacrum, Transverse Processes of T1-T5, Articular Surfaces of C4-C7
Insertion: Transverse Processes of T1-T12, Transverse Processes of C2-C6, Mastoid Process
Action(s): Unilaterally: Lateral Flexion of Trunk; Bilaterally: Extension of Trunk
Innervation: Dorsal Primary Rami of T1-L5
Synergist: Spinalis
Antagonist: Rectus Abdominis

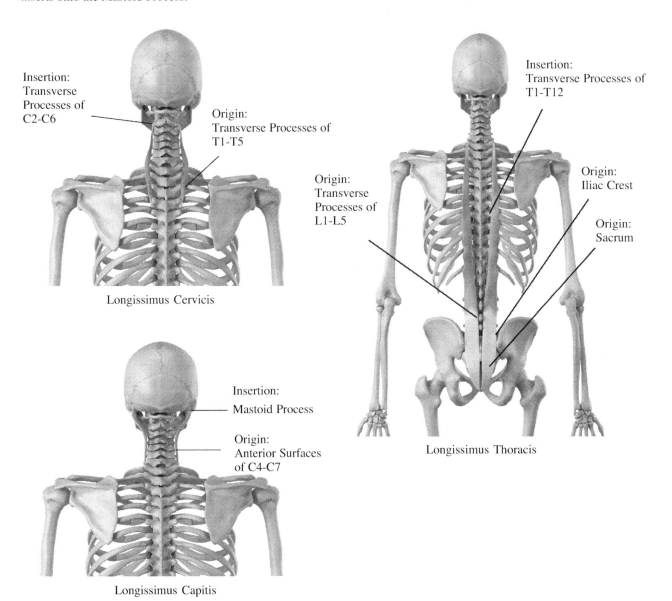

Insertion:
Transverse
Processes of
C2-C6

Origin:
Transverse Processes of
T1-T5

Longissimus Cervicis

Insertion:
Mastoid Process

Origin:
Anterior Surfaces
of C4-C7

Longissimus Capitis

Insertion:
Transverse Processes of
T1-T12

Origin:
Transverse
Processes of
L1-L5

Origin:
Iliac Crest

Origin:
Sacrum

Longissimus Thoracis

Multifidus

Multifidus is a muscle of the back, often grouped together with other multifidus muscles to create the Multifidi.

The Multifidi as a group originate on the Posterior Surface of the Sacrum, the Posterior Superior Iliac Spine (PSIS), Mamillary Processes of L1-L5, the Transverse Processes of T1-T12, and the Articular Processes of C4-C7. The Multifidi insert on the Transverse Processes of C2-L5, spanning essentially the entire vertebral column.

Unilaterally, the Multifidi will laterally flex the trunk, and rotate the trunk. Bilaterally, the Multifidi extend the trunk.

The Multifidi span the most number of vertebrae of any muscle.

Origin: Posterior Surface of Sacrum, Posterior Superior Iliac Spine, Mamillary Processes of L1-L5, Transverse Processes of T1-T12, Articular Processes of C4-C7
Insertion: Spinous Processes of C2-L5
Action(s): Unilaterally: Lateral Flexion of Trunk, Rotation of Trunk; Bilaterally: Extension of Trunk
Innervation: Dorsal Rami of Spinal Nerves
Synergist: Longissimus, Spinalis
Antagonist: Rectus Abdominis

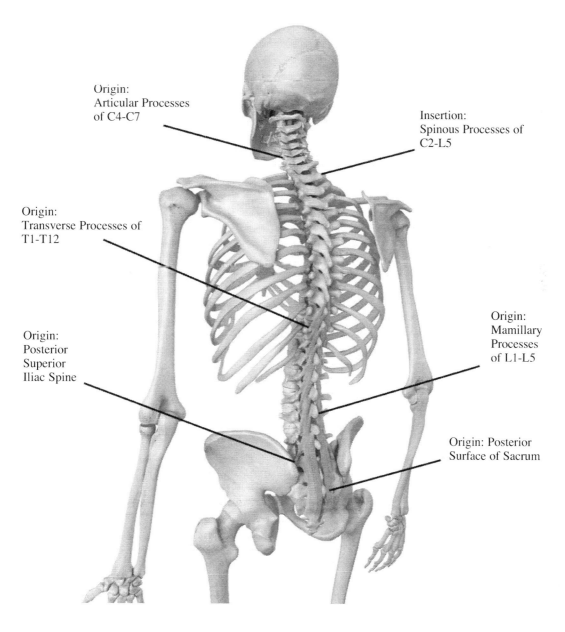

Origin: Articular Processes of C4-C7

Insertion: Spinous Processes of C2-L5

Origin: Transverse Processes of T1-T12

Origin: Posterior Superior Iliac Spine

Origin: Mamillary Processes of L1-L5

Origin: Posterior Surface of Sacrum

Quadratus Lumborum

Quadratus Lumborum is a muscle of the lower back, named after its shape(four sides), and its location(in the lumbar region).

Quadratus Lumborum originates on the Iliac Crest, and inserts onto the 12th Rib, and the Transverse Processes of L1-L4.

Quadratus Lumborum, unilaterally, will assist in lateral flexion of the trunk. Bilaterally, it will assist in extension of the trunk.

If a person suffers from Lordosis(also known as Swayback), it may be caused by hypertonicity in the Quadratus Lumborum, pulling the pelvis anteriorly, thus increasing the curvature of the Lumbar vertebrae.

Origin: Iliac Crest
Insertion: 12th Rib, Transverse Processes of L1-L4
Action(s): Unilaterally: Lateral Flexion of Trunk; Bilaterally: Extension of Trunk
Innervation: Ventral Primary Rami of T12-L3
Synergist: Longissimus, Spinalis
Antagonist: Rectus Abdominis

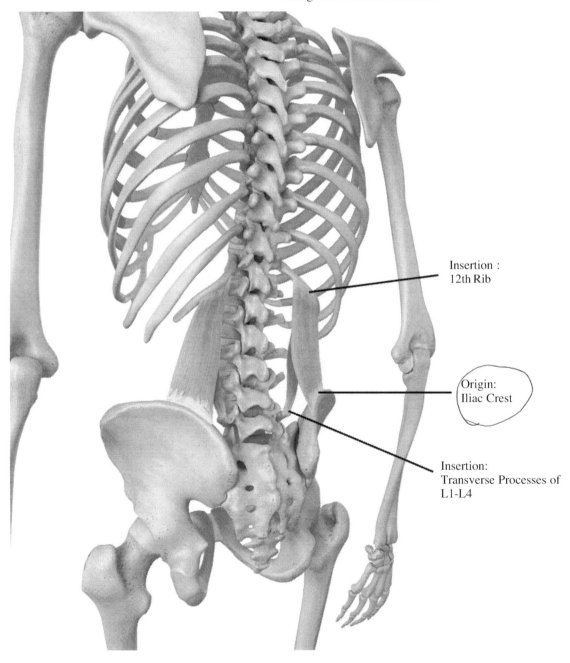

Insertion : 12th Rib

Origin: Iliac Crest

Insertion: Transverse Processes of L1-L4

Rhomboids

The Rhomboids(Rhomboid Major and Rhomboid Minor) are two muscles located on the back. They are named after their shape(rhombus).

Rhomboid Major originates on the Spinous Processes of T3-T5. Rhomboid Minor originates on the Spinous Processes of C7-T2. Together, the Rhomboids insert onto the Medial/Vertebral Border of the Scapula.

When the Rhomboids contract, they pull the Scapula towards the vertebrae. This action is known as retraction/adduction. Two primary antagonists to the Rhomboids are Serratus Anterior and Pectoralis Minor. Both of these muscles protract/abduct the Scapula.

Origin: Rhomboid Minor: Spinous Processes of C7-T2;
Rhomboid Major: Spinous Processes of T3-T5
Insertion: Medial/Vertebral Border of Scapula
Action(s): Retraction/Adduction of Scapula
Innervation: Dorsal Scapular Nerve C5
Synergist: Middle Trapezius
Antagonist: Serratus Anterior, Pectoralis Minor

DID YOU KNOW? *If the Rhomboids are hypertonic on one side, it may contribute to the development of **Scoliosis**!*

Origin:
Spinous Processes of
C7-T5

Insertion:
Medial/Vertebral
Border of Scapula

Rotatores

The Rotatores are a group of muscles that span the entire vertebral column. They are named after their action.

The Rotatores originate on the Transverse Processes of C1-L5, and insert onto the Spinous Processes of the vertebrae just superior. An example, the Rotator muscle that originates on the Transverse Process of C2 would insert onto the Spinous Process of C1.

Unilaterally, the Rotatores will rotate the trunk to the opposite side. Bilaterally, the Rotatores assist in extension of the trunk.

Origin: Transverse Processes of C1-L5
Insertion: Spinous Processes of Vertebrae just superior
Action(s): Unilaterally: Rotate Trunk to opposite side; Bilaterally: Extension of Trunk
Innervation: Dorsal Primary Rami of Spinal Nerves C1- T12
Synergist: Spinalis, Longissimus
Antagonist: Rectus Abdominis

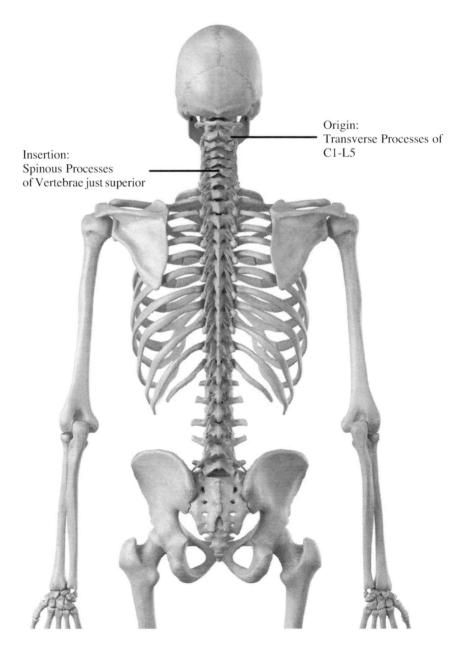

Origin:
Transverse Processes of
C1-L5

Insertion:
Spinous Processes
of Vertebrae just superior

Spinalis

Spinalis is a pair of two muscles, both located on the back. Each muscle is named after its location: Spinalis Thoracis(in the Thoracic region), Spinalis Cervicis(in the Cervical region).

Spinalis Thoracis originates on the Spinous Processes of T11-L2. There may be slight variation of the origin, however, ranging from T10-L3. Spinalis Cervicis originates on the Nuchal Ligament, and Spinous Process of C7. Spinalis Thoracis inserts onto the Spinous Processes of T3-T8. Spinalis Cervicis inserts onto the Spinous Process of C2.

Unilaterally, the Spinalis muscles laterally flex and rotate the trunk to the same side. Bilaterally, they work with other muscles such as Longissimus to extend the trunk.

Origin:Spinalis Thoracis:Spinous Processesof T11-L2;
Spinalis Cervicis: Nuchal Ligament, Spinous Process of C7
Insertion: Spinalis Thoracis: Spinous Processes of T3- T8;
Spinalis Cervicis: Spinous Process of C2
Action(s): Unilaterally: Flex and Rotate Spine to the same side;
Bilaterally: Extend the Trunk
Innervation: Dorsal Rami of Cervical and Thoracic Spinal Nerves
Synergist: Longissimus
Antagonist: Rectus Abdominis

Origin:
Spinous Process
of C7

Insertion.
Spinous Process
of C2

Insertion:
Spinous Processes of
T3-T8

Origin:
Spinous
Processes
of T11-L2

Spinalis Cervicis   Spinalis Thoracis

Subscapularis

Subscapularis is a muscle of the back, named after its location(under the scapula).

Subscapularis originates on the Subscapular Fossa, located on the anterior surface of the Scapula. Subscapularis inserts onto the Lesser Tubercle(sometimes also called the Lesser Tuberosity of the Humerus). It is part of the rotator cuff muscle group, along with Infraspinatus, Teres Minor, and Supraspinatus.

Subscapularis is a synergist to Latissimus Dorsi, performing the same actions on the shoulder. These actions are adduction, extension, and medial rotation.

If a person is affected by Adhesive Capsulitis(Frozen Shoulder), there may be hypertonicity in the Subscapularis, reducing the range-of-motion during actions such as shoulder flexion.

Origin: Subscapular Fossa
Insertion: Lesser Tubercle of Humerus
Action(s): Medial Rotation, Adduction, Extension of the Shoulder
Innervation: Upper and Lower Subscapular Nerves
Synergist: Latissimus Dorsi, Teres Major
Antagonist: Pectoralis Major, Coracobrachialis

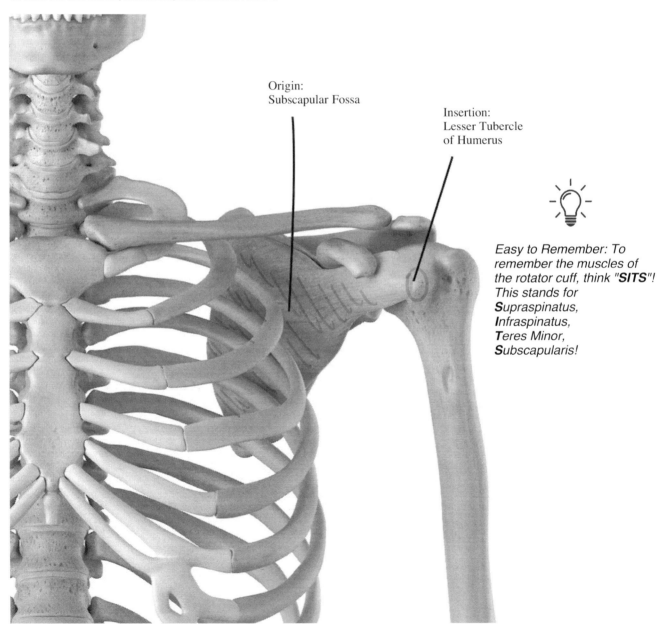

Origin:
Subscapular Fossa

Insertion:
Lesser Tubercle
of Humerus

Easy to Remember: To remember the muscles of the rotator cuff, think "**SITS**"! This stands for **S**upraspinatus, **I**nfraspinatus, **T**eres Minor, **S**ubscapularis!

Supraspinatus

Supraspinatus is a muscle of the back, named after its location (superior to the Spine of the Scapula).

Supraspinatus originates on the Supraspinous Fossa, just above the Spine of the Scapula. Supraspinatus inserts onto the Greater Tubercle (sometimes called the Greater Tuberosity of the Humerus). It is part of the rotator cuff muscle group, along with Infraspinatus, Teres Minor, and Subscapularis.

Supraspinatus has primarily one action: abduction of the shoulder. It is a synergist to the Deltoid in performing this action. Supraspinatus also helps hold the Humerus in place against the Glenoid Fossa, providing stability to the shoulder joint.

Most commonly, if a person suffers from a torn rotator cuff, it likely involves the Supraspinatus more than other muscles. A torn rotator cuff might require surgery to repair, depending on the severity.

Origin: Supraspinous Fossa
Insertion: Greater Tubercle of Humerus
Action(s): Abduction of Shoulder
Innervation: Suprascapular Nerve
Synergist: Deltoid
Antagonist: Latissimus Dorsi, Teres Major

*Easy to Remember: To remember the muscles of the rotator cuff, think "**SITS**"! This stands for **S**upraspinatus, **I**nfraspinatus, **T**eres Minor, **S**ubscapularis!*

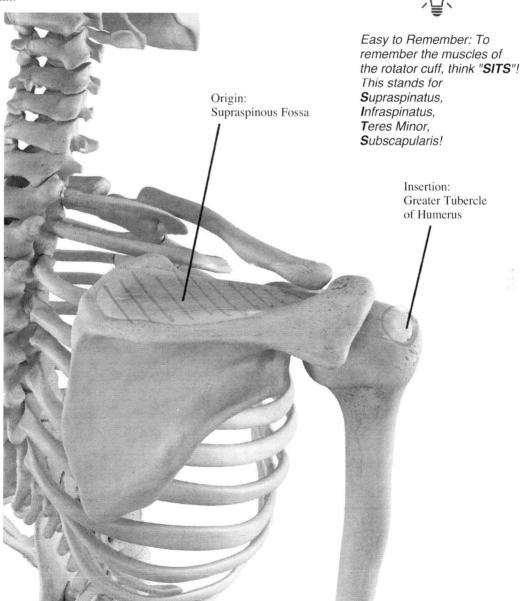

Origin:
Supraspinous Fossa

Insertion:
Greater Tubercle
of Humerus

Teres Major

Teres Major is a muscle of the back. The name "Teres" means "round and long". Teres Major has a long, round shape.

Teres Major originates on the Inferior Angle of the Scapula, and inserts onto the Medial Lip of the Intertubercular Groove. It shares its insertion with Latissimus Dorsi.

Teres Major and Latissimus Dorsi both perform the same actions: medial rotation, extension, and adduction of the shoulder.

Origin: Inferior Angle of Scapula
Insertion: Medial Lip of Intertubercular Groove
Action(s): Medial Rotation, Adduction, Extension of Shoulder
Innervation: Lower Subscapular Nerve
Synergist: Latissimus Dorsi, Subscapularis
Antagonist: Pectoralis Major, Coracobrachialis

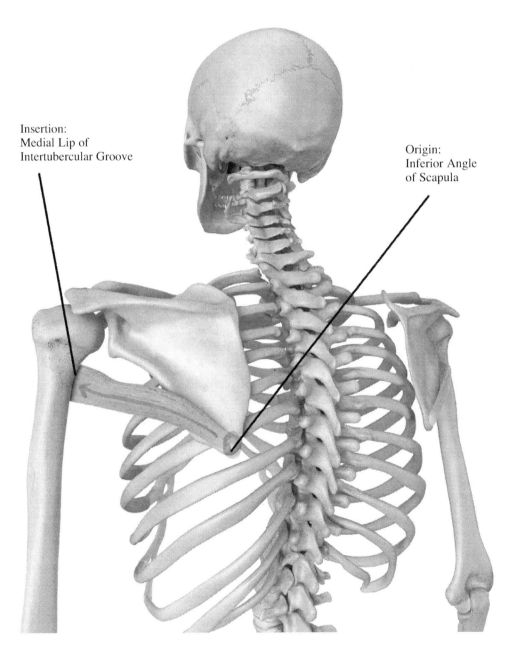

Insertion:
Medial Lip of
Intertubercular Groove

Origin:
Inferior Angle
of Scapula

Teres Minor

Teres Minor is a muscle of the back. The word "Teres" means "round and long". Teres Minor has a long, round shape.

Teres Minor originates on the Lateral/Axillary Border of the Scapula. The term "Axillary" refers to the armpit, which Teres Minor is located next to. Teres Minor inserts onto the Greater Tubercle(sometimes known as the Greater Tuberosity) of the Humerus.

Teres Minor is a member of the rotator cuff muscle group, along with Infraspinatus, Subscapularis, and Supraspinatus.

Teres Minor and Infraspinatus are located immediately next to one another, and sometimes may even fuse together. These muscles perform the same actions: lateral rotation, extension, and horizontal abduction of the shoulder.

Origin: Lateral/Axillary Border of Scapula
Insertion: Greater Tubercle of Humerus
Action(s): Lateral Rotation, Horizontal Abduction of Shoulder
Innervation: Axillary Nerve
Synergist: Infraspinatus
Antagonist: Pectoralis Major

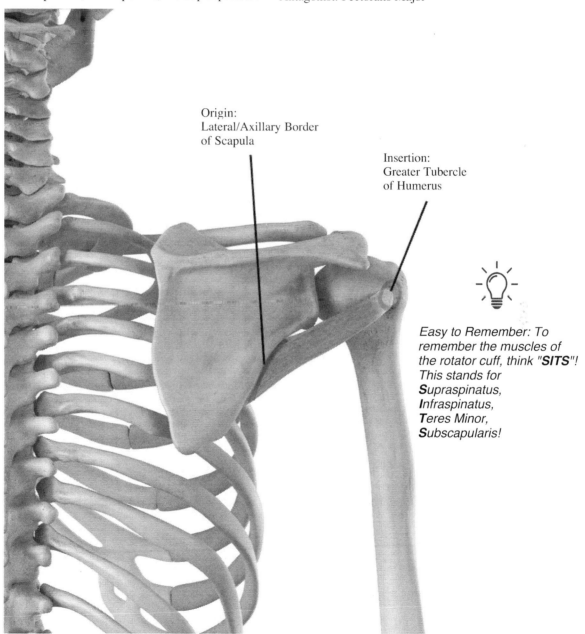

Origin:
Lateral/Axillary Border
of Scapula

Insertion:
Greater Tubercle
of Humerus

*Easy to Remember: To remember the muscles of the rotator cuff, think "**SITS**"! This stands for **S**upraspinatus, **I**nfraspinatus, **T**eres Minor, **S**ubscapularis!*

Trapezius

Trapezius is a large muscle of the back, named after its shape(trapezoid). Trapezius is the most superficial muscle of the back.

Trapezius originates on the External Occipital Protuberance of the Occipital bone, and the Spinous Processes of T1-T12. Trapezius inserts on the Acromion Process, the Spine of the Scapula, and the Lateral 1/3 of the Clavicle.

The Trapezius can be divided into three sections: Upper Trapezius, Middle Trapezius, and Lower Trapezius. When contracting, Upper Trapezius assists in elevation of the scapula. When contracting, Middle Trapezius assists in retraction/adduction of the scapula. When contracting, Lower Trapezius depresses the scapula.

Origin: External Occipital Protuberance, Spinous Processes of T1-T12
Insertion: Lateral 1/3 of Clavicle, Acromion Process, Spine of Scapula
Action(s): Elevation, Retraction/Adduction, Depression of Scapula
Innervation: Accessory Nerve, Cervical Nerves C3 and C4
Synergist: Levator Scapulae(elevation), Rhomboid(retraction), Serratus Anterior(depression)
Antagonist: Serratus Anterior(elevation), Pectoralis Minor (retraction), Levator Scapulae(depression)

inserts @ SAC.

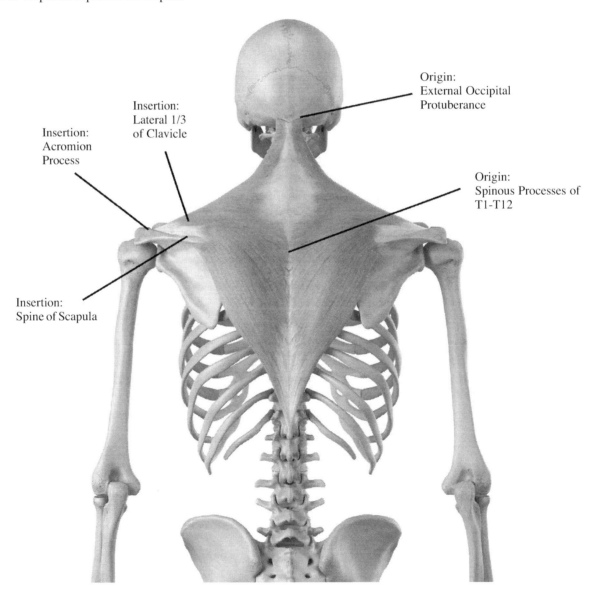

Insertion: Acromion Process

Insertion: Lateral 1/3 of Clavicle

Insertion: Spine of Scapula

Origin: External Occipital Protuberance

Origin: Spinous Processes of T1-T12

Muscles of the Chest

Muscles to Know:
Pectoralis Major
Pectoralis Minor
Serratus Anterior

Terms to Know:
Pector/o: Chest
Serratus: Finely Notched Edge

Pectoralis Major

Pectoralis Major is a large muscle of the chest. The term "pector/o" means "breast" or "chest".

Pectoralis Major originates on the Medial Half of the Clavicle, the Anterior Surface of the Sternum, and the Costal Cartilage of Ribs 1-6. Pectoralis Major inserts onto the Lateral Lip of the Intertubercular Groove.

When contracting, the Pectoralis Major has multiple actions: Flexion, medial rotation, and horizontal adduction of the shoulder. Pectoralis Major also performs extension of the shoulder when the shoulder is already flexed, making it an antagonist to itself.

Origin: Medial Half of Clavicle, Anterior Surface of Sternum, Costal Cartilage 1-6
Insertion: Lateral Lip of Intertubercular Groove
Action(s): Flexion, Medial Rotation, Horizontal Adduction, Extension of Shoulder
Innervation: Lateral and Medial Pectoral Nerves
Synergist: Coracobrachialis, Biceps Brachii, Anterior Deltoid
Antagonist: Latissimus Dorsi, Teres Major, Subscapularis, Posterior Deltoid

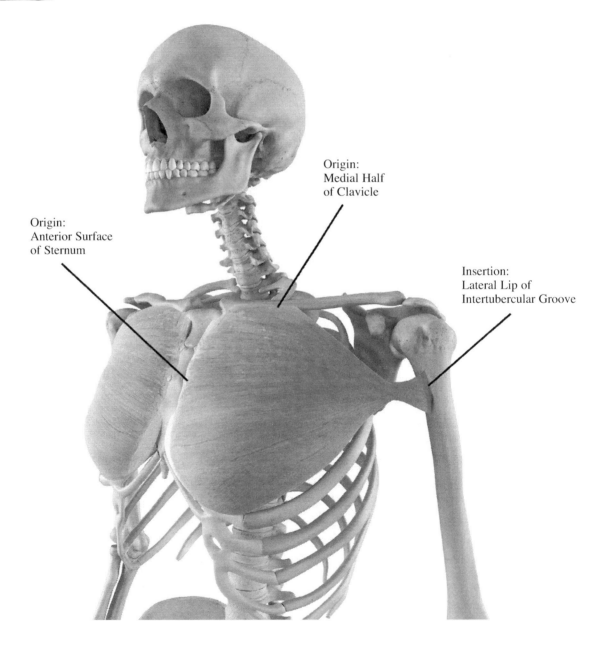

Origin:
Anterior Surface
of Sternum

Origin:
Medial Half
of Clavicle

Insertion:
Lateral Lip of
Intertubercular Groove

Pectoralis Minor ~~ *Kyphosis*

Pectoralis Minor is a muscle of the chest, lying deep to the Pectoralis Major.

Pectoralis Minor originates on the Anterior Surface of Ribs 3-5. Pectoralis Minor inserts onto the Coracoid Process.

When Pectoralis Minor contracts, it protracts/abducts the scapula. Along with Serratus Anterior, it is an antagonist to the Rhomboids.

Pectoralis Minor is often associated with Thoracic Outlet Syndrome. When hypertonic, Pectoralis Minor may compress the Brachial plexus, Subclavian artery, and Subclavian nerve, which may cause a lack of sensation in the upper limb, or restrict blood supply.

Origin: Anterior Surface of Ribs 3-5
Insertion: Coracoid Process of Scapula
Action(s): Protraction/Abduction of Scapula
Innervation: Medial Pectoral Nerve
Synergist: Serratus Anterior
Antagonist: Rhomboids

*Pectoralis Minor is very commonly associated with **Kyphosis**, a rounding of the back in the Thoracic region of the vertebrae(hunch back), caused by Pectoralis Minor being hypertonic, pulling the scapulae anteriorly!*

Origin:
Anterior Surface
of Ribs 3-5

Insertion:
Coracoid Process

Serratus Anterior

Serratus Anterior is a muscle of the chest. "Serratus" means "finely notched edge", such as a serrated knife.

Serratus Anterior originates on the Anterior Surface of Ribs 1-8. Serratus Anterior inserts onto the Anterior Surface of the Medial/ Vertebral Border of the Scapula.

When Serratus Anterior contracts, it moves the scapula anteriorly, producing protraction/abduction. Serratus Anterior also may assist in depression of the scapula.

Origin: Anterior Surface of Ribs 1-8
Insertion: Medial/Vertebral Border of Scapula
Action(s): Protraction/Abduction, Depression of Scapula
Innervation: Long Thoracic Nerve
Synergist: Pectoralis Minor, Lower Trapezius
Antagonist: Rhomboids, Levator Scapulae

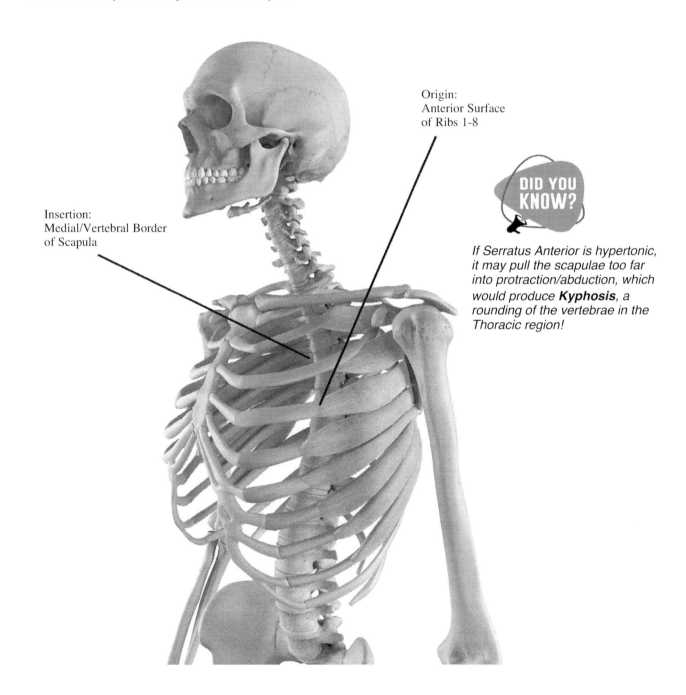

Origin:
Anterior Surface
of Ribs 1-8

Insertion:
Medial/Vertebral Border
of Scapula

DID YOU KNOW?

If Serratus Anterior is hypertonic, it may pull the scapulae too far into protraction/abduction, which would produce Kyphosis, a rounding of the vertebrae in the Thoracic region!

Muscles of the Abdomen

Muscles to Know:
Rectus Abdominis

Terms to Know:
Rectus: Straight

Rectus Abdominis

Rectus Abdominis is a muscle of the abdomen. Rectus Abdominis is the most superficial muscle of the abdomen.

Rectus Abdominis originates on the Pubic Symphysis and the Pubic Crest. Rectus Abdominis inserts onto the Xiphoid Process of the Sternum and the Costal Cartilage of Ribs 5-7.

When Rectus Abdominis contracts, it allows the trunk to flex.

If Rectus Abdominis is too weak, it may lead to a condition known as Lordosis, or Swayback. This causes an increased anterior tilt to the pelvis and Lumbar vertebrae. Strengthening of the Rectus Abdominis may help return the pelvis and vertebrae to their natural state.

Origin: Pubic Symphysis, Pubic Crest
Insertion: Xiphoid Process, Costal Cartilage of Ribs 5-7
Action(s): Flexion of Trunk
Innervation: Anterior Primary Rami T7-T12
Synergist: External Obliques, Internal Obliques
Antagonist: Spinalis, Longissimus

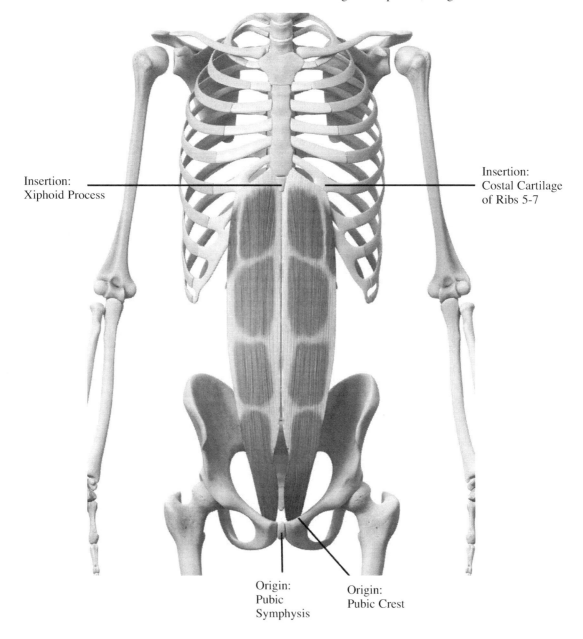

Insertion:
Xiphoid Process

Insertion:
Costal Cartilage
of Ribs 5-7

Origin:
Pubic
Symphysis

Origin:
Pubic Crest

Muscles of the Arm

Muscles to Know:
Biceps Brachii
Brachialis
Coracobrachialis
Deltoid
Triceps Brachii

Terms to Know:
Bi-: Two
-cep: Head
Brachi/o: Arm
Corac/o: Coracoid
Tri-: Three

Biceps Brachii

Biceps Brachii is a muscle of the arm. The term "Biceps" means "two head", and "Brachii" refers to the arm.

Biceps Brachii has two heads. The Short Head of the Biceps Brachii originates on the Coracoid Process. The Long Head of the Biceps Brachii originates on the Supraglenoid Tubercle. Both heads join together in the arm, and together, insert onto the Radial Tuberosity.

When Biceps Brachii contracts, it helps produce flexion of the shoulder, flexion of the elbow, and supination of the forearm. Biceps Brachii is the prime mover of supination.

Origin: Long Head: Supraglenoid Tubercle; Short Head: Coracoid Process
Insertion: Radial Tuberosity
Action(s): Flexion of Shoulder, Flexion of Elbow, Supination of Forearm
Innervation: Musculocutaneous Nerve
Synergist: Pectoralis Major, Brachialis, Supinator
Antagonist: Triceps Brachii, Pronator Teres

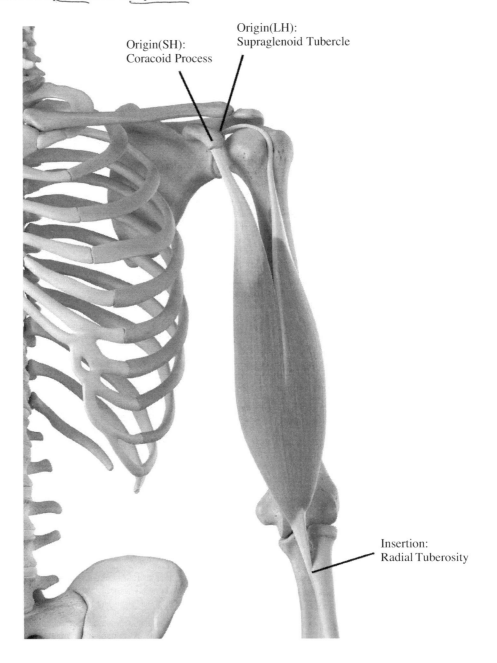

Origin(SH):
Coracoid Process

Origin(LH):
Supraglenoid Tubercle

Insertion:
Radial Tuberosity

Brachialis

Brachialis is a muscle of the arm. It is named after its location, the "brachial" region.

Brachialis originates on the Anterior Distal Shaft of the Humerus, and inserts onto both the Coronoid Process of the Ulna, and the Ulnar Tuberosity.

Brachialis is a powerful muscle. It is the prime mover of elbow flexion. It is located deep to the Biceps Brachii. When Brachialis contracts, it pushes the Biceps Brachii up, allowing Biceps Brachii to be more visible during this action.

Origin: Anterior Distal Shaft of Humerus
Insertion: Coronoid Process and Ulnar Tuberosity
Action(s): Flexion of Elbow
Innervation: Musculocutaneous Nerve
Synergist: Biceps Brachii
Antagonist: Triceps Brachii

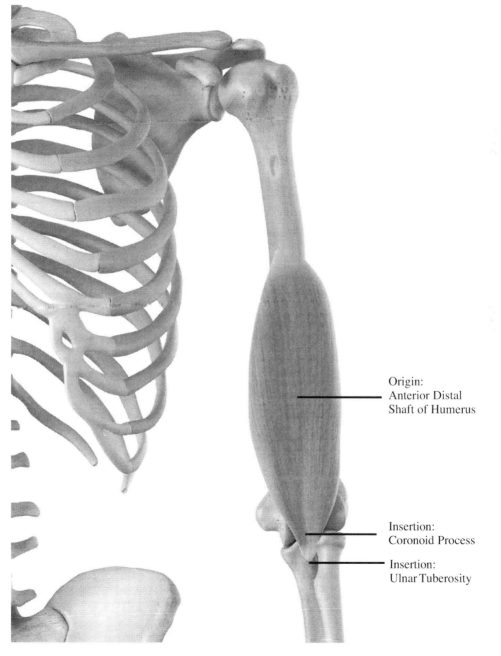

Origin:
Anterior Distal
Shaft of Humerus

Insertion:
Coronoid Process

Insertion:
Ulnar Tuberosity

Coracobrachialis

Coracobrachialis is a muscle of the arm, named after its origin and location.

Coracobrachialis originates on the Coracoid Process, and inserts onto the Medial Proximal Shaft of the Humerus.

Coracobrachialis is primarily a synergist to Pectoralis Major. When Coracobrachialis contracts, it flexes and horizontally adducts the shoulder.

Origin: Coracoid Process
Insertion: Medial Proximal Shaft of Humerus
Action(s): Flexion, Horizontal Adduction of Shoulder
Innervation: Musculocutaneous Nerve
Synergist: Pectoralis Major, Biceps Brachii
Antagonist: Infraspinatus, Teres Minor

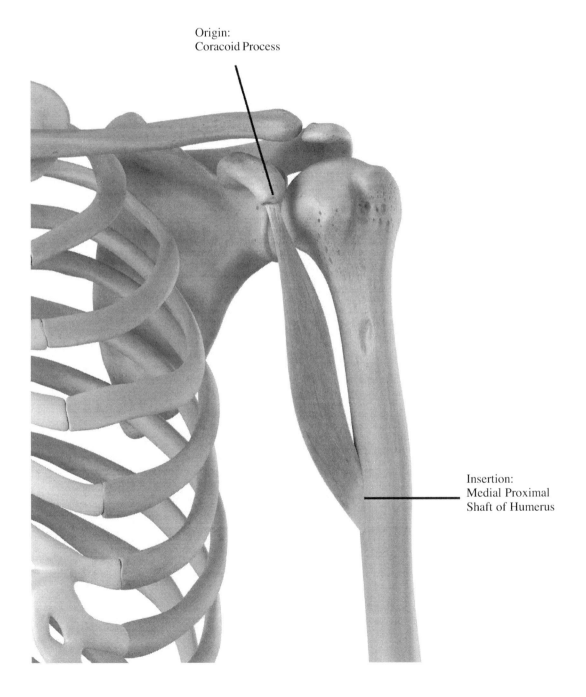

Origin:
Coracoid Process

Insertion:
Medial Proximal
Shaft of Humerus

Deltoid

Deltoid is a muscle of the arm/shoulder, named after the Greek letter "delta", which is shaped like an equilateral triangle(all sides are the same length).

Deltoid has three different portions that make up the muscle: Anterior Deltoid, Middle Deltoid, and Posterior Deltoid. All three combined create the Deltoid muscle.

Anterior Deltoid originates on the lateral third of the clavicle. Middle Deltoid originates on the Acromion Process. Posterior Deltoid originates on the Spine of the Scapula. All three join together distally and insert onto the Deltoid Tuberosity.

The Deltoid has many different actions, depending on which fibers of the muscle are contracting. Anterior Deltoid assists in flexion, horizontal adduction, and medial rotation of the shoulder. Posterior Deltoid assists in extension, horizontal abduction, and lateral rotation of the shoulder. Middle Deltoid, in conjunction with the two other Deltoid fibers, abducts the shoulder.

Origin: Anterior Deltoid: Lateral Third of Clavicle; Middle Deltoid: Acromion Process; Posterior Deltoid: Spine of Scapula
Insertion: Deltoid Tuberosity
Action(s): Abduction, Medial Rotation, Lateral Rotation, Horizontal Adduction, Horizontal Abduction, Flexion, Extension of Shoulder
Innervation: Axillary Nerve
Synergist: Supraspinatus(abduction), Pectoralis Major(flexion, horizontal adduction, medial rotation), Infraspinatus (extension, horizontal abduction, lateral rotation)
Antagonist: Latissimus Dorsi(abduction), Infraspinatus(flexion, horizontal adduction, medial rotation), Pectoralis Major(extension, horizontal abduction, lateral rotation)

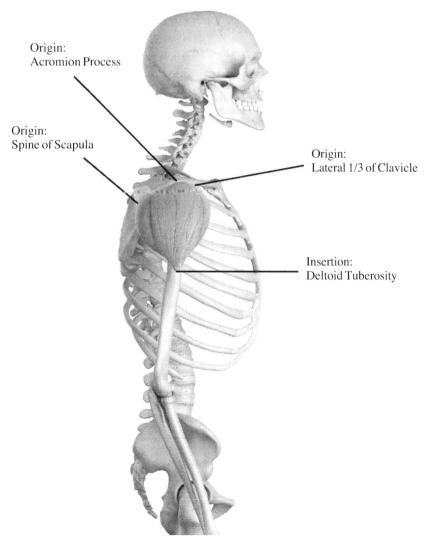

Origin:
Acromion Process

Origin:
Spine of Scapula

Origin:
Lateral 1/3 of Clavicle

Insertion:
Deltoid Tuberosity

Triceps Brachii

Triceps Brachii is a muscle of the posterior arm. The name "Triceps" means "three heads", and "Brachii" refers to the arm.

Triceps Brachii has three heads. The Long Head originates on the Infraglenoid Tubercle of the Humerus. The Medial Head originates on the Posterior Shaft of the Humerus, on the medial side. The Lateral Head originates on the Posterior Shaft of the Humerus, on the lateral side. All three heads join together and insert on the Olecranon Process.

Triceps Brachii, when it contracts, extends the shoulder and extends the elbow.

Origin: Long Head: Infraglenoid Tubercle; Medial Head: Posterior Shaft of Humerus; Lateral Head: Posterior Shaft of Humerus
Insertion: Olecranon Process
Action(s): Extension of Shoulder, Extension of Elbow
Innervation: Radial Nerve
Synergist: Latissimus Dorsi, Anconeus
Antagonist: Pectoralis Major, Biceps Brachii

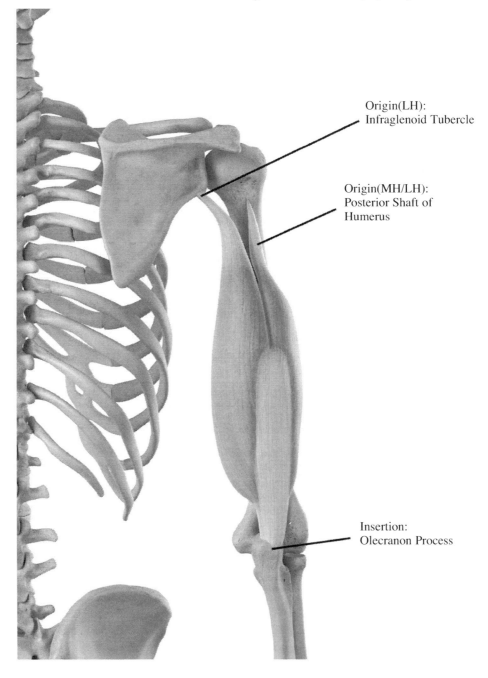

Origin(LH):
Infraglenoid Tubercle

Origin(MH/LH):
Posterior Shaft of
Humerus

Insertion:
Olecranon Process

Muscles of the Forearm

Muscles to Know:
Anconeus
Brachioradialis
Pronator Teres

Terms to Know:
Agkon: Elbow
Brachi/o: Arm
Teres: Round and Long

Anconeus

Anconeus is a muscle of the forearm. Its name derives from the Greek "agkon", which means "elbow".

Anconeus originates on the Lateral Epicondyle of the Humerus, and inserts onto the Olecranon Process.

Anconeus is primarily only a synergist to the Triceps Brachii, assisting to perform elbow extension.

Origin: Lateral Epicondyle of Humerus
Insertion: Olecranon Process
Action(s): Extension of Elbow
Innervation: Radial Nerve
Synergist: Triceps Brachii
Antagonist: Brachialis

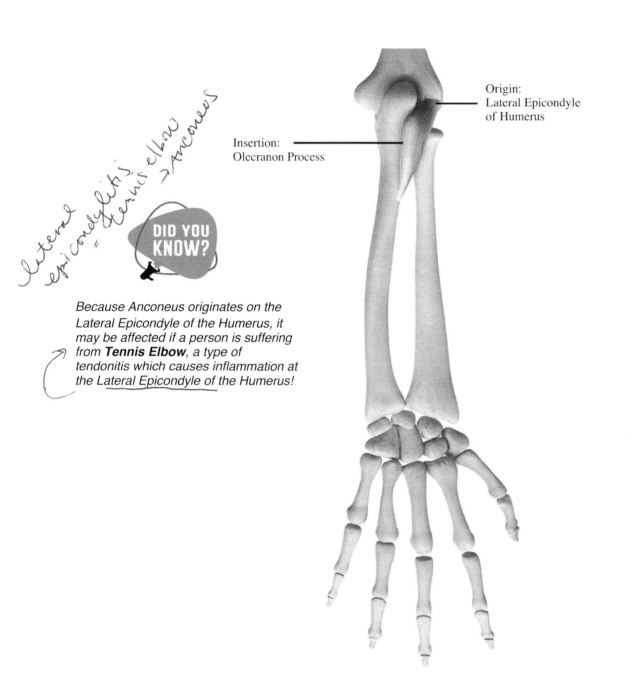

lateral epicondylitis = tennis elbow > Anconeus

DID YOU KNOW?

Because Anconeus originates on the Lateral Epicondyle of the Humerus, it may be affected if a person is suffering from **Tennis Elbow**, a type of tendonitis which causes inflammation at the Lateral Epicondyle of the Humerus!

Origin: Lateral Epicondyle of Humerus

Insertion: Olecranon Process

Brachioradialis

Brachioradialis is a muscle of the forearm, named after its location and insertion. "Brachio" refers to the arm, and "radialis" refers to the Radius.

Brachioradialis originates on the Lateral Supracondylar Ridge of the Humerus, the ridge just superior to the Lateral Epicondyle. Brachioradialis inserts onto the Styloid Process of the Radius.

Brachioradialis primarily performs flexion of the elbow with the hand in the neutral position(neither in pronation or supination).

Origin: Lateral Supracondylar Ridge of Humerus
Insertion: Styloid Process of Radius
Action(s): Flexion of Elbow
Innervation: Radial Nerve
Synergist: Biceps Brachii
Antagonist: Triceps Brachii

Origin:
Lateral Supracondylar
Ridge of Humerus

Insertion:
Styloid Process
of Radius

Pronator Teres

Pronator Teres is a muscle of the forearm, named for its action and shape ("Teres" means "round and long". Pronator Teres has a long, round shape).

Pronator Teres originates on the Medial Epicondyle of the Humerus and the Coronoid Process of the Ulna. Pronator Teres inserts onto the Middle of the Lateral Surface of the Radius.

Pronator Teres, as the name suggests, is the strongest pronator of the forearm. Because Pronator Teres crosses the elbow joint, it also assists in flexion of the elbow.

Origin: Medial Epicondyle of Humerus, Coronoid Process of Ulna
Insertion: Middle of Lateral Surface of Radius
Action(s): Pronation of Forearm, Flexion of Elbow
Innervation: Median Nerve
Synergist: Pronator Quadratus, Brachialis
Antagonist: Biceps Brachii, Triceps Brachii

Origin:
Medial Epicondyle
of Humerus

Origin:
Coronoid Process

Insertion:
Middle of Lateral
Surface of Radius

Muscles of the Pelvis

Muscles to Know:
Gluteus Maximus
Iliacus
Piriformis
Psoas Major

Terms to Know:
Iliac: Ilium
Pirum: Pear
Psoa: Loin Region

Gluteus Maximus

Gluteus Maximus is a muscle of the pelvis, named for its location and size.

Gluteus Maximus originates on the Posterior Iliac Crest, the Posterior Sacrum and Coccyx, and the Sacrotuberous Ligament. Gluteus Maximus inserts partially onto the Gluteal Tuberosity, and into the Iliotibial Band.

Gluteus Maximus is primarily responsible for assisting in extension of the hip, and abduction of the hip.

The Gluteus Maximus is the largest muscle in the human body. It is also the most superficial of the gluteus muscle group.

Origin: Posterior Iliac Crest, Posterior Sacrum and Coccyx, Sacrotuberous Ligament
Insertion: Gluteal Tuberosity, Iliotibial Band
Action(s): Extension, Abduction of Hip
Innervation: Inferior Gluteal Nerve
Synergist: Hamstrings, Piriformis
Antagonist: Rectus Femoris, Adductor Magnus

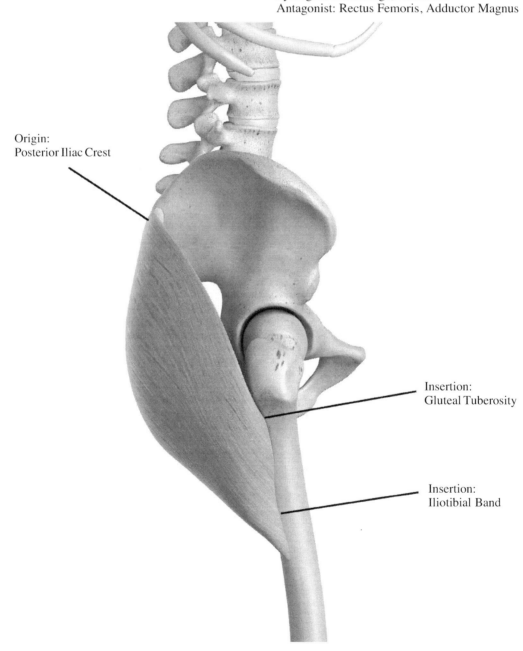

Origin:
Posterior Iliac Crest

Insertion:
Gluteal Tuberosity

Insertion:
Iliotibial Band

Iliacus

Iliacus is a muscle of the pelvis, named for its origin.

Iliacus originates in the Iliac Fossa, and crosses the hip joint to insert onto the Lesser Trochanter.

Iliacus is one of the prime movers of hip flexion. It often is joined with the Psoas Major, which also aids in hip flexion, to make a single muscle named the Iliopsoas.

If the Iliacus is hypertonic, it may pull the pelvis anteriorly. This shift of the pelvis results in a hypercurvature in the lumbar vertebrae, a condition known as Lordosis(Swayback).

Origin: Iliac Fossa
Insertion: Lesser Trochanter
Action(s): Flexion of Hip
Innervation: Femoral Nerve
Synergist: Psoas Major
Antagonist: Hamstrings

Origin:
Iliac Fossa

Insertion:
Lesser
Trochanter

Piriformis

Piriformis is a muscle of the pelvis, named for its shape("piri" refers to "pirum", which means "pear" in Latin. Piriformis is shaped like a pear).

Piriformis originates on the Anterior Surface of the Sacrum, and inserts onto the Greater Trochanter.

Piriformis works with the Gluteus Maximus to perform abduction and lateral rotation of the hip.

Piriformis is part of the Deep Six muscle group.

Piriformis, when hypertonic, may place substantial pressure on the Sciatic Nerve, which passes by, and sometimes through, the muscle itself. This is known as Piriformis Syndrome. This can result in pain in the hip, posterior thigh, posterior leg, and plantar surface of the foot.

Origin: Anterior Surface of Sacrum
Insertion: Greater Trochanter
Action(s): Abduction, Lateral Rotation of Hip
Innervation: Piriformis Nerve
Synergist: Gluteus Maximus, Sartorius
Antagonist: Adductor Magnus, Pectineus

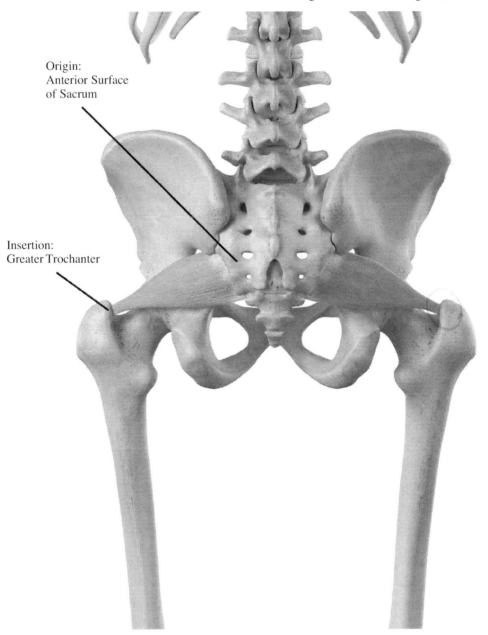

Origin:
Anterior Surface
of Sacrum

Insertion:
Greater Trochanter

Psoas Major

Psoas Major is a muscle of the abdomen and pelvis, named for its location ("psoas" comes from the Greek word "psoa", which means "loin region") and size.

Psoas Major originates on the Anterior Surface of the Lumbar Vertebrae. Psoas Major inserts onto the Lesser Trochanter.

Psoas Major is responsible for flexion of the hip, along with Iliacus. Psoas Major often joins with Iliacus to form one muscle known as the Iliopsoas.

If the Psoas Major is hypertonic, it pulls the Lumbar Vertebrae anteriorly, which may also force the pelvis anteriorly. This is a condition known as Lordosis (Swayback).

Origin: Anterior Surface of Lumbar Vertebrae
Insertion: Lesser Trochanter
Action(s): Flexion of Hip, Flexion of Trunk
Innervation: Lumbar Plexus
Synergist: Iliacus, Rectus Abdominis
Antagonist: Hamstrings, Spinalis

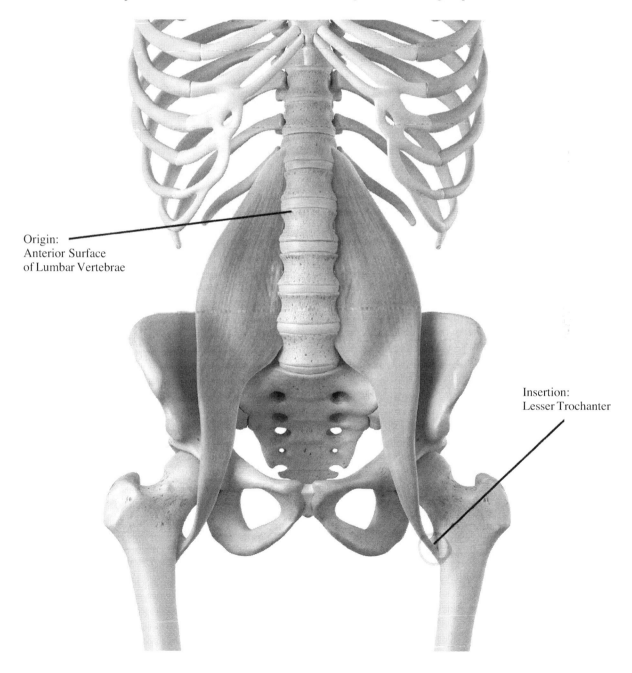

Origin:
Anterior Surface
of Lumbar Vertebrae

Insertion:
Lesser Trochanter

Muscles of the Thigh

Muscles to Know:
Adductor Magnus
Biceps Femoris
Gracilis
Rectus Femoris
Sartorius
Semimembranosus
Semitendinosus
Tensor Fasciae Latae

Terms to Know:
Magnus: Great
Bi-: Two
-cep: Head
Gracilis: Slender
Rectus: Straight
Sartor: Tailor
Semi-: Half
Membranosus: Skin
Tendere: To Stretch
Fasciae: Band
Latae: Side

Adductor Magnus

Adductor Magnus is a muscle of the thigh, named after its action (adduction) and size("Magnus" means "great" in Latin).

Adductor Magnus has multiple origins. It originates on the Inferior Ramus of the Pubis and Ischial Tuberosity. Adductor Magnus inserts onto the Medial Lip of the Linea Aspera, and the Adductor Tubercle.

Adductor Magnus is an antagonist to itself. It can flex and extend the hip. It also, as the name implies, adducts the hip.

Adductor Magnus is the largest muscle of the Adductor muscle group, which also consists of Adductor Longus, Adductor Brevis, Gracilis, and Pectineus.

Origin: Inferior Ramus of Pubis, Ischial Tuberosity
Insertion: Linea Aspera, Adductor Tubercle
Action(s): Adduction, Flexion, Extension of Hip
Innervation: Obturator Nerve, Sciatic Nerve(Tibial branch)
Synergist: Adductor Longus(adduction), Iliacus(flexion), Gluteus Maximus(extension)
Antagonist: Piriformis(adduction), Hamstrings(flexion), Rectus Femoris(extension)

Origin:
Ischial Tuberosity

Origin:
Inferior Ramus
of Pubis

Insertion:
Linea Aspera

Insertion:
Adductor Tubercle

Biceps Femoris

Biceps Femoris is a muscle of the posterior thigh, named after the number of heads it has("Biceps" means "two heads") and its location(Femur).

Biceps Femoris has two origins: The Long Head of Biceps Femoris originates on the Ischial Tuberosity. The Short Head of Biceps Femoris originates on the Lateral Lip of the Linea Aspera, on the distal end of the femur. Biceps Femoris inserts onto the Head of the Fibula.

Biceps Femoris crosses the hip and the knee. When it contracts, it extends the hip, and flexes the knee.

Biceps Femoris is a member of the Hamstrings muscle group. It is the most lateral Hamstring muscle, the only Hamstring muscle that attaches to the Fibula.

Origin: Long Head: Ischial Tuberosity; Short Head: Lateral Lip of Linea Aspera
Insertion: Head of Fibula
Action(s): Extension of Hip, Flexion of Knee
Innervation: Sciatic Nerve(Tibial branch)
Synergist: Semimembranosus, Semitendinosus
Antagonist: Rectus Femoris

Origin(LH):
Ischial Tuberosity

Origin(SH):
Lateral Lip
of Linea Aspera

Insertion:
Head of Fibula

Gracilis

Gracilis is a muscle of the medial thigh. The word "Gracilis" means "slender" in Latin. The Gracilis is a thin, slender, long muscle.

Gracilis originates on the Inferior Ramus of the Pubis, along with Adductor Magnus. Gracilis inserts onto the Pes Anserinus, located on the Medial Proximal Shaft of the Tibia, just medial to the Tibial Tuberosity.

Gracilis performs adduction and flexion of the hip. Gracilis also crosses the knee, and will assist in flexion of the knee.

Gracilis is a member of the Adductor muscle group, the most medial muscle of the group. The Gracilis is the only Adductor muscle that crosses two joints. All the other Adductor muscles (Adductor Magnus, Adductor Longus, Adductor Brevis, Pectineus) only cross the hip.

Origin: Inferior Ramus of Pubis
Insertion: Pes Anserinus
Action(s): Adduction, Flexion of Hip, Flexion of Knee
Innervation: Obturator Nerve
Synergist: Adductor Magnus, Gastrocnemius
Antagonist: Gluteus Maximus, Hamstrings, Rectus Femoris

Origin:
Inferior Ramus
of Pubis

Insertion:
Pes Anserinus

Rectus Femoris

Rectus Femoris is a muscle of the thigh, named after its function ("rectus" in Latin means "straight", referring to ones ability to stand straight) and location.

Rectus Femoris originates on the Anterior Inferior Iliac Spine(AIIS), and inserts onto the Tibial Tuberosity.

Rectus Femoris is the prime mover of both hip flexion and knee extension.

Rectus Femoris is the most anterior muscle of the Quadriceps muscle group.

Origin: Anterior Inferior Iliac Spine
Insertion: Tibial Tuberosity
Action(s): Flexion of Hip, Extension of Knee
Innervation: Femoral Nerve
Synergist: Sartorius, Vastus Lateralis
Antagonist: Hamstrings

*Rectus Femoris is also the only Quadriceps muscle that crosses **two joints**(hip and knee). The rest of the Quadriceps muscles only cross the knee!*

Origin:
Anterior Inferior
Iliac Spine

Insertion:
Tibial Tuberosity

248

Sartorius

Sartorius is a muscle of the thigh, named for its action("sartor" is Latin for "tailor". It is named as such due to the actions of the muscle, which are the position a tailor places their leg into while working).

Sartorius originates on the Anterior Superior Iliac Spine (ASIS), and inserts onto the Pes Anserinus, located just medial to the Tibial Tuberosity.

Sartorius is responsible for flexion and lateral rotation of the hip, and flexion of the knee.

Origin: Anterior Superior Iliac Spine
Insertion: Pes Anserinus
Action(s): Flexion, Abduction, Lateral Rotation of Hip, Flexion of Knee
Innervation: Femoral Nerve
Synergist: Rectus Femoris(hip flexion), Gluteus Maximus (abduction), Piriformis(lateral rotation), Gastrocnemius (knee flexion)
Antagonist: Biceps Femoris(hip flexion), Adductor Magnus(abduction), Pectineus(lateral rotation), Rectus Femoris(knee flexion)

DID YOU KNOW?

*Sartorius is the **longest muscle** in the human body!*

Origin:
Anterior Superior
Iliac Spine

Insertion:
Pes Anserinus

Semimembranosus

Semimembranosus is a muscle of the thigh, named after its appearance("semi" means "half", "membranosus" means "skin". Semimembranosus is about half muscle, half membranous tendon).

Semimembranosus originates on the Ischial Tuberosity, and inserts onto the Posterior Medial Condyle of the Tibia.

Semimembranosus is one muscle responsible for extension of the hip, and flexion of the knee.

Semimembranosus is a member of the Hamstring muscle group, located on the posterior thigh. Semimembranosus is the most medial of the Hamstring muscles.

Origin: Ischial Tuberosity
Insertion: Posterior Medial Condyle of Tibia
Action(s): Extension of Hip, Flexion of Knee
Innervation: Sciatic Nerve(Peroneal branch)
Synergist: Semitendinosus
Antagonist: Rectus Femoris

Origin:
Ischial Tuberosity

Insertion:
Posterior Medial
Condyle of Tibia

Semitendinosus

Semitendinosus is a muscle of the thigh, named for its appearance("semi" means "half", "tendinosus" refers to the Latin word "tendere", which means "to stretch").

Semitendinosus originates on the Ischial Tuberosity, and inserts onto the Pes Anserinus, located just medial to the Tibial Tuberosity.

Semitendinosus is one muscle responsible for extending the hip and flexing the knee, along with Semimembranosus and Biceps Femoris.

Semitendinosus is a member of the Hamstring muscle group, located on the posterior thigh. Semitendinosus sits atop Semimembranosus, and is the intermediate Hamstring muscle.

Origin: Ischial Tuberosity
Insertion: Pes Anserinus
Action(s): Extension of Hip, Flexion of Knee
Innervation: Sciatic Nerve(Peroneal branch)
Synergist: Biceps Femoris
Antagonist: Rectus Femoris

Origin:
Ischial Tuberosity

Insertion:
Pes Anserinus

Tensor Fasciae Latae

Tensor Fasciae Latae is a muscle of the thigh, named after its appearance("tensor" comes from the Latin "tensere", which means "to stretch". "Fasciae" is Latin for "band". "Latae" is Latin for "side ", such as the term "lateral").

Tensor Fasciae Latae originates on the Anterior Superior Iliac Spine (ASIS) and the Iliac Crest. Tensor Fasciae Latae inserts into the Iliotibial Tract(also known as the IT Band).

Tensor Fasciae Latae is a synergist in hip flexion.

Origin: Anterior Superior Iliac Spine, Iliac Crest
Insertion: Iliotibial Tract
Action(s): Flexion of Hip
Innervation: Superior Gluteal Nerve
Synergist: Rectus Femoris
Antagonist: Hamstrings

Origin:
Iliac Crest

Origin:
Anterior Superior
Iliac Spine

Insertion:
Iliotibial Tract

Muscles of the Leg

Muscles to Know:
Gastrocnemius
Peroneus Longus
Plantaris
Soleus
Tibialis Anterior
Tibialis Posterior

Terms to Know:
Gastr/o: Stomach
Kneme: Leg
Longus: Long

Gastrocnemius

Gastrocnemius is a muscle of the posterior leg. Its name means stomach(gastro) of the leg(kneme), from Greek origin.

Gastrocnemius originates on the Medial and Lateral Epicondyles of the Femur on the posterior side. The two muscle bellies join together at the Calcancal Tendon, and insert at the Calcaneus. The Calcaneal Tendon is the strongest tendon in the body. Another name for the Calcaneal Tendon is "Achilles Tendon", so named after the Greek legend of Achilles.

Gastrocnemius, when contracted, assists the Hamstrings in performing flexion of the knee. Gastrocnemius is the prime mover of plantarflexion.

A primary synergist to Gastrocnemius is the Soleus, the muscle deep to the Gastrocnemius. Soleus joins with the Gastrocnemius at the Calcaneal Tendon, and assists in plantarflexion.

Origin: Medial and Lateral Epicondyles on Posterior Femur
Insertion: Calcaneus via Calcaneal Tendon
Action(s): Flexion of Knee, Plantarflexion
Innervation: Tibial Nerve
Synergist: Hamstrings, Soleus
Antagonist: Rectus Femoris, Tibialis Anterior

Origin:
Lateral Epicondyle
of Femur

Origin:
Medial Epicondyle
of Femur

Insertion:
Calcaneus

Peroneus Longus

Peroneus Longus is a muscle of the lateral leg, named after its origin ("perone" means "fibula" and the two arc interchangeable) and length.

Peroneus Longus originates on the Proximal Lateral Shaft of the Fibula, and the Head of the Fibula. It wraps beneath the Lateral Malleolus and onto the plantar surface of the foot, inserting onto the Base of the 1st Metatarsal and Cuneiform I (also known as the Medial Cuneiform).

When Peroneus Longus contracts, it is the prime mover of eversion/pronation of the foot. It also assists the Gastrocnemius and Soleus in performing plantarflexion.

Origin: Head of Fibula, Proximal Shaft of Fibula
Insertion: Base of 1st Metatarsal, Cuneiform I
Action(s): Plantarflexion, Eversion/Pronation of Foot
Innervation: Superficial Peroneal Nerve
Synergist: Peroneus Brevis
Antagonist: Tibialis Anterior

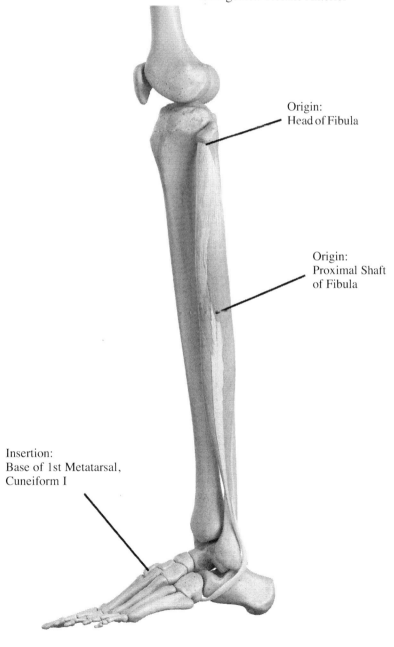

Origin:
Head of Fibula

Origin:
Proximal Shaft
of Fibula

Insertion:
Base of 1st Metatarsal,
Cuneiform I

Plantaris

Plantaris is a muscle of the posterior leg, named after its action (plantarflexion).

Plantaris originates on the Lateral Supracondylar Ridge of the Femur, just above the Lateral Epicondyle. It crosses the knee and ankle, inserting onto the Calcaneus.

Plantaris is a synergist in all of its actions. At the knee, it assists the Hamstrings and Gastrocnemius in flexion. At the ankle, it assists Gastrocnemius and Soleus in plantarflexion.

If a person injures the Plantaris, they may be diagnosed with a condition known as Tennis Leg, a straining of not just the Plantaris, but the other calf muscles.

Origin: Lateral Supracondylar Ridge of Femur
Insertion: Calcaneus
Action(s): Flexion of Knee, Plantarflexion
Innervation: Tibial Nerve
Synergist: Gastrocnemius
Antagonist: Tibialis Anterior

Origin:
Lateral Supracondylar
Ridge of Femur

DID YOU KNOW?

The **longest tendon** in the body connects the **plantaris** to the calcaneus!

longest tendon

Insertion:
Calcaneus

Soleus

Soleus is a muscle of the posterior leg, named after its appearance (resembles a sole fish in shape).

Soleus originates on the Soleal Line, a ridge located on the posterior proximal surface of the Tibia, and the Head of the Fibula. Soleus joins with the Gastrocnemius at the Calcaneal Tendon, inserting onto the Calcaneus.

Soleus is primarily a synergist to the Gastrocnemius, performing plantarflexion.

Origin: Soleal Line, Head of Fibula
Insertion: Calcaneus via Calcaneal Tendon
Action(s): Plantarflexion
Innervation: Tibial Nerve
Synergist: Gastrocnemius
Antagonist: Tibialis Anterior

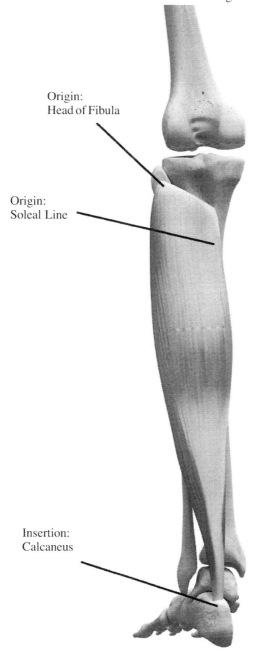

Origin:
Head of Fibula

Origin:
Soleal Line

Insertion:
Calcaneus

Tibialis Anterior

Tibialis Anterior is a muscle of the anterior leg, named after its origin(Tibia) and location(Anterior).

Tibialis Anterior originates on the Lateral Proximal Shaft of the Tibia, beside the Fibula. Tibialis Anterior wraps onto the medial plantar surface of the foot, inserting onto the Base of the 1st Metatarsal, and Cuneiform I(also known as the Medial Cuneiform). It shares its insertion with Peroneus Longus, its direct antagonist.

Tibialis Anterior is the prime mover of inversion/supination of the foot, pulling the soles of the feet in towards the midline when the muscle contracts. It is also the prime mover of dorsiflexion, pulling the foot up.

If a person is affected by paralysis in the Deep Peroneal Nerve, the Tibialis Anterior is severely weakened. This results in inability to dorsiflex, a condition known as Drop Foot.

Origin: Lateral Proximal Shaft of Tibia
Insertion: Base of 1st Metatarsal, Cuneiform I
Action(s): Dorsiflexion, Inversion/Supination of Foot
Innervation: Deep Peroneal Nerve
Synergist: Extensor Digitorum Longus, Tibialis Posterior
Antagonist: Peroneus Longus

Origin:
Lateral Proximal
Shaft of Tibia

Insertion:
Base of 1st Metatarsal,
Cuneiform I

Tibialis Posterior

Tibialis Posterior is a muscle of the posterior leg, named after its location(on the posterior Tibia).

Tibialis Posterior originates on the Posterior Proximal Shaft of the Tibia and Fibula. It crosses the ankle and runs into the plantar surface of the foot, inserting onto the Navicular, Cuneiform I(also called the Medial Cuneiform), and Metatarsals 2-4.

Tibialis Anterior is primarily a synergist, assisting Tibialis Anterior in inversion/supination of the foot, and assisting Gastrocnemius and Soleus in plantarflexing the ankle.

Origin: Posterior Proximal Shaft of Tibia and Fibula
Insertion: Navicular, Cuneiform I, Metatarsals 2-4
Action(s): Inversion of Foot, Plantarflexion
Innervation: Tibial Nerve
Synergist: Tibialis Anterior, Gastrocnemius
Antagonist: Peroneus Longus, Extensor Digitorum Longus

Origin:
Posterior Proximal
Shaft of Tibia

Origin:
Posterior Proximal
Shaft of Fibula

Insertion:
Navicular, Cuneiform I,
Metatarsals 2-4

Kinesiology Matching

__C.__ : Action performed by Brachialis

__L.__ : Insertion of Brachioradialis

__N.__ : Muscle that inserts on the Mastoid Process of the Temporal bone

__F.__ : Insertion of Gracilis

__M__ : Origin of Temporalis

__T__ : Action shared by Tibialis Anterior and Tibialis Posterior

__A__ : Muscle inserting onto the Radial Tuberosity

__E.__ : Prime mover of shoulder abduction

__R.__ : Insertion of Rectus Abdominis

__K.__ : Muscle inserting onto the Pes Anserinus (medial proximal tibia)

__B.__ : Origin of Sartorius

__R.__ : Muscles responsible for retracting/adducting the scapula

__S.__ : Action performed by the Biceps Brachii, in which it is the prime mover

__I.__ : Bipennate muscle that crosses the hip and knee on the anterior thigh

__Q.__ : Origin of the Infraspinatus

__J.__ : Insertion of the Quadriceps

__H.__ : Action performed by the Latissimus Dorsi   e m a

__D.__ : Muscle originating in the Supraspinous Fossa

__O.__ : Primary action performed by the Pectoralis Major

__G__ : Action of the Hamstrings and Gastrocnemius

A: Biceps Brachii

B: Anterior Superior Iliac Spine

C: Elbow Flexion

D: Supraspinatus

E: Deltoid

F: Pes Anserinus med. prox tib

G: Knee Flexion

H: Shoulder Adduction

I: Rectus Femoris

J: Tibial Tuberosity

K: Sartorius

L: Styloid Process of Radius

M: Temporal Fossa

N: Sternocleidomastoid

O: Horizontal Adduction of the Shoulder

P: Rhomboids

Q: Infraspinous Fossa

R: Xiphoid Process

S: Supination

T: Inversion

Answer Key on Page 271

Kinesiology

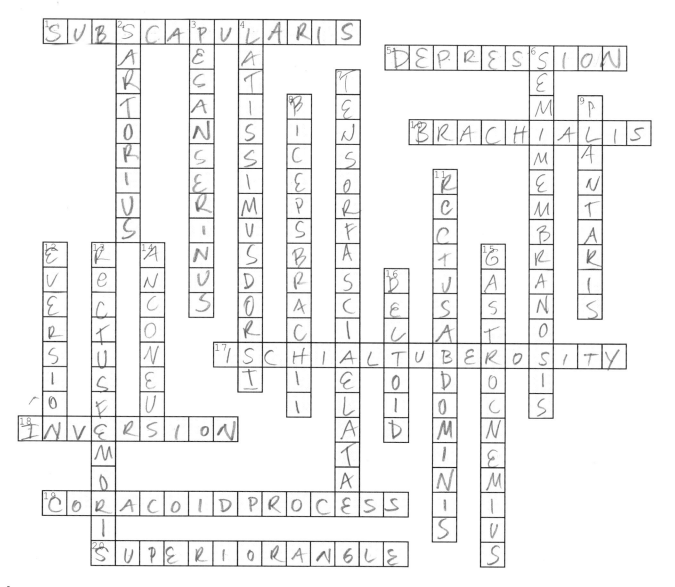

The crossword grid contains the following filled-in answers:

Across:
- 1. SUBSCAPULARIS
- 5. DEPRESSION
- 10. BRACHIALIS
- 17. ISCHIALTUBEROSITY
- 18. INVERSION
- 19. CORACOIDPROCESS
- 20. SUPERIORANGLE

Down (letters visible in grid):
- 2. SARTORIUS
- 3. PESANSERINUS
- 4. LATISSIMUSDORSI
- 6. SEMIMEMBRANOSUS
- 7. TENSORFASCIALATA
- 8. BICEPSBRACHII
- 9. PLANTARIS
- 11. RECTUSABDOMINIS
- 12. EVERSIO
- 13. RECTUSFEMORIS
- 14. ANCONEUS
- 15. GASTROCNEMIUS
- 16. DELTOID

Across

1. Muscle assisting latissimus dorsi and teres major in extension and adduction of the shoulder
5. Action of the serratus anterior on the scapula
10. Prime mover of elbow flexion
17. Origin of all three hamstring muscles
18. Action of the tibialis anterior and tibialis posterior
19. Insertion of pectoralis minor
20. Insertion of levator scapulae

Down

2. The longest muscle in the body
3. Insertion of sartorius, gracilis, and semitendinosus
4. The widest muscle in the body
6. Most medial hamstring muscle
7. Muscle attaching to the IT Band that assists in hip flexion
8. Muscle inserting onto the radial tuberosity
9. The longest tendon in the body attaches to this muscle
11. Muscle responsible for flexion of the trunk
12. Action of the peroneus longus
13. Bipennate muscle responsible for flexion of the hip and extension of the knee
14. Muscle originating on lateral epicondyle of humerus and inserting onto the olecranon process
15. Muscle that flexes the knee and plantarflexes the ankle
16. Muscle responsible for shoulder abduction

Answer Key on Page 277

calcaneal tendon

temporalis

(middle) deltoid

brachioradialis

pec major

biceps brachii

gluteus maximus

gastrocnemius

fibularis longus

Answer Key on Page 278

Masseter

Buccinator

serratus anterior

rectus abdominis

sartorius

rectus femons

Gracilis

adductor magnus

Answer Key on Page 278

(upper)
trapezius

triceps
brachii

latissimus
dorsi

biceps
femoris

soleus
?

Answer Key on Page 278

265

clavicle

humerus

sternum
(body)

rib

ulna

radius

carpal—
trapezoid?

metacarpal

phalange

femur

fibula

patella

tibia

metatarsal

phalanges

Answer Key on Page 279

cervical
vertebrae

spine of
scapula

thoracic
vertebra
T7

lumbar
vertebrae
L3

ilium

sacrum

calcaneus

Answer Key on Page 279

Kinesiology Practice Exam

1. Most medial muscle of the erector spinae muscle group
A. Longissimus
B. Semispinalis
C. Spinalis ✓
D. Iliocostalis

2. Insertion of the adductor longus
A. Lesser trochanter
B. Pectineal line
C. Linea aspera ✓
D. Greater trochanter

3. Elbow extension and shoulder extension is performed by the following muscle
A. Triceps brachii ✓
B. Biceps brachii
C. Coracobrachialis
D. Anconeus

4. Part of the scapula serratus anterior inserts onto
A. Medial border ✓
B. Lateral border
C. Spine
D. Inferior angle

5. Muscle originating in the subscapular fossa
A. Pectoralis Minor
B. Supraspinatus
C. Infraspinatus
D. Subscapularis ✓

6. Large bony structures located at the proximal end of the humerus
A. Trochlea and capitulum
B. Medial and lateral epicondyles
C. Deltoid tuberosity and olecranon fossa
D. Greater and lesser tubercles ✓

7. An antagonist to the biceps brachii is
A. Coracobrachialis
B. Brachialis
C. Pronator Teres ✓
D. Supinator   _ ramus + ischium_

8. Adductor magnus has a common origination site with which muscle group
A. Wrist flexors
B. Quadriceps
C. Rotator cuff
D. Hamstrings ✓

9. All of the following are located on the femur except
A. Medial condyle _tibia_ ✓
B. Greater trochanter
C. Linea alba ✓
D. Adductor tubercle

10. The second cervical vertebrae is also known as
A. Atlas
B. Axis ✓
C. Occiput
D. Temporal

11. Muscle originating on the spinous processes of T7-L5, the iliac crest, and lumbar aponeurosis
A. Quadratus lumborum
B. Latissimus dorsi ✓
C. Spinalis
D. Psoas major

12. Which fiber of the deltoid originates on the acromion process of the scapula
A. Inferior deltoid
B. Anterior deltoid
C. Posterior deltoid
D. Middle deltoid ✓

13. Shoulder flexion, elbow flexion, and forearm supination are all performed by which muscle
A. Brachialis
B. Coracobrachialis
C. Brachioradialis
D. Biceps Brachii ✓

14. Which of the following is a hinge joint
A. Knee ✓
B. Hip
C. Shoulder
D. Wrist

15. Muscle inserting onto the medial lip of the linea aspera and adductor tubercle of the femur
A. Adductor longus
B. Adductor magnus ✓
C. Adductor brevis
D. Gracilis

16. The linea aspera is located on which side of the femur
A. Anterior
B. Posterior ✓
C. Medial
D. Lateral

17. The following muscle inserts onto the lateral lip of the intertubercular groove
A. Pectoralis minor
B. Pectoralis major ✓
C. Latissimus dorsi
D. Teres major

18. The origin of teres minor
A. Lateral border of the scapula ✓
B. Medial border of the scapula
C. Spine of the scapula
D. Inferior angle of the scapula

19. Origin of the rectus femoris
A. Anterior Superior Iliac Spine
B. Anterior Inferior Iliac Spine ✓
C. Ischial tuberosity
D. Body of the pubis

20. Which two structures form the hip joint
A. Head of femur and obturator foramen
B. Head of femur and acetabulum
C. Head of humerus and glenoid fossa
D. Head of humerus and acromion process

21. Contraction of the middle fibers of the trapezius result in
A. Retraction
B. Protraction
C. Elevation
D. Depression

22. The coronal suture connects the following bones of the cranium
A. Occipital and parietal
B. Parietal and parietal
C. Parietal and frontal
D. Temporal and parietal

23. The interphalangeal joints can perform which actions
A. Adduction and abduction
B. Rotation
C. Flexion and extension
D. Protraction and retraction

24. Brachioradialis inserts onto which part of the radius
A. Styloid process
B. Radial tuberosity
C. Head
D. Interosseous border

25. A massage therapist is working on the lateral side of the forearm. The bone they are working on top of is the
A. Radius
B. Ulna
C. Humerus
D. Fibula

26. Muscles originating on the spinous processes of C7-T5
A. Levator scapulae
B. Serratus anterior
C. Trapezius
D. Rhomboids

27. The socket of the hip is also called the
A. Ischial tuberosity
B. Obturator foramen
C. Acetabulum
D. Iliac crest

28. Primary muscle a massage therapist palpates on the lateral edge of the leg
A. Soleus
B. Tibialis anterior
C. Peroneus longus
D. Gastrocnemius

29. The ankle joint is comprised of which two bones
A. Tibia and talus
B. Tibia and fibula
C. Talus and calcaneus
D. Talus and fibula

30. Origin of pectoralis minor
A. Coracoid process
B. Ribs 3-5
C. Ribs 1-3
D. Sternum

31. Extension of the thumb can be accomplished by contraction of which muscle
A. Extensor pollicis longus
B. Flexor pollicis longus
C. Extensor hallucis longus
D. Flexor hallucis longus

32. The saddle joint is located where
A. Elbow
B. Thumb
C. Knee
D. Ankle

33. Structure located on the lateral distal end of the humerus
A. Medial epicondyle
B. Greater tubercle
C. Lateral epicondyle
D. Trochlea

34. Antagonist to the rhomboids, responsible for abduction of the scapula
A. Latissimus dorsi
B. Pectoralis major
C. Trapezius
D. Serratus anterior

35. Proximal attachment of coracobrachialis
A. Coracoid process
B. Coronoid process
C. Medial proximal shaft of humerus
D. Radial tuberosity

36. Joint located between the occiput and first cervical vertebrae, responsible for flexion and extension of the head
A. Atlantoaxial
B. Atlantooccipital
C. Occipitofrontalis
D. Occipitoaxial

37. Three of the four rotator cuff muscles insert onto the greater tubercle of the humerus. The only one that does not is
A. Teres Minor
B. Supraspinatus
C. Infraspinatus
D. Subscapularis

38. Which of the following muscles crosses the glenohumeral joint
A. Pectoralis minor
B. Trapezius
C. Coracobrachialis
D. Brachialis

39. Distal attachment of the peroneus longus
A. Head of the fibula
B. Tuberosity of the fifth metatarsal
C. Base of first metatarsal
D. Lateral condyle of the tibia

40. Synergist to the hamstrings while flexing the knee
A. Gastrocnemius
B. Soleus
C. Tibialis anterior
D. Rectus femoris

41. A concentric contraction of this muscle causes the hip to extend and the knee to flex
A. Gastrocnemius
B. Rectus femoris
C. Biceps brachii
D. Semitendinosus

42. Structure located immediately distal to the coronoid process of the ulna
A. Ulnar tuberosity
B. Coronoid fossa
C. Olecranon fossa
D. Styloid process

43. If a client were to resist the actions of the pectineus, *adduction* *flexion* how would they move their body
A. Adduction and flexion of the hip
B. Abduction and extension of the hip
C. Abduction and flexion of the hip
D. Adduction and extension of the hip

44. Muscle originating on the sternum and clavicle, responsible for neck flexion and unilateral head rotation to the opposite side
A. Levator scapulae
B. Sternocleidomastoid
C. Scalenes
D. Pectoralis major   *ulna?*

45. The capitulum articulates with
A. Head of the radius
B. Tibial plateau
C. Coracoid process
D. Greater trochanter

46. Which muscle originates on the sternum, ribs, and medial half of the clavicle
A. Teres minor
B. Pectoralis minor
C. Anterior deltoid
D. Pectoralis major

47. What are the two actions performed by the rectus femoris
A. Hip flexion, knee flexion
B. Hip extension, knee extension
C. Hip flexion, knee extension
D. Hip extension, knee flexion

48. Where does the biceps brachii insert?
A. Ulnar Tuberosity
B. Radial Process
C. Coronoid Process
D. Radial Tuberosity

49. Muscle originating on the medial epicondyle of the humerus
A. Brachioradialis
B. Biceps brachii
C. Brachialis
D. Pronator teres

50. Triceps brachii is innervated by the following nerve
A. Ulnar
B. Radial
C. Musculocutaneous
D. Median

Answer Key on Page 280

Matching Answer Key

Massage Matching(p 23):

K	G
H	I
M	O
E	T
R	N
L	S
D	C
A	F
Q	B
J	P

Word Root Matching(p 37):

R	H
M	A
G	D
J	E
K	T
L	S
P	I
Q	F
C	O
B	N

Prefix Matching(p 38):

S	D
C	K
P	I
B	M
O	E
A	H
J	N
R	Q
T	L
G	F

Suffix Matching(p 39):

M	I
L	C
R	Q
S	K
O	J
A	D
P	F
H	T
B	E
G	N

Anatomy Matching(p 78):

C	P
K	N
E	A
T	H
O	S
D	J
M	F
L	G
B	I
Q	R

Pathology Matching(p 169):

D	R
P	B
G	I
O	M
A	L
N	H
T	C
J	F
S	K
E	Q

Kinesiology Matching (p 261):

C	P
L	S
N	I
F	Q
M	J
T	H
A	D
E	O
R	G
K	
B	

Medical Term Breakdown and Building(p 40):

1. Arteriosclerosis: Artery/Hard/Condition
2. Pyelonephritis: Renal pelvis/Kidney/Inflammation
3. Encephalitis: Brain/Inflammation
4. Lymphedema: Lymph/Swelling
5. Hyperthyroidism: Excessive/Thyroid/Condition
6. Cholecystitis: Bile/Bladder/Inflammation
7. Hepatitis: Liver/Inflammation
8. Phlebitis: Vein/Inflammation

1. Without blood: An/Emia
2. Fatty plaque hard condition: Athero/Scler/Osis
3. Stomach inflammation: Gastr/Itis
4. Black tumor: Melan/Oma
5. Fiber muscle pain: Fibro/My/Algia
6. Bone joint inflammation: Osteo/Arthr/Itis
7. Bladder inflammation: Cyst/Itis
8. Without breath: A/Pnea

Massage Therapy Answers

Critical Thinking Answers

1. Katie forgot to clean the door handle! The client, who had not washed their hand, opened the door. This contaminated the door handle. Katie cleaned the table, bolsters, and head rest perfectly, but her hand became contaminated when she grabbed the door handle without cleaning it first. She then shook the hand of her next client, which resulted in cross-contamination. Make sure you clean anything the client touches!

2. Brandon has violated confidentiality. Anything the client states during the massage is to be kept confidential, and should only be discussed with the client in a massage setting. By asking Stan about the marathon and the work on his hamstrings in a public setting, he has violated the confidentiality established with Stan.

3. Johnny has knowingly and intentionally performed chiropractic work, which is outside of his scope of practice. If this action had resulted in the client becoming hurt in any way, Brandon could be sued for malpractice and negligence. If a joint pops during the course of massage naturally, that is fine. But because Johnny knowingly attempted to perform work outside of his scope of practice, he could be held liable for damages. Do not work outside your scope of practice!

4. Steph has committed a violation of ethics. The client is seeing Steph for a massage, and nothing more. Attempting to solicit a client anything that is not directly massage related is a violation of ethics, and should not be done. Instead, Steph should have recommended the client go to a vendor that sells used ski boots.

5. Amber is crossing in to counter-transference and dual relationships. If a massage therapist begins feeling any sort of attraction towards a client, they should end the business relationship before it becomes a problem. If the therapist is working for someone, they should notify their employer of the situation so the client can be booked with another therapist. If the therapist wishes to date a client, the therapist needs to make sure they are no longer that client's therapist.

6. Jonah has likely witnessed a theft in progress. Jonah should report the potential theft to his employer. Jonah should not approach or confront the co-worker suspected of stealing. Doing so could create many issues between co-workers if there is no proof of any wrong doing, an altercation could ensue, etc. If any issue arises between co-workers, the issue should be brought to the attention of the employer.

7. The client has violated Charlie's boundaries. Boundaries set limitations on where the massage therapist works, and are set by both the therapist and client. When Charlie sets the drape, the boundary is established, and Charlie is non-verbally telling the client that there will be no massage past this point on the back. By pulling the sheet down, the client has violated Charlie's boundaries. Charlie should explain to the client that the sheet is setting the boundary, and needs to stay where it is. If the client insists on the sheet being lowered, Charlie may tell the client that the session will end.

8. Sasha should immediately leave the massage room and report the incident to the employer. The client should be escorted off the property and barred from returning. This type of incident, in which a massage therapist is physically assaulted, can happen to anyone, and should never be tolerated. Side note, this exact circumstance happened to me once! Like I said, it can happen to anyone!

Anatomy and Physiology

Complete the crossword below

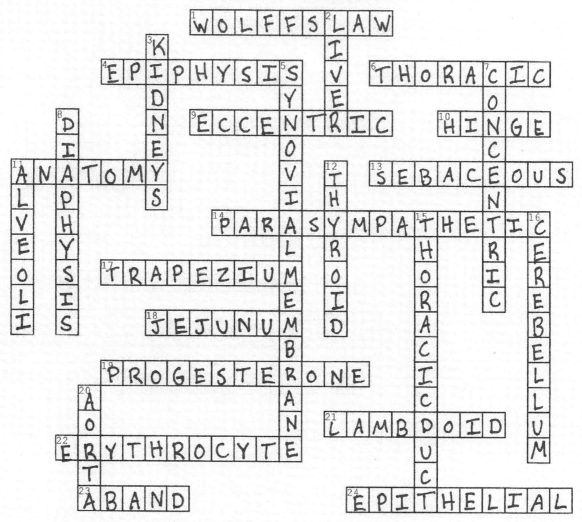

1. WOLFFSLAW
2. IVE
3. KIDNEYS
4. EPIPHYSIS
5. SYNOVIALMEMBRANE
6. THORACIC
7. CONCENTRIC
8. DIAPHYSIS
9. ECCENTRIC
10. HINGE
11. ANATOMY
12. THYROID
13. SEBACEOUS
14. PARASYMPATHETIC
15. THORACIC
16. CEREBELLUM
17. TRAPEZIUM
18. JEJUNUM
19. PROGESTERONE
20. AORTA
21. LAMBDOID
22. ERYTHROCYTE
23. ABAND
24. EPITHELIAL

ALVEOLI

ABDUC

Pathology

Complete the crossword below

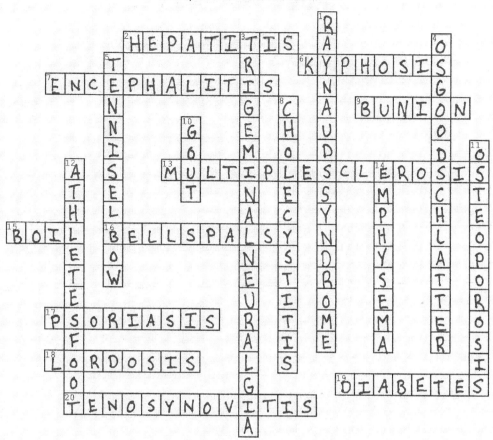

Medications

Find the medications based on what they're used for!

```
W  J  A  P  K  D  H  D  W  E  A  N  T  I  F  U  N  G  A  L
V  S  M  C  I  Q  T  N  J  Q  W  W  B  Y  E  Y  X  F  J  X
C  B  L  X  A  E  N  I  M  A  T  S  I  H  I  T  N  A  U  N
M  I  A  Z  N  A  N  T  I  B  I  O  T  I  C  L  H  S  B  Q
N  A  Q  W  T  K  T  F  U  K  C  D  L  O  L  B  V  R  R  G
A  N  T  I  I  N  F  L  A  M  M  A  T  O  R  Y  O  P  X  Z
T  D  R  U  V  Z  U  J  Z  S  L  H  C  G  O  N  A  B  V  J
H  B  Q  E  I  I  N  M  X  J  R  A  H  X  C  N  E  L  W  O
P  Y  R  F  R  U  N  Z  I  C  L  F  O  H  T  K  V  V  X  E
B  R  M  B  A  I  N  B  V  A  U  G  O  I  N  I  I  O  D  X
P  Y  A  I  L  S  D  X  N  I  T  D  P  P  A  M  T  N  W  C
K  A  Z  U  G  Y  S  E  A  F  I  Y  Z  S  T  X  A  Z  R  X
B  G  S  X  Z  F  S  N  D  L  R  J  R  G  S  V  D  S  Z  N
S  N  J  X  U  T  T  N  A  E  B  T  P  G  E  D  E  G  I  W
I  Z  Y  B  H  A  N  T  T  T  A  N  A  L  G  E  S  I  C  P
O  S  Q  E  C  A  O  I  F  T  K  P  I  P  N  U  E  N  J  O
G  T  T  I  R  R  C  I  S  V  Z  I  Z  L  O  M  M  B  H  S
E  I  D  J  S  N  G  K  W  S  L  K  W  U  C  C  B  Y  A  Y
C  T  N  A  L  U  G  A  O  C  I  T  N  A  E  H  G  S  M  J
C  I  T  E  R  U  I  D  E  F  L  B  Y  R  D  V  I  K  O  M
```

Kinesiology

Complete the crossword below

Across / Down answers filled in:

1. SUBSCAPULARIS
2. SARTORIUS
3. ESANSERINUS
4. LATISSIMUSDORSI
5. DEPRESSION
6. SEMIMEMBRANOSUS
7. TENSORFASCIALATA
8. BICEPSBRACHII
9. PLANTARIS
10. BRACHIALIS
11. RECTUSABDOMINIS
12. EVERSION
13. RECTUSFEMORIS
14. ANCONEUS
15. GASTROCNEMIUS
16. DELTOID
17. ISCHIALTUBEROSITY
18. INVERSION
19. CORACOIDPROCESS
20. SUPERIORANGLE

Muscle Labeling(p 263)

Temporalis

Deltoid

Brachioradialis

Pectoralis Major

Biceps Brachii

Gluteus Maximus

Gastrocnemius

Peroneus Longus

Masseter

Serratus Anterior

Rectus Abdominis

Trapezius

Triceps Brachii

Latissimus Dorsi

Biceps Femoris

Sartorius

Rectus Femoris

Gracilis

Soleus

Bone Labeling(p 266)

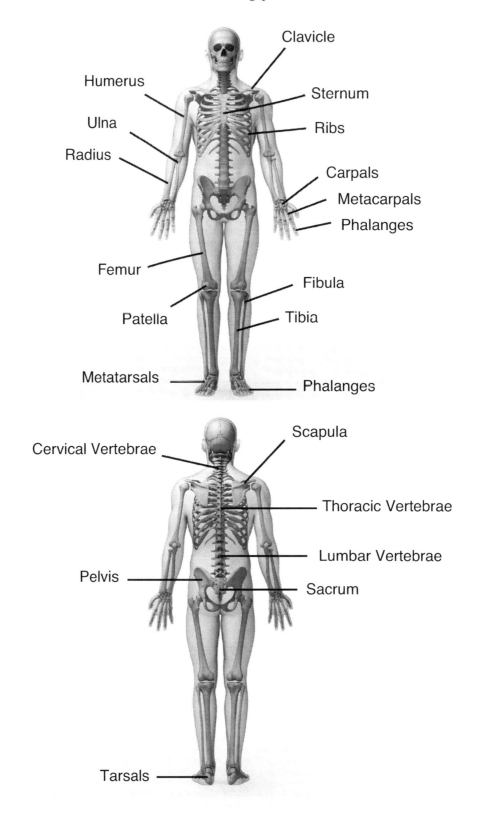

Clavicle

Humerus

Sternum

Ulna

Ribs

Radius

Carpals

Metacarpals

Phalanges

Femur

Fibula

Patella

Tibia

Metatarsals

Phalanges

Cervical Vertebrae

Scapula

Thoracic Vertebrae

Lumbar Vertebrae

Pelvis

Sacrum

Tarsals

Individual Subject Practice Exam Answer Keys

Massage Therapy(p 28)		Anatomy(p 80)		Pathology(p 172)		Kinesiology(p 268)	
01. C	26. A	01. C	26. C	01. C	26. C	01. C	26. D
02. D	27. C	02. B	27. C	02. C	27. A	02. C	27. C
03. B	28. A	03. A	28. D	03. C	28. D	03. A	28. C
04. D	29. A	04. B	29. A	04. A	29. C	04. A	29. A
05. A	30. D	05. D	30. C	05. B	30. D	05. D	30. B
06. A	31. A	06. A	31. D	06. D	31. A	06. D	31. A
07. C	32. B	07. C	32. C	07. B	32. C	07. C	32. B
08. B	33. C	08. A	33. A	08. A	33. B	08. D	33. C
09. C	34. D	09. A	34. D	09. C	34. A	09. C	34. D
10. C	35. A	10. D	35. B	10. C	35. D	10. B	35. A
11. C	36. B	11. D	36. B	11. A	36. C	11. B	36. B
12. D	37. A	12. B	37. A	12. D	37. D	12. D	37. D
13. B	38. C	13. A	38. C	13. A	38. A	13. D	38. C
14. D	39. B	14. D	39. D	14. B	39. B	14. A	39. C
15. A	40. C	15. A	40. D	15. C	40. A	15. B	40. A
16. D	41. C	16. D	41. C	16. B	41. D	16. B	41. D
17. A	42. A	17. B	42. C	17. B	42. A	17. B	42. A
18. B	43. D	18. B	43. B	18. C	43. C	18. A	43. B
19. B	44. C	19. A	44. C	19. D	44. C	19. B	44. B
20. D	45. B	20. A	45. A	20. C	45. C	20. B	45. A
21. C	46. A	21. A	46. B	21. A	46. C	21. A	46. D
22. D	47. A	22. D	47. D	22. B	47. A	22. C	47. C
23. A	48. A	23. C	48. B	23. D	48. B	23. C	48. D
24. B	49. D	24. C	49. C	24. A	49. C	24. A	49. D
25. B	50. A	25. B	50. A	25. B	50. A	25. A	50. B

For detailed answer explanations, watch the
videos at mblextestprep.com/resources.html

Practice Exams

This is one of the most important parts of the book! Practice exams! This is where you can finally put your knowledge to use and see what you know, what you don't, what you need to work on, and using your test-taking techniques!

Just be aware: THESE ARE NOT THE EXACT SAME QUESTIONS YOU WILL SEE ON THE MBLEx. I DO NOT WORK FOR, NOR HAVE ANY ASSOCIATION WITH, THE FSMTB OR HAVE ANY INSIGHT INTO THE QUESTIONS ASKED ON THE EXAM. These questions were created by me, and only me.

These questions test you on the material you MAY see on the exam! There are even questions in these practice exams covering information not seen in this study guide. Just like the MBLEx, you will have questions on things you've never seen or learned before. This is where your test-taking techniques come in! Practice answering questions on things you've never learned before, and it can help you do the exact same thing on the MBLEx! If you're tested on information you've never seen before, look it up! Learn about that information, and if that information comes up on the MBLEx, you'll be even more prepared!

What I always recommend my students do while taking their exams is, if they have access to a piece of paper, write down as many test-taking techniques as they can remember at the very beginning of the test, even before trying to answer any questions. This way, while they're taking the MBLEx, they can look at their test-taking techniques and remind themselves to do them. Write down things like: Take your time, don't change answers, identify key words, eliminate answers, stay relaxed, and read the entire question.

On the MBLEx, you may have questions giving you scenarios involving clients, therapists, coworkers, etc, similar to the Critical Thinking assignment earlier in this study guide, and it expects you to deconstruct the situation and give the appropriate answer. With regards to ethical questions like these, I've mostly left them out of the practice exams. I'd rather test you on more difficult information than something that should be common sense. The simplest way to approach any ethical question is simple: Just ask yourself, "If I wanted to keep my job, what would I do?" It can't get much easier than that!

For a reminder of your test-taking techniques, visit page 4.

For more practice exams, go online to: http://www.mblextestprep.com/resources.html

Practice Test 1

1. Plan information is

A. Information the client shares about themselves
B. Measurable information visible to the massage therapist
C. Medical conditions the client has been assessed with
D. Recommendations for future massage sessions

2. If a client experiences lower back pain due to a hypertonic psoas major while in the supine position, a bolster should be placed

A. Under the knees
B. Under the ankles
C. Between the legs
D. Under the hips

3. Most common form of arthritis

A. Rheumatoid arthritis
B. Gouty arthritis
C. Osteoarthritis
D. Periostitis

4. Elbow extension and shoulder extension is performed by the following muscle

A. Triceps brachii
B. Biceps brachii
C. Coracobrachialis
D. Anconeus

5. The sympathetic nervous system is also referred to as

A. Housekeeping
B. Rest and digest
C. Fight or flight
D. Central

6. The longest vein in the body, located on the medial aspect of the leg and thigh

A. Great saphenous
B. Femoral
C. External iliac
D. Brachial

7. Cryotherapy treatment used for an acute strain or sprain

A. PPALM
B. SOAP
C. PRICE
D. CAR

8. Technique primarily used to work on trigger points

A. Wringing
B. Ischemic compression
C. Cross-fiber friction
D. Myofascial release

9. Primary function of a gland

A. Secretion
B. Protection
C. Absorption
D. Contraction

10. Branching muscle tissue is also called

A. Smooth
B. Skeletal
C. Cardiac
D. Striated

11. Mastication is more commonly known as

A. Chewing
B. Swallowing
C. Sneezing
D. Defecating

12. Part of the scapula serratus anterior inserts onto

A. Medial border
B. Lateral border
C. Spine
D. Inferior angle

13. The leading cause of lung, oral, and esophageal cancer

A. Industrial dust
B. Cigarette smoking
C. Asbestos
D. Cystic fibrosis

14. The most common substance used in body scrubs

A. Salt
B. Sugar
C. Ground coffee
D. Powdered milk

15. Stoppage of range of motion due to trauma to an area

A. Soft end feel
B. Hard end feel
C. Empty end feel
D. Nervous end feel

16. Goals are

A. Measurable or attainable accomplishments
B. A generalized statement about the purpose of a business
C. The theme of a business
D. Business plans detailing projected income

17. Growth hormone, prolactin, and follicle- stimulating hormone are all produced by the

A. Thalamus
B. Pituitary
C. Testes
D. Thyroid

18. All of the following are contagious conditions except

A. Mononucleosis
B. Hepatitis A
C. Psoriasis
D. Osteomyelitis

19. Antiarrhythmics

A. Medication that controls rate of heart contraction
B. Medication that reduces the amount on inflammation in an area
C. Medication that controls the cholesterol levels in the blood
D. Medication that controls urine output

20. How many muscles attach to the scapula

A. 10
B. 16
C. 11
D. 14

21. A certification is obtained via

A. Passing a jurisprudence exam
B. Paying a fee to a jurisdiction licensing agency
C. Obtaining liability insurance to protect against malpractice
D. Completing educational requirements in a school setting

22. Synergist to the hamstrings while flexing the knee

A. Gastrocnemius
B. Soleus
C. Tibialis anterior
D. Rectus femoris

23. A concentric contraction of this muscle causes the hip to extend and the knee to flex

A. Gastrocnemius
B. Rectus femoris
C. Biceps brachii
D. Semitendinosus

24. A client comes in for a massage, complaining of pain in the right upper trapezius and neck. The first thing a massage therapist should do in this situation is

A. Ask the client if they are taking any medications for the pain
B. Ask the client to perform range-of-motion on the affected area
C. Palpate the area to locate any adhesions present
D. Determine any causes of the pain

25. There are seven vertebrae in which region of the vertebral column

A. Thoracic
B. Cervical
C. Lumbar
D. Coccygeal

26. An active stretch

A. Client stretches into resistance without the help of a massage therapist
B. Client stretches into resistance with the assistance of a massage therapist
C. Massage therapist stretches the client into resistance with assistance from the client
D. Massage therapist stretches the client into resistance without assistance from the client

27. Erythrocytes

A. Carry oxygen and carbon dioxide throughout the body
B. Are also called neutrophils and perform phagocytosis
C. Produce thrombi at an area of trauma
D. Allow transport of blood cells throughout the body

28. Peristalsis is controlled by which of the following types of muscle

A. Cardiac
B. Skeletal
C. Smooth
D. Striated

29. Vitamin D is produced in the following organ

A. Liver
B. Skin
C. Pancreas
D. Spleen

30. Structural realignment therapy working on muscles and fascia over the course of ten sessions

A. Rolfing
B. Trager method
C. Feldenkrais
D. Myofascial release

31. Massage results in increased production of

A. Cortisol
B. Blood cells
C. Pathogens
D. Water retention

32. Part of the respiratory passage that divides into the left and right bronchus

A. Larynx — voice box
B. Pharynx — throat
C. Trachea
D. Epiglottis

33. Information the client shares about themselves is documented under which section of SOAP notes

A. Objective
B. Subjective
C. Assessment
D. Plan

34. A massage therapist should wash their hands

A. Only after using the restroom
B. Before each massage
C. After each massage
D. Before and after each massage

35. Phlebitis

A. Swelling of veins as a result of valve incompetence, causing blood to flow backwards
B. Inflammation of a vein due to trauma to a vein
C. Swelling of a vein due to excessive lymph fluid in a limb
D. Inflammation of an artery due to immobility as a result of surgery

36. Dilation of blood vessels during the inflammatory stage is controlled by

A. Histamines
B. Leukocytes
C. Neutrophils
D. Fibrosis

37. Psoriasis

A. Inflammation of skin resulting in skin coming into contact with an irritant
B. Autoimmune disorder resulting in thick, dry, silvery patches of skin
C. Blockage of sebaceous glands, resulting in pustules
D. Skin irritation caused by exposure to cold, affecting blood vessels and hair follicles

38. Observable information the massage therapist can physically see is documented under what category in SOAP notes

A. Subjective
B. Objective
C. Assessment
D. Plan

39. Keeping a client covered while performing a massage

A. Bolstering
B. Draping
C. Covering
D. Wrapping

40. Function of red blood cells

A. Clot to prevent hemorrhage
B. Fight diseases and eat dead cells
C. Transport oxygen and carbon dioxide
D. Transport blood cells throughout the body

41. Cells in the peripheral nervous system can perform an action that cells in the central nervous system generally cannot. What is this action

A. Die
B. Regenerate
C. Produce neurotransmitters
D. Communicate with one another

42. Structure located directly inferior to the coronoid process of the ulna

A. Ulnar tuberosity
B. Coronoid fossa
C. Olecranon fossa
D. Styloid process

43. The esophagus passes through the following structure on its way to the stomach

A. Peritoneum
B. Liver
C. Pericardium
D. Diaphragm

44. Liabilities are

A. Large companies free to operate independently
B. Possessions owned by a business
C. Raising the price of a product for sale
D. Debts owed to a person or business

45. Percussion strokes, used to loosen phlegm in the respiratory tract and activate muscle spindle cells

A. Petrissage
B. Effleurage
C. Friction
D. Tapotement

46. The functional unit of tissue is called

A. Cell
B. Nerve
C. Blood
D. Muscle

47. A patient with severe bradycardia [slow] would most likely need a pacemaker implanted into their body to regulate

A. Embolism formation
B. Lipid accumulation
C. Heart rhythm
D. Phlebitis

48. Body temperature below 90 degrees results in

A. Hypothermia
B. Heat stroke
C. Heat cramps
D. Frostbite

49. If a client were to resist the actions of the pectineus, how would they move their body

A. Adduction and flexion of the hip
B. Abduction and extension of the hip
C. Abduction and flexion of the hip
D. Adduction and extension of the hip

50. Adhesive capsulitis

A. Adhesions forming in the liver, causing decreased bile production and blood detoxification B. Joint capsule surrounding the glenohumeral joint adhering to the head of the humerus, reducing movement
C. Tearing of fascia along the medial tibia, causing increased pain upon walking
D. Autoimmune disorder causing degeneration of myelin sheaths in the central nervous system, resulting in scarring of an axon

51. Most superior portion of the sternum

A. Costal cartilage
B. Body
C. Xiphoid process
D. Manubrium

52. Stimulation of tsubo points to stimulate nerves and increase circulation

A. Shiatsu
B. Reflexology
C. Amma
D. Ayurveda

53. Holding and carrying a heavy item in one hand requires which type of contraction of the upper fibers of the trapezius

A. Isotonic
B. Concentric
C. Isometric
D. Eccentric

54. What personal information is usually listed on a W2

A. The independent contractor's full name and address
B. The employee's full name, address, and complete social security number
C. The name of the business owner and their home address
D. The amount the business made and royalties paid out to the contracted associate

55. All of the following carry blood away from the heart except

A. Capillaries
B. Arteries
C. Arterioles
D. Veins

56. Protein fiber that gives bone its strength

A. Cartilage
B. Elastin
C. Collagen
D. Periosteum

57. An end feel is

A. Also known as a foot massage
B. A very light massage stroke performed at the end of a massage
C. Stoppage of range of motion due to factors such as muscle, bone, or an injury
D. A passive joint mobilization performed by a massage therapist

58. An injury that tears skin, producing jagged edges

A. Laceration
B. Incision
C. Puncture
D. Abrasion

59. When reading blood pressure, the lower number represents

A. Diastolic pressure
B. Systolic pressure
C. Venous pressure
D. Pulmonary pressure

60. Muscle originating on the sternum and clavicle, responsible for neck flexion and unilateral head rotation to the opposite side

A. Levator scapulae
B. Sternocleidomastoid
C. Scalenes
D. Pectoralis major

61. The adrenal glands are located atop which organs

A. Large intestine
B. Small intestine
C. Kidneys
D. Ureters

62. Dopamine is an example of a

A. Neurotransmitter
B. Synapse
C. Neuron
D. Dendrite

63. A client who suffers from psoriasis schedules a massage. An appropriate treatment modification would be

A. Performing vigorous friction on the patches to exfoliate dead skin
B. Avoiding the affected pouches to not worsen them
C. Working on the dry patches if pain is not present
D. Reschedule the massage as psoriasis is contagious

64. A vertebral curvature positioned anteriorly is called

A. Lordotic
B. Kyphotic
C. Scoliotic
D. Amniotic

65. A license is obtained by a massage therapist in order to

A. Perform massage services but not receive monetary compensation
B. Perform massage services and receive monetary compensation
C. Protect the massage therapist against malpractice lawsuits
D. Perform diagnoses and prognoses

66. Amoxicillin and methicillin are forms of

A. Macrolides
B. Penicillin
C. Cephalosporins
D. Tetracyclines

67. The cardiac sphincter is located in which body system

A. Urinary
B. Cardiovascular
C. Nervous
D. Digestive

68. Bone found in the region of the forearm

A. Radius
B. Humerus
C. Fibula
D. Hamate

69. The capitulum articulates with

A. Head of the radius
B. Tibial plateau
C. Coracoid process
D. Greater trochanter

70. Which muscle originates on the sternum, ribs, and medial half of the clavicle

A. Teres minor
B. Pectoralis minor
C. Anterior deltoid
D. Pectoralis major

71. Water is absorbed by the

A. Large intestine
B. Pancreas
C. Esophagus
D. Liver

72. Which of the following is an example of an exocrine gland

A. Hypothalamus
B. Thymus
C. Adrenal
D. Sudoriferous

73. The rectus femoris is biarticular. What are the two actions performed by this muscle

A. Hip flexion, knee flexion
B. Hip extension, knee extension
C. Hip flexion, knee extension
D. Hip extension, knee flexion

74. Where does the biceps brachii insert

A. Ulnar Tuberosity
B. Radial Process
C. Coronoid Process
D. Radial Tuberosity

75. Gliding movements are performed with

A. Petrissage
B. Effleurage
C. Tapotement
D. Friction

76. Contraindications for hydrotherapy include all of the following except

A. Contagious conditions
B. Hypertension
C. Acne
D. Skin rash

77. Tendons

A. Connect ligaments to muscles to prevent friction
B. Connect bones to bones to provide stability
C. Connect muscles to muscles to allow synergists
D. Connect bones and muscles to allow movement

78. Massage may have all of the following psychological effects except

A. Increased relaxation
B. Decreased stress
C. Increased stress
D. Increased energy

79. Rectus femoris has what shape

A. Bipennate
B. Circular
C. Convergent
D. Spiral

80. The pineal gland is located

A. In the neck
B. In the chest
C. In the abdomen
D. In the skull

81. Bronchial tubes branch out into smaller tubes called

A. Larynx
B. Alveoli
C. Trachea
D. Bronchioles

82. Drug used to treat acute asthma

A. Bronchodilator
B. Expectorant
C. Decongestant
D. Anticoagulant

83. Blood passes from the right atrium through the tricuspid valve into the

A. Left ventricle
B. Left atrium
C. Right ventricle
D. Pulmonary artery

84. Muscle originating on the medial lip of the linea aspera

A. Vastus medialis
B. Vastus lateralis
C. Semimembranosus
D. Semitendinosus

85. Muscle primarily responsible for supination of the forearm

A. Biceps brachii
B. Triceps brachii
C. Brachioradialis
D. Brachialis

86. Balancing electrolyte and acid levels in the body is regulated by

A. Stomach
B. Bladder
C. Large intestine
D. Kidneys

87. Vibration of air produces speech, which is the responsibility of

A. Larynx
B. Pharynx
C. Trachea
D. Epiglottis

88. Most superior portion of the tibia

A. Soleal line
B. Tibial tuberosity
C. Medial malleolus
D. Tibial plateau

89. Epinephrine and norepinephrine are produced by which glands

A. Adrenal
B. Pituitary
C. Pineal
D. Ovaries

90. Virus resulting in the development of warts

A. Herpes simplex
B. Human papilloma virus
C. Epstein-Barr virus
D. Urticaria

91. Application of hot and cold on the skin results in the blood vessels

A. Breaking down and building up
B. Constricting and closing
C. Dilating and opening
D. Dilating and constricting

92. ABMP and AMTA offer

A. Business plans
B. Massage licensure
C. Massage certification
D. Liability insurance

93. Stimulating massage strokes include all of the following except

A. Friction
B. Effleurage
C. Tapotement
D. Vibration

94. Type of cell broken down inside the spleen

A. Osteocyte
B. Leukocyte
C. Thrombocyte
D. Erythrocyte

95. Vein running from the medial surface of the foot to the inguinal region

A. Great saphenous vein
B. Femoral vein
C. Obturator vein
D. Superficial tibial vein

96. What action does this muscle perform

A. Adduction
B. Retraction
C. Protraction
D. Abduction

288

100. Hypertonicity of the iliacus, associated with psoas major, may result in
A. Lordosis
B. Scoliosis
C. Ankylosing Spondylitis
D. Kyphosis

97. If a client complains of straining of this muscle, what action may be affected

A. Knee extension
B. Hip flexion
C. Shoulder extension
D. Hip extension

98. While performing the following action, what position is the shoulder in

A. Flexion
B. Abduction
C. Lateral Rotation
D. Horizontal Adduction

99. The primary function of the following muscle on the elbow

A. Pronation
B. Extension
C. Supination
D. Flexion

Practice Test 2

1. Insertion of pectoralis major

A. Deltoid tuberosity
B. Medial lip of intertubercular groove
C. Lateral lip of intertubercular groove
D. Acromion process

2. The elbow joint performs the following actions

A. Flexion and extension
B. Adduction and abduction
C. Medial and lateral rotation
D. Protraction and retraction

3. Tissue specializing in protection, absorption, and secretion

A. Muscular
B. Connective
C. Nervous
D. Epithelial

4. Keeping client information private and protected

A. Self-disclosure
B. Assurance
C. Confidentiality
D. Closed-ended

5. Phenol, bleach, and alcohol are all examples of

A. Disinfectants
B. Soap
C. Hand sanitizers
D. Oil removers

6. Heat creation is produced by which type of muscle tissue

A. Smooth
B. Cardiac
C. Skeletal
D. Adipose

7. Autoimmune disorder affecting myelin sheaths in the central nervous system

A. Multiple sclerosis
B. Myasthenia gravis
C. Parkinson's disease
D. Alzheimer's disease

8. After a massage, the massage therapist notifies the client of stretches that the therapist thinks might help with a client's range-of-motion. This information would be documented under which section of SOAP notes

A. Subjective
B. Objective
C. Assessment
D. Plan

9. The primary goal of a massage performed after a sporting event is

A. Move metabolic waste out of tissues
B. Increase circulation
C. Stimulate muscle fibers
D. Break up adhesions between tissues

10. Distal attachment of what muscle is located at the tibial tuberosity

A. Biceps Femoris
B. Rectus Femoris
C. Sartorius
D. Tibialis Anterior

11. Insertion of levator scapulae

A. Superior angle of scapula
B. Transverse processes of C1-C4
C. Spinous processes of C5-T1
D. Inferior angle of scapula

12. Nociceptors detect

A. Pain
B. Temperature
C. Chemical concentration
D. Body position

13. The glenohumeral joint is considered what kind of synovial joint

A. Hinge
B. Pivot
C. Gliding
D. Ball and socket

14. Autoimmune disorder resulting in increased epithelial production, producing thick scaly patches of skin

A. Psoriasis
B. Rosacea
C. Wart
D. Lupus

15. Ibuprofen is an example of

A. Non-steroidal anti-inflammatory drug
B. Statin
C. Bronchodilator
D. Expectorant

16. Herpes simplex is a

A. Bacteria
B. Virus
C. Fungus
D. Parasite

17. Anatomical law stating bone adapts to load under which it is placed

A. Davis' Law
B. Wolff's Law
C. Johnson's Law
D. Merlino's Law

18. Mammary glands produce what substance

A. Oil
B. Sweat
C. Milk
D. Testosterone

19. The thoracic and sacral vertebrae are curved in which way

A. Lordotic
B. Kyphotic
C. Scoliotic
D. Amniotic

20. Movement of the limbs is controlled by which type of muscle tissue

A. Cardiac
B. Skeletal
C. Smooth
D. Hyaline

21. An asset is

A. Nontaxable income
B. A weakness in a company's business model
C. A business with no liabilities
D. A possession of a business

22. All of the following companies provide liability insurance for massage therapists except

A. NCBTMB
B. ABMP
C. AMTA
D. NAMT

23. There are how many pairs of spinal nerves in the peripheral nervous system

A. 24
B. 12
C. 18
D. 31

24. Epiphyses are covered in the following

A. Elastic cartilage
B. Periosteum
C. Hyaline cartilage
D. Mesentery

25. The thoracic vertebrae contains how many bones

A. Twelve
B. Seven
C. Five
D. Eleven

26. Technique used to treat adhesions found between fascia and muscles

A. Rolfing
B. Myofascial release
C. Deep tissue
D. Osteosymmetry

27. The descending order of the small intestine is

A. Duodenum, ileum, jejunum
B. Ileum, jejunum, duodenum
C. Duodenum, jejunum, ileum
D. Jejunum, duodenum, ileum

28. If systolic pressure measures 140 or higher, a person may be diagnosed with

A. Hypotension
B. Hypertension
C. Hyperemia
D. Myocardial infarction

29. A podiatrist is a doctor that specializes in the

A. Ears
B. Mouth
C. Feet
D. Bladder

30. Plantarflexion and dorsiflexion take place at which joint

A. Tibiofemoral
B. Talocalcaneal
C. Talotibial
D. Tibiofibular

31. Motor axons carry nerve impulses

A. Towards the cerebellum
B. Towards the brain
C. Away from the brain
D. Away from muscle

32. Certain leukocytes perform phagocytosis, which is when cells perform what action

A. Eat substances
B. Absorb nutrients
C. Move from an area of high concentration to an area of low concentration
D. Transportation of oxygen and carbon dioxide

33. Insertion of the adductor magnus

A. Inferior ramus of the pubis
B. Ischial tuberosity
C. Lateral epicondyle of the femur
D. Medial lip of linea aspera and adductor tubercle

34. Lateral curvature of the thoracic vertebrae

A. Swayback
B. Dowager's hump
C. Scoliosis
D. Bamboo spine

35. Fungal infection affecting the epidermis, resulting in a circular rash

A. Cordyceps
B. Athlete's foot
C. Ringworm
D. Whitlow

36. Irregular heart beat

A. Myocardial infarction
B. Heart murmur
C. Arrhythmia
D. Angina pectoris

37. The cervical vertebrae contains how many bones

A. Twelve
B. Seven
C. Five
D. One

38. Serous membranes

A. Secrete synovial fluid into a joint cavity to lubricate a joint
B. Are filled with interstitial fluid to fight disease
C. Separate organs to prevent friction
D. Surround fasciculi in muscle tissue

39. Muscle originating on the anterior surface of the sacrum

A. Psoas major
B. Pectineus
C. Sartorius
D. Piriformis

40. The styloid process of the ulna lies where in relation to the olecranon process

A. Posterior
B. Proximal
C. Anterior
D. Distal

41. Business expenses include all of the following except

A. Massages
B. Advertising
C. Electricity
D. Credit card fees

42. Slightly bent knees, straight back, and limp wrists are all examples of

A. Proper massage modalities
B. Improper body mechanics
C. Proper body mechanics
D. Improper massage modalities

43. The pyloric sphincter is located between which two structures

A. Stomach and small intestine
B. Stomach and esophagus
C. Pancreas and small intestine
D. Small intestine and large intestine

44. Involuntary painful contraction of a muscle caused by lack of oxygen or dehydration

A. Cramp
B. Spasm
C. Twitch
D. Strain

45. Ulceration may occur in the fingers and toes in severe cases of

A. Emphysema
B. Cyanosis
C. Raynaud's syndrome
D. Paraplegia

46. A synapse is

A. Where two or more neurons meet
B. Where the brain meets the cerebellum
C. Where a dendrite meets a cell body
D. Where a nerve cell body meets an axon

47. Stance in which the feet are placed parallel to the table

A. Warrior
B. Horse
C. Archer
D. Swimmer

48. An employee receives the following tax form detailing income and tax information

A. W-2
B. 1040
C. Schedule K1
D. 1099

49. The rest and digest response is also known as

A. Peripheral
B. Sympathetic
C. Parasympathetic
D. Fight or flight

50. If a client is unable to withstand any amount of pressure during a massage, a treatment the therapist might recommend would be

A. Reiki
B. Rolfing
C. Myofascial release
D. Lymphatic drainage

51. Storage of urine is found in the

A. Kidneys
B. Gallbladder
C. Bladder
D. Urethra

52. The inguinal region is located near which part of the body

A. Elbow
B. Knee
C. Shoulder
D. Hip

53. All of the following are located on the ilium except

A. Ischial spine
B. Anterior superior iliac spine
C. Anterior inferior iliac spine
D. Iliac fossa

54. Gastrocnemius takes what action on the ankle when contracted

A. Dorsiflexes
B. Plantarflexes
C. Inverts
D. Everts

55. Nerve running deep to the flexor retinaculum of the wrist, which may be compressed, resulting in loss of sensation in the hand

A. Radial
B. Ulnar
C. Median
D. Tibial

56. Contraction of hepatitis B is most likely due to exposure to

A. Blood
B. Feces
C. Saliva
D. Semen

57. Substance produced by the liver which aids in the digestion of lipids

A. Bile
B. Vitamin A
C. Insulin
D. Glucagon

58. Superficial muscle to the vastus intermedius

A. Rectus femoris
B. Vastus lateralis
C. Vastus medialis
D. Pectineus

59. Hypotension is also referred to as

A. Low blood pressure
B. High blood pressure
C. Arrhythmia
D. Varicose veins

60. Massage has the following effect on blood vessels

A. Constriction
B. Dilation
C. Toning
D. Formation

61. An electroencephalogram measures

A. Muscle contractions
B. Heart rhythm
C. Blood pressure
D. Brain wave activity

62. The "I" in PRICE stands for

A. Immersion
B. Ice
C. Inflammation
D. Increase

63. Hormone responsible for increasing heart rate and moving blood from digestive organs into the muscles

A. Aldosterone
B. Oxytocin
C. Growth hormone
D. Norepinephrine

64. Basal cell carcinoma is what type of tumor

A. Idiopathic
B. Malignant
C. Benign
D. Lymphatic

65. The study of the cause of disease

A. Oncology
B. Etiology
C. Radiology
D. Idiopathology

66. Periosteum

A. Surrounds the heart
B. Surrounds the epiphysis of a long bone
C. Covers articular surface of bones to prevent friction
D. Surrounds the shaft of long bones

67. Over-production in melanocytes results in a tumor known as

A. Sarcoma
B. Carcinoma
C. Melanoma
D. Lymphoma

68. The pancreas empties pancreatic juices into the duodenum and they mix with

A. Feces
B. Bolus
C. Chyme
D. Water

69. In a herniated disc, the nucleus pulposus protrudes through the

A. Annulus fibrosis
B. Vertebral body
C. Intervertebral facet
D. Sacral foramina

70. Hawaiian massage similar to Swedish massage, utilizing rhythmic massage strokes that flow freely up and down the body

A. Watsu
B. Thai Massage
C. Amma
D. Lomi Lomi

71. Muscle inserting on the pes anserinus

A. Gracilis
B. Semimembranosus
C. Rectus femoris
D. Biceps femoris

72. Cartilage found surrounding the glenoid fossa which aids in structural support of the shoulder joint

A. Labrum
B. Coracoid process
C. Bicipital tendon
D. Acetabulum

73. Expectorants help in

A. Thinning mucous
B. Draining sinuses
C. Blocking histamines
D. Dilating respiratory passages

74. Cranial nerve VII is involved in

A. Bell's palsy
B. Cerebral palsy
C. Trigeminal neuralgia
D. Hemotaxis

75. Proprioceptive neuromuscular facilitation utilizes what specific kind of contraction before the secondary stretch

A. Eccentric
B. Isotonic
C. Isometric
D. Concentric

76. A massage license from one jurisdiction being recognized as valid in another jurisdiction

A. Reciprocity
B. Certification
C. Liability
D. Malpractice

77. Function of insulin

A. Digestion of protein
B. Absorption of glucose
C. Absorption of lipids
D. Elimination of wastes

78. Aged red blood cells are destroyed in the following organ

A. Liver
B. Stomach
C. Pancreas
D. Spleen

79. A bolster is placed between the legs and arms and under the head in which position

A. Slightly elevated
B. Supine
C. Prone
D. Side-lying

80. Swedish massage is based on the Western principals of

A. Anatomy and physiology
B. Energy
C. Life force
D. Chi

81. Migraine headaches are also known as

A. Trigeminal headaches
B. Muscular tension headaches
C. Glycemic headaches
D. Vascular headaches

82. Each of the following are contagious conditions except

A. Mononucleosis
B. Ringworm
C. Meningitis
D. Lupus

83. Type of metal vital in the formation of hemoglobin

A. Tin
B. Aluminum
C. Iron
D. Steel

84. Penicillin is a form of

A. Antiviral
B. Anti-inflammatory
C. Antibiotic
D. Antifungal

85. All of the following are parts of the ulna except

A. Trochlea
B. Olecranon process
C. Coronoid process
D. Styloid process

86. The pylorus is found at the exit of what organ

A. Small intestine
B. Stomach
C. Large intestine
D. Esophagus

87. A client experiences acute pain during shoulder abduction. Which muscle is most likely involved

A. Teres minor
B. Infraspinatus
C. Deltoid
D. Coracobrachialis

88. The sagittal suture is located between which two cranial bones

A. Occipital and parietal
B. Parietal bones
C. Parietal and frontal
D. Temporal and parietal

89. Rolfing aligns major body segments, known as

A. Structural realignment
B. Somatic holding pattern
C. Mentastics
D. Balance of body and mind

90. Stretch technique in which a muscle is stretched to resistance, followed by an isometric contraction by the client, then the muscle stretched further after the contraction

A. Active static stretch
B. Proprioceptive neuromuscular facilitation
C. Strain counter-strain
D. Myofascial release

91. Lungs and kidneys are both examples of

A. Paired organs
B. Digestive organs
C. Respiratory organs
D. Urinary organs

92. Cartilage found covering the surface of articulating bones

A. Dense
B. Elastic
C. Hyaline
D. Loose

93. Angina pectoris, hypertension, and migraines may all be treated with

A. Vasodilators
B. Antihistamines
C. Beta-blockers
D. Corticosteroids

94. Hookworm, ascariasis, and pinworm are all forms of

A. Parasite
B. Virus
C. Bacteria
D. Fungus

95. A set of guiding moral principles is known as

A. Regulations
B. Scope of practice
C. Ethics
D. Reputation

96. Actions of the following muscle

A. Elevation, retraction, depression
B. Medial rotation, protraction, abduction
C. Depression, flexion
D. Flexion, protraction, extension

97. Name the following condition

A. Cellulitis
B. Herpes Simplex
C. Decubitus Ulcer
D. Impetigo

98. This type of cell is known as

A. Basophil
B. Erythrocyte
C. Neuron
D. Nociceptor

100. Insertion of the following muscle

A. Lateral lip of the intertubercular groove
B. Greater tubercle
C. Medial lip of the intertubercular groove
D. Lesser trochanter

99. Synergist to the following muscle

A. Soleus
B. Tibialis Anterior
C. Extensor Digitorum Longus
D. Rectus Femoris

Practice Test 3

1. The thyroid produces the following hormone

A. Insulin
B. Calcitonin
C. Testosterone
D. Progesterone

2. Cryotherapy treatment used for an acute strain or sprain

A. PPALM
B. SOAP
C. PRICE
D. CAR

3. The pituitary gland produces all of the following hormones except

A. Growth hormone ✓
B. Testosterone
C. Follicle stimulating hormone ✓
D. Prolactin ✓

4. Perirenal fat is found surrounding the

A. Rectum
B. Bladder
C. Liver
D. Kidneys

5. Elbow extension and shoulder extension is performed by the following muscle

A. Triceps brachii
B. Biceps brachii
C. Coracobrachialis
D. Anconeus

6. Part of the scapula that serratus anterior inserts onto

A. Medial border
B. Lateral border
C. Spine
D. Inferior angle

7. Medication prescribed to fight off bacterial infections

A. Anti-inflammatory
B. Antivenoms
C. Antipyretics
D. Antibiotics

8. Adductor magnus has a common origination site with which muscle group

A. Wrist flexors
B. Quadriceps
C. Rotator cuff
D. Hamstrings

9. T-lymphocytes are produced by which gland

A. Thymus
B. Thalamus
C. Pituitary
D. Pineal

10. Goals are

A. Measurable or attainable accomplishments
B. A generalized statement about the purpose of a business
C. The theme of a business
D. Business plans detailing projected income

11. A glove should be worn by the massage therapist if

A. The client has an open wound on the back
B. The client has an open wound on the arm
C. The massage therapist has an open wound on the leg
D. The massage therapist has an open wound on the hand

12. The most common site of sprain

A. Shoulder
B. Knee
C. Elbow
D. Ankle

13. Nausea, vomiting, and fatigue with yellowing of the skin may be the result of

A. Hepatitis
B. Food poisoning
C. Diarrhea
D. Meningitis

14. Another name for a leukocyte is

A. Thrombocyte
B. Red blood cell
C. Platelet
D. White blood cell

15. A dermatologist is a doctor who specializes in the

A. Heart
B. Kidneys
C. Skin
D. Brain

16. If a massage therapist begins to feel sexual attraction towards a client, what should the Massage Therapist do

A. Act upon these urges
B. Do nothing
C. Tell the client
D. Recommend the client see another therapist

17. A client with Bell's palsy would be referred to which doctor

A. Cardiologist
B. Neurologist
C. Rheumatologist
D. Dermatologist

18. There are seven vertebrae in which region of the vertebral column

A. Thoracic
B. Cervical
C. Lumbar
D. Coccygeal

19. Erythrocytes

A. Carry oxygen and carbon dioxide throughout the body
B. Are also called neutrophils and perform phagocytosis
C. Produce thrombi at an area of trauma
D. Allow transport of blood cells throughout the body

20. Technique primarily used to work on trigger points

A. Wringing
B. Ischemic compression
C. Cross-fiber friction
D. Myofascial release

21. HIPAA ensures client information remains

A. Confidential
B. In the government's possession
C. With the client's spouse
D. Unimportant

22. Muscle originating on the spinous processes of T7-L5, the iliac crest, and lumbar aponeurosis

A. Quadratus lumborum
B. Latissimus dorsi
C. Spinalis
D. Psoas major

23. The ethmoid bone is found in which part of the face

A. Eye socket
B. Nose
C. Cheek
D. Ear canal

24. Absorption of nutrients primarily takes place in what part of the small intestine

A. Jejunum
B. Ileum
C. Duodenum
D. Cecum

25. Information the client shares about themselves is documented under which section of SOAP notes

A. Objective
B. Subjective
C. Assessment
D. Plan

26. If a person were to fall forward, landing on their outstretched arms, the shoulder joint could most likely become dislocated in which direction

A. Medially
B. Anteriorly
C. Distally
D. Posteriorly

27. The second cervical vertebrae is also called the

A. Occiput
B. Atlas
C. Axis
D. Dens

28. Areas of the body in which caution is advised during massage of a pregnant client include all of the following except

A. Face
B. Abdomen
C. Ankles
D. Lumbar

29. Rheumatoid arthritis is what type of disorder

A. Sarcoma
B. Viral
C. Bacterial
D. Autoimmune

30. The most fatal form of tumor is

A. Cystic
B. Benign
C. Malignant
D. Gangrenous

31. Cilia contain glands that secrete

A. Sebum
B. Mucous
C. Sweat
D. Ear wax

32. Perception of your own body parts and position of your body

A. Integration
B. Proprioception
C. Reflexes
D. Nociceptor

eye
ethmoid bone
cilia r secrete —
mucous

298

33. In a client with herpes simplex, exposure to sunlight, stress, or hormonal changes may result in the development of

A. Impetigo
B. Decubitus ulcers
C. Cold sores
D. Acne

34. Massage stroke directed toward the heart used to increase circulation, transition between strokes, and apply massage lubricant

A. Friction
B. Petrissage
C. Effleurage
D. Vibration

35. A pre-event sports massage requires the following kinds of strokes to be performed

A. Relaxing
B. Invigorating
C. Slow
D. Sedative

36. Which type of gland is found in the skin

A. Adrenal
B. Mammary
C. Pineal
D. Sebaceous

37. The alimentary canal

A. Is also known as the circulatory system
B. Contains the brain and spinal cord
C. Consists of the mouth, esophagus, stomach, and intestines
D. Brings blood from the heart to the lungs and back to the heart

38. A trigger point that results in pain only when being palpated

A. Acute
B. Active
C. Passive
D. Latent

39. An antipyretic is a type of medication responsible for

A. Eliminating increased glucose
B. Decreasing inflammation
C. Destroying bacteria
D. Lowering fever

40. Protein found inside of red blood cells, responsible for transporting oxygen and carbon dioxide throughout the body

A. Mitochondria
B. Hemoglobin
C. Hemophilia
D. Leukocyte

41. The vagus nerve controls which autonomic nervous system

A. Fight or flight
B. Sympathetic
C. Autonomic
D. Parasympathetic

42. An upper respiratory tract infection may result in

A. Acute bronchitis
B. Emphysema
C. Asthma
D. Pleurisy

43. An aura stroke is a massage stroke in which

A. The hands are pressed firmly into the body
B. The hands are touching the body very lightly
C. The hands are held just above the body
D. The hands are placed on the body without substantial pressure

44. Hair is made of which type of tissue

A. Muscular
B. Connective
C. Epithelial
D. Nervous

45. A resistive joint movement

A. Client moves the joint without the assistance of a massage therapist
B. A client moves the joint with the assistance of a massage therapist
C. A client resists a movement being performed by a massage therapist
D. A massage therapist moves a client's joint without the help of the client

46. Essential oil commonly used to aid in relaxation of smooth muscles in the respiratory tract

A. Eucalyptus
B. Grapefruit
C. Lemongrass
D. Peppermint

47. All of the following are located on the femur except

A. Medial condyle
B. Greater trochanter
C. Linea alba
D. Adductor tubercle

48. Origin of pectoralis minor

A. Coracoid process
B. Ribs 3-5
C. Ribs 1-3
D. Sternum

49. The most distal structure on the tibia

A. Lateral condyle
B. Lateral malleolus
C. Medial condyle
D. Medial malleolus

50. Release of urine from the bladder is controlled by which nervous system

A. Sympathetic
B. Parasympathetic
C. Fight or flight
D. Autonomic

51. Pain felt at the lateral epicondyle of the humerus is associated with

A. Tennis elbow
B. Golfer's elbow
C. Carpal tunnel syndrome
D. Synovitis

52. Another term for a blood clot within a blood vessel

A. Thrombus
B. Embolus
C. Aneurysm
D. Fibrin

53. Hyper-curvature in the thoracic region

A. Swayback
B. Dowager's hump
C. Scoliosis
D. Bamboo spine

54. A disease that has an unknown cause is known as

A. Pathological
B. Carcinogenic
C. Etiologic
D. Idiopathic

55. A constant ringing in the ear is known as

A. Tinnitus
B. Acromegaly
C. Pinocytosis
D. Vertigo

56. Eversion of the foot is also known as

A. Pronation
B. Supination
C. Plantarflexion
D. Dorsiflexion

57. The condyles of the femur articulate with which structures on the tibia

A. Tuberosities
B. Malleoli
C. Head
D. Condyles

58. Protection from malpractice lawsuits is gained by obtaining

A. Limited Liability Corporation
B. Massage certification
C. Licensure
D. Professional liability insurance

59. A soft end feel is felt at the end of a range of motion due to

A. Tight muscle
B. Bone
C. Injuries
D. Inflammation

60. The most abundant form of connective tissue found in the body

A. Fascia
B. Bone
C. Cartilage
D. Blood

61. Allergic reactions in the body may be controlled with use of

A. Vasodilators
B. Statins
C. Antihistamines
D. Beta-blockers

62. Dilation of a small portion of an artery, caused by a weakened arterial wall

A. Embolism
B. Aneurysm
C. Thrombus
D. Murmur

63. During the fight or flight response, what body function shuts down

A. Movement
B. Circulation
C. Respiration
D. Digestion

64. An independent contractor is responsible for filing which tax form

A. Schedule K1
B. W2
C. 1099
D. Schedule C

65. Nociceptors detect which sensation

A. Temperature
B. Pain
C. Light pressure
D. Deep pressure

300

66. A massage therapist bringing their own unresolved issues into the therapeutic relationship

A. Self-disclosure
B. Transference
C. Counter-transference
D. Ethics

67. The femur connects to the tibia via the

A. Anterior cruciate ligament
B. Meniscus
C. Articular cartilage
D. Interosseous membrane

68. Normal cells growing uncontrollably results in

A. Inflammation
B. Cyst
C. Cancer
D. Edema

69. Compression of the following nerve by the transverse carpal ligament results in carpal tunnel syndrome

A. Median
B. Ulnar
C. Radial
D. Musculocutaneous

70. Inflammation of a tendon and its surrounding sheath is known as

A. Tendonitis
B. Carpal Tunnel Syndrome
C. Sprain
D. Tenosynovitis

71. Slow heart rhythm

A. Bradycardia
B. Tachycardia
C. Atrial fibrillation
D. Myocarditis

72. Lateral rotation of the shoulder is performed by which two rotator cuff muscles

A. Supraspinatus, Infraspinatus
B. Infraspinatus, Teres Major
C. Teres Minor, Infraspinatus
D. Supraspinatus, Subscapularis

73. Pressure felt as blood passes through an artery

A. Diastolic
B. Systolic
C. Venous
D. Cardiac

74. Nerve responsible for facial expression

A. Cranial nerve VII
B. Cranial nerve V
C. Cranial nerve I
D. Cranial nerve X

75. Decreasing the angle of a joint

A. Extension
B. Flexion
C. Rotation
D. Abduction

76. Bile aids in the digestion of

A. Lipids
B. Glucose
C. Carbohydrates
D. Protein

77. With a client lying supine, a bolster should be placed

A. Between the legs and arms, and under the head
B. Under the ankles and neck
C. Under the knees
D. Under the head only

78. Ability to perform services legally according to occupational standards and licensing

A. Certification
B. Scope of practice
C. Reciprocity
D. Regulations

79. Cryotherapy is used to reduce

A. Inflammation
B. Frostbite
C. Hypoxia
D. Edema

80. A contusion is also known as

A. Bruise
B. Wart
C. Fracture
D. Hives

81. Chris, who has recently suffered from a heart attack, has requested a massage. The proper course a massage therapist should take is

A. Reschedule the massage until medical clearance has been provided from the client's physician
B. Perform the massage to promote circulation
C. Perform the massage and use a cold compress to lower blood pressure
D. Perform the massage while avoiding shaking or trembling actions

82. The lungs

A. Exchange oxygen and carbon monoxide in the blood
B. Exchange sodium and potassium in the blood
C. Exchange oxygen and carbon dioxide in the blood
D. Exchange nitrogen and carbon monoxide in the blood

83. The largest lymph vessel in the body

A. Thoracic duct
B. Subclavian vein
C. Superior vena cava
D. Aorta

84. Basal cell carcinoma

A. Most common, most serious, fastest growing form of skin cancer
B. Least common, most serious, fastest growing form of skin cancer
C. Most common, least serious, slowest growing form of skin cancer
D. Least common, least serious, slowest growing form of skin cancer

85. Digestive enzyme located in the stomach that aids in breaking down food into usable parts for absorption

A. Insulin
B. Bile
C. Bilirubin
D. Pepsin

86. The term "massage" became popularized in America by

A. Johann Mezger
B. The Taylor Brothers
C. Douglas Graham
D. Per Henrik Ling

87. Tapotement

A. Light gliding strokes towards the heart, used to increase circulation and apply lubricant
B. Strokes that move across tissue, used to break up adhesions
C. Kneading strokes, used to release adhesions and increase circulation
D. Percussion strokes, used to stimulate muscle spindle cells

88. Urine flows from the kidneys through the ureters on its way to the

A. Urethra
B. Bladder
C. Bloodstream
D. Liver

89. The deltoid is an antagonist to itself. What does this mean?

A. It has actions that aren't connected
B. It has two of the same actions
C. It has actions that are similar
D. It has two opposing actions

90. Form of compression in which a muscle fiber is compressed between the thumb and fingers

A. Pincer compression
B. Transverse compression
C. Cross-fiber compression
D. Longitudinal compression

91. Which of the following is a function of connective tissue

A. Absorb nutrients
B. Hold structures together
C. Sensory input
D. Regulation of hormones

92. Tinea is a form of

A. Virus
B. Fungus
C. Bacteria
D. Parasite

93. Depletion of water content in the body results in

A. Hypothermia
B. Hydronephrosis
C. Dehydration
D. Frostbite

94. Name of the joint found between the atlas and axis

A. Spinous joint
B. Atlantooccipital
C. Occipitotemporal
D. Atlantoaxial

95. The long head of the biceps brachii originates where

A. Supraglenoid tubercle
B. Infraglenoid tubercle
C. Coracoid process
D. Radial tuberosity

96. The following type of cancer is known as

A. Basal Cell Carcinoma
B. Malignant Melanoma
C. Squamous Cell Carcinoma
D. Kaposi's Sarcoma

97. Law which states that bone density and strength will increase as a result of increased load on a bone

A. Newton's Law
B. Hilton's Law
C. Davis's Law
D. Wolff's Law

98. The origin of the teres minor is

A. Lateral Border
B. Greater Tubercle
C. Intertubercular Groove
D. Inferior Angle

99. With reference to the above image, which muscle group is being stretched

A. Hamstrings
B. Adductors
C. Quadriceps
D. Calf

100. Name the bone highlighted in the image

A. Calcaneus
B. Talus
C. Cuboid
D. Hamate

Practice Test 4

1. The knee is considered which type of synovial joint

A. Ellipsoid
B. Pivot
C. Ball and socket
D. Hinge

2. A trigger point that causes pain without palpation

A. Acute
B. Latent
C. Active
D. Chronic

3. Sebaceous glands produce what substance

A. Oil
B. Sweat
C. Milk
D. Epinephrine

4. Tendon attaching the gastrocnemius to the calcaneus

A. Tibial
B. Calcaneal
C. Gastroc
D. Patellar

5. A rheumatologist is a doctor that specializes in

A. Connective tissue
B. Stomach
C. Kidneys
D. Urinary bladder

6. Complete rupture of a ligament

A. Grade 3 strain
B. Grade 3 sprain
C. Grade 2 strain
D. Grade 2 sprain

7. The smallest type of blood vessel

A. Capillary
B. Artery
C. Vein
D. Arteriole

8. Gait analysis is observation and interpretation of a person's

A. Walking pattern
B. Somatic holding pattern
C. Sitting pattern
D. Range of motion

9. All of the following are local contraindications except

A. Herniated disc
B. Grade 2 sprain
C. Trigeminal neuralgia
D. Acute osteoarthritis

10. Shearing of the anterior cruciate ligament most commonly results from force placed on the femur, causing it to move too far in which direction

A. Posteriorly
B. Medially
C. Anteriorly
D. Laterally

11. Another term for inversion of the foot is

A. Supination
B. Pronation
C. Dorsiflexion
D. Plantarflexion

12. The thoracic body cavity

A. Contains the liver, stomach, small intestine, large intestine, pancreas, spleen, and gallbladder
B. Is separated from the dorsal body cavity via the diaphragm
C. Contains the lungs, heart, and major blood vessels
D. Holds the spleen against the stomach to prevent rupture of the spleen

13. Which of the following is not a part of the axial skeleton

A. Sacrum
B. Ribs
C. Skull
D. Clavicle

14. Objective information is

A. Information the client shares about themselves
B. Measurable information visible to the massage therapist
C. Medical conditions the client has been assessed with
D. Recommendations for future massage sessions

15. Tennis elbow is also known as

A. Olecranon bursitis
B. Medial epicondylitis
C. Tuberculitis
D. Lateral epicondylitis

16. Tearing of a muscle is considered a

A. Sprain
B. Strain
C. Contracture
D. Subluxation

17. The first cervical vertebrae is also known as

A. Atlas
B. Axis
C. Occiput
D. Temporal

18. Which of the following massage strokes is best in aiding lung decongestion

(A.) Tapotement
B. Effleurage
C. Friction
D. Petrissage

19. Changes in temperature can be detected by

A. Chemoreceptors
(B.) Thermoreceptors
C. Nociceptors
D. Baroreceptors

20. Nephrons are responsible for reabsorption of

A. Staphylococci
(B.) Urea — *out*
(C.) Vitamins
D. Lactic acid

Nephrons reasborb water + nutrients

21. If diastolic pressure measures 90 or higher, a person may be diagnosed with

A. Myocardial infarction
B. Hypotension
C. Hyperemia
(D.) Hypertension

Hair

22. Follicle-stimulating hormone, produced by the pituitary gland, affects what other structure in the body

(A. Ovaries)
B. Thymus
C. Pancreas
(D.) Thyroid

23. An accountant may handle all of the following except

A. Bookkeeping
B. Taxes
C. Accounting
(D.) Advertising

24. A blockage of a blood vessel may result in

A. Arrhythmia
B. Phlebitis
(C.) Ischemia
D. Hypotension

25. The origin of gracilis is found at what body region

(A.) Inguinal
B. Popliteal
C. Cubital
D. Antecubital

26. Extension is

A. Moving a structure toward the midline
B. Decreasing the angle of a joint
(C.) Increasing the angle of a joint
D. Taking a structure away from the midline

27. A cancer spreading from one location in the body to another makes it

A. Asymptomatic
B. Benign
(C.) Malignant
D. Asymmetrical

28. Which type of gland plays an important role in maintaining body temperature

A. Pineal
B. Sebaceous
(C.) Sudoriferous
D. Adrenal

29. Which of the following is not a characteristic of muscle tissue

A. Extensibility
(B.) Protectability
C. Contractility
D. Elasticity

30. A client demonstrating range of motion is an example of which joint movement

(A.) Active
B. Assistive
C. Passive
D. Resistive

31. Flexion of the lumbar vertebrae can be accomplished by contraction of the following muscle

(A.) Rectus abdominis
B. Iliacus
C. Quadratus lumborum
D. Latissimus dorsi

32. Which of the following is not a function of connective tissue

(A.) Insulating the body *fat* — *cartilage*
(B.) Protection *o*
C. Separating tissues *~ fascia*
(D. Hormone release)

33. Tearing of the fascia on the bottom of the foot

A. Flat feet
B. Plantar warts
(C.) Plantarfasciitis
D. Bunion

34. Antagonist to the quadriceps, responsible for hip extension and knee flexion

A. Calf
B. Adductors
C. Rotators
(D.) Hamstrings

35. Sympathetic nervous system

A. Is voluntary and increases heart rate and blood pressure
B. Is involuntary and increases heart rate and blood pressure
C. Is involuntary and decreases heart rate and blood pressure
D. Is voluntary and decreases heart rate and blood pressure

36. The three types of muscle tissue are

A. Striated, dense, cardiac
B. Skeletal, cardiac, epithelial
C. Epithelial, smooth, branching
D. Skeletal, cardiac, smooth

37. A person trembling during fine motor movements is a sign of

A. Alzheimer's disease
B. Parkinson's disease
C. Anemia
D. Bell's palsy

38. Anatomical law that states a nerve that innervates a muscle will also innervate surrounding tissues

A. Campbell's Law
B. Davis' Law
C. Wolff's Law
D. Hilton's Law

39. All of the following muscles insert onto the scapula except

A. Rhomboids ✓
B. Supraspinatus ✓
C. Serratus anterior ✓
D. Pectoralis minor ✓

40. Hemoglobin is a substance made of iron, located where

A. Erythrocytes
B. Leukocytes
C. Lymph
D. Thrombocytes

41. Calcitonin is responsible for

A. Converting calcium into carbohydrates in the liver
B. Increasing calcium synthesis in the stomach
C. Converting calcium into insulin in the pancreas
D. Reducing calcium levels in the blood

42. Stretching of the quadriceps muscle group is achieved by moving the body in what ways

A. Knee extension, hip flexion
B. Knee extension, hip extension
C. Knee flexion, hip flexion
D. Knee flexion, hip extension

43. Action of psoas major on the hip

A. Medial rotation
B. Extension
C. Flexion
D. Lateral rotation

44. Multiple sclerosis is what type of disorder

A. Bacterial
B. Autoimmune
C. Viral
D. Ulcerative

45. There are how many bones in the ankle

A. Eight
B. Two
C. Seven
D. Five

46. The largest part of the brain is also known as

A. Cerebellum
B. Cerebrum
C. Spinal cord
D. Diencephalon

47. Actions of the tibialis anterior

A. Supination and plantarflexion
B. Pronation and plantarflexion
C. Supination and dorsiflexion
D. Pronation and dorsiflexion

48. Massage stroke best utilized to sedate an area

A. Petrissage
B. Vibration
C. Friction
D. Tapotement

49. A massage therapist solicits a product to a client not related to a massage session or treatment. This could be a violation of

A. Ethics
B. Scope of Practice
C. Licensure
D. Reciprocity

not use — decrease

50. Anatomical law which states soft tissue will change length under specific amounts of load or tension

A. Davis' Law
B. Hilton's Law
C. Campbell's Law
D. Wolff's Law *or bone density?*

51. Insertion of supraspinatus

A. Greater Tubercle
B. Lesser Tubercle
C. Supraspinous Fossa
D. Infraspinous Fossa

52. An increased amount of interstitial fluid in an area results in

A. Aneurysm
B. Inflammation
C. Edema
D. Thrombus

306

8.

53. Dead white blood cells in a localized area will form

A. Pus
B. Wart
C. Mole
D. Cancer

54. Blood passes from the right atrium into which chamber

A. Left ventricle
B. Left atrium
C. Right ventricle
D. Aorta

55. Circumduction is

A. Moving a structure around the circumference of a joint
B. Bringing a structure closer to the midline
C. Rotating a structure laterally
D. Flexing a joint

56. Another name for thrombocytes is

A. Red blood cells
B. Platelets
C. White blood cells
D. Plasma

57. The sheet or towel used to cover a client while performing a massage

A. Top cover
B. Full sheet
C. Diaper
D. Full towel

58. Streptococci infection which enters the body through wounds, resulting in infection of the skin and surrounding tissues

A. Cold sore
B. Boil
C. Rosacea
D. Cellulitis

59. Another name for cardiac muscle is

A. Smooth
B. Striated
C. Non-striated
D. Branching

60. During the course of a massage, the massage therapist notices a pre-existing contusion on the client's leg. The massage therapist should

A. Avoid the contusion, notify the client where the contusion is located, and document the contusion in SOAP notes
B. Work over the contusion to help break up potential blood clots that may have formed during the course of healing
C. Apply a cold compress to the affected contusion to reduce blood flow to the contusion
D. Reschedule the massage until the contusion has resolved

61. The aorta carries blood to the liver via the

A. Carotid artery
B. Renal artery
C. Hepatic artery
D. Pulmonary artery

62. The longest tendon in the body connects to which muscle

A. Gastrocnemius
B. Biceps Brachii
C. Semimembranosus
D. Plantaris

63. Primary muscle involved in adhesive capsulitis which tightens and restricts range of motion

A. Pectoralis major
B. Supraspinatus
C. Subscapularis
D. Trapezius

64. An active assistive stretch

A. Client stretches into resistance without the help of a massage therapist
B. Client stretches into resistance with the assistance of a massage therapist
C. The client stretches the Massage Therapist into resistance
D. Massage therapist stretches the client into resistance without assistance from the client

65. Glands are made of which type of tissue

A. Nervous
B. Connective
C. Muscular
D. Epithelial   Sweat oil

66. Muscles inserting onto the medial border of the scapula, responsible for adduction of the scapula

A. Serratus anterior
B. Rhomboids
C. Upper fibers of the trapezius
D. Latissimus dorsi

67. Attack of the epithelial cells of the skin by the body's immune system results in   auto-immune

A. Rosacea
B. Acne
C. Psoriasis
D. Systemic lupus

68. Which of the following describes a fossa

A. Articulation
B. Small protrusion
C. Large protrusion
D. Shallow depression

69. Autoimmune disorder in which the immune system attacks the inner linings of the digestive tract, possibly causing ulcers and scarring

A. Crohn's Disease
B. Diverticulosis
C. Pyelonephritis
D. Gastroesophageal Reflux Disease

70. The nucleus pulposus is located in

A. Stratum germinativum
B. Vertebral bodies
C. Squamous epithelium
D. Intervertebral discs

71. Upon dilation of blood vessels in the inflammatory response, the following type of cell moves into the location to destroy bacteria and debris

A. Leukocytes
B. Thrombocytes
C. Erythrocytes
D. Osteoclasts

72. Actions of the hamstring muscle group

A. Hip extension, knee flexion
B. Knee extension, hip flexion
C. Knee flexion, hip flexion
D. Knee extension, hip extension

73. Abrupt stoppage of range of motion due to structures such as bone

A. Soft end feel
B. Hard end feel
C. Empty end feel
D. Nervous end feel

74. The four types of tissue found in the body

A. Muscular, smooth, skeletal, cardiac
B. Epithelial, connective, nervous, muscular
C. Epithelial, skeletal, connective, nervous
D. Connective, epithelial, nervous, smooth

75. Most common form of arthritis

A. Rheumatoid arthritis
B. Gouty arthritis
C. Osteoarthritis
D. Periostitis

76. The region of the body found at the back of the knee is known as

A. Popliteal
B. Crural
C. Inguinal
D. Antecubital

77. Which of the following massage strokes is best in increasing venous circulation

A. Tapotement
B. Friction
C. Effleurage
D. Petrissage — specific area

78. A system of movements performed in specific ways to achieve certain results is known as

A. Stroke
B. Process
C. Modality
D. Treatment

79. An ophthalmoscope is used to view the inside of a person's

A. Eyeball
B. Large intestine
C. Mouth
D. Ear

80. Bacterial infection that affects the kidneys, usually occuring acutely

A. Uremia
B. Kidney stones
C. Pyelonephritis
D. Cystitis Bladder

81. Muscle inserting into the fascia of the upper chest

A. Sternocleidomastoid
B. Platysma
C. Pectoralis major
D. Subclavian

82. The most common form of papilloma

A. Wart
B. Acne
C. Psoriasis
D. Cyst

83. Alveoli are located at the ends of lungs?

A. Pulmonary veins
B. Bronchial tubes
C. Bronchioles
D. Trachea

84. Chronic inflammation located at the tibial tuberosity, caused by overuse of the quadriceps

A. Osgood-Schlatter disease
B. Grave's disease
C. Raynaud's disease
D. Knock-knee

85. The glenohumeral joint is made by combining the head of the humerus with which structure on the scapula

A. Supraglenoid tubercle
B. Acromion process
C. Coracoid process
D. Glenoid fossa

86. Sartorius attaches proximally to what structure of the pelvis

A. Anterior superior iliac spine
B. Anterior inferior iliac spine
C. Ischial tuberosity
D. Superior ramus of pubis

87. A question asked that is used when asking for a yes or no response

A. Open-ended
B. Close-ended
C. Confidential
D. Tactful

88. Connective tissue holding bones together

A. Tendon
B. Ligament
C. Cartilage
D. Periosteum

89. The trigeminal nerve is which numbered cranial nerve

A. X
B. VII
C. V
D. III

90. A red-ringed rash is found in

A. Tinea pedis
B. Ringworm
C. Shingles
D. Psoriasis

91. An assessment is performed

A. Only before and after a massage
B. Only before a massage
C. Only after a massage
D. Before, during, and after the massage

92. Melanin

A. Provides pigmentation to the skin
B. Allows protection by producing a thickened area of skin
C. Waterproofs the skin
D. Allows absorption of water into the skin

93. A short general statement detailing the goal of a business

A. Public image
B. Purpose
C. Mission statement
D. Business plan

94. A doctor that specializes in the feet is known as a

A. Podiatrist
B. Oncologist
C. Radiologist
D. Rheumatologist

95. The outer most membrane of a serous membrane is called

A. Peritoneal membrane X
B. Visceral serous membrane
C. Temporal serous membrane
D. Parietal serous membrane

96. Primary actions of the latissimus dorsi ena

A. Extension, abduction, lateral rotation
B. Flexion, abduction, lateral rotation
C. Extension, adduction, medial rotation
D. Flexion, adduction, lateral rotation

97. A step backwards psychologically when faced with stress is known as

A. Repression
B. Denial
C. Displacement
D. Regression

98. If a massage therapist begins to feel sexually attracted to a client, what should the best course of action be

A. No longer book appointments with the client
B. Ignore the feelings because they are natural
C. Act on the feelings
D. Ask the client out on a date

99. There are seven vertebrae in which region of the vertebral column

A. Thoracic
B. Lumbar
C. Cervical
D. Sacral

100. Carrying a heavy bucket with one hand for an extended period of time may result in soreness in the following muscle, the result of an isometric contraction

A. Levator scapulae
B. Rectus abdominis
C. Sternocleidomastoid
D. Scalenes

Practice Test 5

1. Reiki originated in

A. Japan
B. China
C. India
D. America

2. Massage strokes directed towards the heart are called

A. Centrifugal
B. Centripetal
C. Chucking
D. Superficial

3. Muscle group primarily responsible for extension of the hip and flexion of the knee

A. Glutes
B. Quadriceps
C. Adductors
D. Hamstrings

4. High altitudes can cause altitude sickness, a common form of

A. Hypoxia
B. Hypothermia
C. Hyperplasia
D. Frostbite

5. The definition of physiology is

A. Studying movement
B. Studying the structure of the body
C. Studying the cause of disease
D. Studying the function of the body

6. Structure bringing air into the lungs

A. Epiglottis
B. Pharynx
C. Trachea
D. Uvula

7. A body out of vertical alignment might most benefit from the following treatment

A. Swedish massage
B. Lymphatic drainage
C. Rolfing
D. Thai massage

8. Self-disclosure

A. The client sharing feelings and emotions during a massage session
B. The massage therapist sharing their feelings and emotions during a massage session
C. A massage therapist disclosing their scope of practice
D. A client viewing a massage therapist as they would a significant person in their early life

9. The lesser trochanter is positioned where in relation to the greater trochanter

A. Lateral
B. Medial
C. Anterior
D. Posterior

10. A lack of erythrocytes in the body results in

A. Myocardial infarction
B. Raynaud's syndrome
C. Anemia
D. Decreased immune response

11. Excessive alcohol consumption may result in

A. Nephritis
B. Cirrhosis
C. Gastritis
D. Diverticulitis

12. Tachycardia, a form of arrhythmia, results in

A. Slow heart beat
B. Rapid heart beat
C. Heart murmur
D. Angina pectoris

13. A sitz bath is a bath in which the client immerses their body up to

A. The knees
B. The chest
C. The neck
D. The hips

14. The ovaries produce

A. Luteinizing hormone
B. Testosterone
C. Progesterone
D. Melatonin

15. The radiocarpal joint is considered which type of synovial joint

A. Hinge
B. Ball and socket
C. Condyloid
D. Pivot

16. Infection caused by bacteria or virus that causes inflammation of the meninges, resulting in vomiting, headache, and fever

A. Osteomyelitis
B. Meningitis
C. Impetigo
D. Encephalitis

17. Jasmine, sandalwood, and grapefruit are all examples of

A. Massage table materials
B. Gemstones
C. Essential oils
D. Perfumes

18. An empty end feel is felt at the end of a range of motion due to

A. Tight muscle
B. Bone
C. Trauma to a joint
D. Resistance

19. The inferior five pairs of ribs are also called

A. True ribs
B. False ribs
C. Superior ribs
D. Inferior ribs

20. Abduction of the scapula can be accomplished by contraction of which muscle

A. Serratus anterior
B. Rhomboids
C. Latissimus dorsi
D. Trapezius

21. The cerebellum is formed by which type of tissue

A. Connective
B. Nervous
C. Epithelial
D. Muscular

22. Which part of a long bone is the diaphysis

A. Shaft
B. End
C. Articular surface
D. Growth plate

23. A massage table, chair, and music source are located in

A. Massage room
B. Business area
C. Changing room
D. Bathroom

24. Lymphatic drainage massage involves light strokes and

A. Application of heat
B. Deep strokes
C. Tapotement
D. Pumping actions

25. All of the following are local contraindications except

A. Raynaud's syndrome
B. Phlebitis
C. Fracture
D. Acne

26. The atlantooccipital joint is responsible for producing which two actions on the head

A. Lateral deviation
B. Rotation
C. Flexion and extension
D. Adduction and abduction

27. Plane joint connecting the scapula to the clavicle

A. Sternoclavicular
B. Acromioclavicular
C. Atlantooccipital
D. Atlantoaxial

28. The lumbar region contains how many vertebrae

A. Seven
B. Twelve
C. Five
D. One

29. Transference

A. Keeping a client's information private and protected
B. The massage therapist bringing their own unresolved issues into the therapeutic relationship
C. The client viewing a massage therapist as a significant person in their early life D.Relocating from one office to another

30. Which type of muscle tissue is controlled voluntarily

A. Epithelial
B. Cardiac
C. Smooth
D. Skeletal

31. Polarity therapy helps clients to balance

A. Mind and soul
B. Hips and shoulders
C. Knees and ankles
D. Body and mind

32. Pain is detected by

A. Photoreceptors
B. Baroreceptors
C. Mechanoreceptors
D. Nociceptors

33. A furuncle is a

A. Bacterial infection of hair follicles
B. Bacterial infection of mucous membranes
C. Viral infection of mucous membranes
D. Bacterial infection of bone

34. Primary action of the pronator teres

A. Elbow extension
B. Supination
C. Elbow flexion
D. Pronation

35. Gentle, rhythmic massage strokes may be

A. Centrifugal
B. Stimulating
C. Sedative
D. Deep

36. The pattern or design of a massage treatment is known as

A. Deliberation
B. Process
C. Sequence
D. Contact

37. Sebaceous glands connect to

A. Arrector pili
B. Hair follicles
C. Skin openings
D. Kidneys

38. Muscle inserting on the pes anserinus, responsible for flexing and externally rotating the hip, and flexing the knee

A. Gracilis
B. Sartorius
C. Semitendinosus
D. Biceps femoris

39. Massage technique targeting reflex points on the hands, feet, and ears to stimulate organs and tissue throughout the body

A. Mentastics
B. Reiki
C. Trager method
D. Reflexology

40. Sprain

A. Tearing of cartilage
B. Tearing of a tendon
C. Over-stretching of a muscle
D. Over-stretching of a ligament

41. Muscle primarily responsible for elevation of the scapula

A. Middle fibers of trapezius
B. Supraspinatus
C. Levator scapulae
D. Sternocleidomastoid

42. Etiology

A. Study of movement
B. Study of cause of disease
C. Study of tumors
D. Study of tissue

43. Vein found in the region of the arm

A. Femoral vein
B. Brachial vein
C. Great saphenous vein
D. Axillary vein

44. Medications given to help control hypertension are known as

A. Statins
B. Antihistamines
C. Chemotherapy
D. Nitrates

45. Stance used to perform massage strokes such as petrissage, friction, and tapotement

A. Archer
B. Horse
C. Bow
D. Swimmer

46. Medial and lateral rotation can be performed at which of the following joints

A. Hip
B. Elbow
C. Ankle
D. Wrist

47. Physical effects of massage therapy are called

A. Emotional effects
B. Mechanical effects
C. Reflex effects
D. Sensory effects

48. The epiglottis

A. Allows food to move from the mouth into the pharynx
B. Allows food to move from the pharynx into the esophagus
C. Prevents food from moving from the pharynx into the nasal sinus
D. Prevents food and liquid from moving into the larynx upon swallowing

49. Exocrine glands secrete their substances where

A. Onto a surface
B. Into the blood
C. Onto the brain
D. Into endocrine glands

50. Suggestions for future treatments by the massage therapist would be documented under which section of SOAP notes

A. Subjective
B. Objective
C. Assessment
D. Plan

51. A massage therapist is working on the lateral side of the forearm. The bone they are working on top of is the

A. Radius
B. Ulna
C. Humerus
D. Fibula

52. An injury to the adductor magnus muscle would make which movements more difficult to perform

A. Hip flexion, abduction, and extension
B. Hip flexion, adduction, and extension
C. Hip extension, abduction, and medial rotation
D. Hip flexion, abduction, and medial rotation

53. All of the following are forms of parasites except

A. Ringworm
B. Tapeworm
C. Hookworm
D. Pinworm

54. The small intestine

A. Breaks down food into usable parts for absorption
B. Absorbs water from feces and eliminates waste
C. Absorbs nutrients from chyme into the blood
D. Transports food from the mouth to the stomach

55. Over-stretching of veins resulting from excessive pressure

A. Arteriosclerosis
B. Phlebitis
C. Edema
D. Varicose veins

56. Good body mechanics are important to

A. Perform a shorter massage
B. Prevent injuries to the therapist
C. Massage the head and neck
D. Prevent injuries to the client

57. All of the following muscles extend the shoulder except

A. Teres major
B. Latissimus dorsi
C. Supraspinatus
D. Subscapularis

58. Mononucleosis, warts, and cold sores are all caused by

A. Fungus
B. Bacteria
C. Virus
D. Parasite

59. Aromatherapy affects which portion of the brain

A. Limbic System
B. Midbrain
C. Occipital Lobe
D. Pons

60. Periosteum is a form of which type of tissue

A. Nervous
B. Connective
C. Epithelial
D. Muscular

61. The hip joint is also known as

A. Coaxal joint
B. Tibiofemoral joint
C. Talocrural joint
D. Glenohumeral joint

62. Anemia results in

A. Varicose veins
B. Myocardial infarction
C. Lack of oxygen traveling through the body
D. Increased lipid content in the blood

63. Glucagon is a digestive enzyme produced by the pancreas responsible for

A. Decreasing glucose levels in the blood
B. Increasing glucose levels in the blood
C. Increasing potassium levels in the blood
D. Decreasing potassium levels in the blood

64. Movement of a joint through the entire extent of its action is known as

A. Stretching
B. Range of motion
C. Traction
D. Active movement

65. Antagonist to sartorius with regards to knee flexion

A. Biceps femoris
B. Rectus femoris
C. Semitendinosus
D. Semimembranosus

66. Dilation of blood vessels during the inflammatory stage is controlled by

A. Histamines
B. Leukocytes
C. Neutrophils
D. Fibrosis

67. Psoriasis

A. Inflammation of skin resulting in skin coming into contact with an irritant
B. Autoimmune disorder resulting in thick, dry, silvery patches of skin
C. Blockage of sebaceous glands, resulting in pustules
D. Skin irritation caused by exposure to cold, affecting blood vessels and hair follicles

68. The left ventricle is located directly inferior to

A. Bicuspid valve
B. Tricuspid valve
C. Right atrium
D. Right ventricle

69. Proximal attachment of the short head of biceps brachii

A. Coracoid process
B. Supraglenoid tubercle
C. Infraglenoid tubercle
D. Coronoid process

70. Contrast baths utilize

A. Warm and lukewarm water
B. Hot and cold water
C. Hot and warm water
D. Cold water and ice

71. The medial epicondyle of the humerus is the origination site of which muscle group

A. Adductors
B. Wrist extensors
C. Wrist flexors
D. Abductors

72. An antagonist to the biceps brachii is

A. Coracobrachialis
B. Brachialis
C. Pronator Teres
D. Pectoralis Major

73. The floating ribs are considered

A. A local contraindication
B. An absolute contraindication
C. An endangerment site
D. Not a contraindication

74. The fight or flight response is also known as

A. Sympathetic
B. Parasympathetic
C. Autonomic
D. Peripheral

75. Medical conditions the client has been assessed with are documented on which section of SOAP notes

A. Subjective
B. Objective
C. Assessment
D. Plan

76. Muscle responsible for external rotation and extension of the shoulder

A. Subscapularis
B. Supraspinatus
C. Infraspinatus
D. Latissimus Dorsi

77. The ulna is positioned where in relation to the radius

A. Proximal
B. Lateral
C. Medial
D. Distal

78. Paralysis of the lower limbs

A. Quadriplegia
B. Hemiplegia
C. Paraplegia
D. Triplegia

79. The jejunum is responsible for

A. Absorption of nutrients into the blood stream
B. Digestion and excretion of waste
C. Filtration of electrolytes into the kidneys
D. Mastication of food in the alimentary canal

80. A client is looking for structural realignment therapy. The type of massage they are requesting is

A. Myofascial release
B. Feldenkrais
C. Rolfing
D. Sports massage

81. Muscle located on the lateral side of the leg, responsible for pronation and plantarflexion of the foot

A. Tibialis anterior
B. Peroneus longus
C. Gastrocnemius
D. Soleus

82. Another name for a nerve cell

A. Neuron
B. Axon
C. Neuroglia
D. Brain

83. The "R" in PRICE stands for

A. Rest
B. Resist
C. Reflex
D. Regain

84. Paralysis of one half of the face, caused by stimulation of the Herpes Simplex virus, which affects the Facial nerve

A. Graves disease
B. Cerebral palsy
C. Trigeminal neuralgia
D. Bell's palsy

85. The skeletal system

A. Absorbs substances into the blood stream
B. Connects tissues together
C. Protects organs and creates blood cells
D. Circulates blood throughout the body

86. Friction

A. Light gliding strokes towards the heart, used to increase circulation and apply lubricant
B. Strokes that move across tissue, used to break up adhesions
C. Kneading strokes, used to release adhesions and increase circulation
D. Percussion strokes, used to stimulate muscle spindle cells

87. Muscle originating on the temporal bone, inserting onto the coronoid process of the mandible

A. Pterygoid
B. Buccinator
C. Masseter
D. Temporalis

88. A client notifies a massage therapist that they have a small area of skin affected by cellulitis. The appropriate response by the massage therapist would be

A. Apply heat to the affected area to allow increased circulation to enter the area
B. Work on the affected area to help break up fat deposits under the skin
C. Avoid the affected area but continue massaging the rest of the body
D. Reschedule the massage until the cellulitis has completely cleared up

89. All of the following are structures that pass through the diaphragm except

A. Inferior vena cava
B. Esophagus
C. Abdominal aorta
D. Stomach

90. Deltoid and supraspinatus share a common action. That action is

A. Extension of the shoulder
B. Abduction of the shoulder
C. Flexion of the shoulder
D. Adduction of the shoulder

91. Long gliding stroke in which the hands are held just above the body, not touching

A. Nerve stroke
B. Effleurage
C. Aura stroke
D. Feather stroke

92. Urea and ammonia are filtered from the blood by the

A. Large intestine
B. Bladder
C. Kidneys
D. Spleen

93. Arteriosclerosis

A. Hardening of the walls of the arteries
B. Fatty plaque buildup in the arteries
C. Bulging of an arterial wall
D. Inflammation of a vein

94. The three muscles that attach to the coracoid process

A. Long head of biceps brachii, coracobrachialis, pectoralis major
B. Coracobrachialis, brachialis, pectoralis minor
C. Short head of biceps brachii, coracobrachialis, pectoralis minor
D. Short head of biceps femoris, coracobrachialis, pectoralis minor

95. Using the same linen between two separate clients is known as

A. Common sheet
B. Same linen
C. Common towel
D. Same towel

96. Increasing the temperature in a room may be useful in treating the following condition

A. Rosacea
B. Psoriasis
C. Carpal Tunnel Syndrome
D. Raynaud's Disease

97. The longest tendon in the body connects to the following muscle, pictured above

A. Soleus
B. Tibialis Posterior
C. Plantaris
D. Peroneus Longus

98. Draping establishes

A. Scope of practice
B. Ethics
C. Boundaries
D. Liabilities

99. If a client presents with trigeminal neuralgia, the best modification to the massage table would be

A. Remove the head rest and have client lay with their head turned to the side, or supine
B. Elevate the right hip with bolsters
C. Only position the client in a semi-reclined position
D. Have the client place both arms across the chest to relax the platysma

100. The muscle group being stretched in this picture is

A. Elbow extensors
B. Wrist flexors
C. Elbow flexors
D. Wrist extensors

Practice Test 1 Answer Key

01. D	26. A	51. D	76. C
02. A	27. A	52. A	77. D
03. C	28. C	53. C	78. C
04. A	29. B	54. B	79. A
05. C	30. A	55. D	80. D
06. A	31. B	56. C	81. D
07. C	32. C	57. C	82. A
08. B	33. B	58. A	83. C
09. A	34. D	59. A	84. A
10. C	35. B	60. B	85. A
11. A	36. A	61. C	86. D
12. A	37. B	62. A	87. A
13. B	38. B	63. C	88. D
14. A	39. B	64. A	89. A
15. C	40. C	65. B	90. B
16. A	41. B	66. B	91. D
17. B	42. A	67. D	92. D
18. C	43. D	68. A	93. B
19. A	44. D	69. A	94. D
20. B	45. D	70. D	95. A
21. D	46. A	71. A	96. A
22. A	47. C	72. D	97. B
23. D	48. A	73. C	98. D
24. D	49. B	74. D	99. D
25. B	50. B	75. B	100. A

Practice Test 2 Answer Key

01. C	26. B	51. C	76. A
02. A	27. C	52. D	77. B
03. D	28. B	53. A	78. D
04. C	29. C	54. B	79. D
05. A	30. C	55. C	80. A
06. C	31. C	56. A	81. D
07. A	32. A	57. A	82. D
08. D	33. D	58. A	83. C
09. A	34. C	59. A	84. C
10. B	35. C	60. B	85. A
11. A	36. C	61. D	86. B
12. A	37. B	62. B	87. C
13. D	38. C	63. D	88. B
14. A	39. D	64. B	89. A
15. A	40. D	65. B	90. B
16. B	41. A	66. D	91. A
17. B	42. C	67. C	92. C
18. C	43. A	68. C	93. C
19. B	44. A	69. A	94. A
20. B	45. C	70. D	95. C
21. D	46. A	71. A	96. A
22. A	47. C	72. A	97. C
23. D	48. A	73. A	98. C
24. C	49. C	74. A	99. A
25. A	50. A	75. C	100. A

Practice Test 3 Answer Key

01. B	26. B	51. A	76. A
02. C	27. C	52. A	77. C
03. B	28. A	53. B	78. B
04. D	29. D	54. D	79. A
05. A	30. C	55. A	80. A
06. A	31. B	56. A	81. A
07. D	32. B	57. D	82. C
08. D	33. C	58. D	83. A
09. A	34. C	59. A	84. C
10. A	35. B	60. D	85. D
11. D	36. D	61. C	86. C
12. D	37. C	62. B	87. D
13. A	38. D	63. D	88. B
14. D	39. D	64. C	89. D
15. C	40. B	65. B	90. A
16. D	41. D	66. C	91. B
17. B	42. A	67. A	92. B
18. B	43. C	68. C	93. C
19. A	44. C	69. A	94. D
20. B	45. C	70. D	95. A
21. A	46. A	71. A	96. B
22. B	47. C	72. C	97. D
23. A	48. B	73. B	98. A
24. A	49. D	74. A	99. C
25. B	50. B	75. B	100. A

Practice Test 4 Answer Key

01. D	26. C	51. A	76. A
02. C	27. C	52. C	77. C
03. A	28. C	53. A	78. C
04. B	29. B	54. C	79. A
05. A	30. A	55. A	80. C
06. B	31. A	56. B	81. B
07. A	32. D	57. A	82. A
08. A	33. C	58. D	83. C
09. C	34. D	59. D	84. A
10. C	35. B	60. A	85. D
11. A	36. D	61. C	86. A
12. C	37. B	62. D	87. B
13. D	38. D	63. C	88. B
14. B	39. B	64. B	89. C
15. D	40. A	65. D	90. B
16. B	41. D	66. B	91. D
17. A	42. D	67. C	92. A
18. A	43. C	68. D	93. C
19. B	44. B	69. A	94. A
20. C	45. C	70. D	95. D
21. D	46. B	71. A	96. C
22. A	47. C	72. A	97. D
23. D	48. B	73. B	98. A
24. C	49. A	74. B	99. C
25. A	50. A	75. C	100. A

Practice Test 5 Answer Key

01. A	26. C	51. A	76. C
02. B	27. B	52. B	77. C
03. D	28. C	53. A	78. C
04. A	29. C	54. C	79. A
05. D	30. D	55. D	80. C
06. C	31. D	56. B	81. B
07. C	32. D	57. C	82. A
08. A	33. A	58. C	83. A
09. B	34. D	59. A	84. D
10. C	35. C	60. B	85. C
11. B	36. C	61. A	86. B
12. B	37. B	62. C	87. D
13. D	38. B	63. B	88. C
14. C	39. D	64. B	89. D
15. C	40. D	65. B	90. B
16. B	41. C	66. A	91. C
17. C	42. B	67. B	92. C
18. C	43. B	68. A	93. A
19. B	44. A	69. A	94. C
20. A	45. B	70. B	95. C
21. B	46. A	71. C	96. D
22. A	47. B	72. C	97. C
23. A	48. D	73. C	98. C
24. D	49. A	74. A	99. A
25. A	50. D	75. C	100. B

REFLEXOLOGY CHART

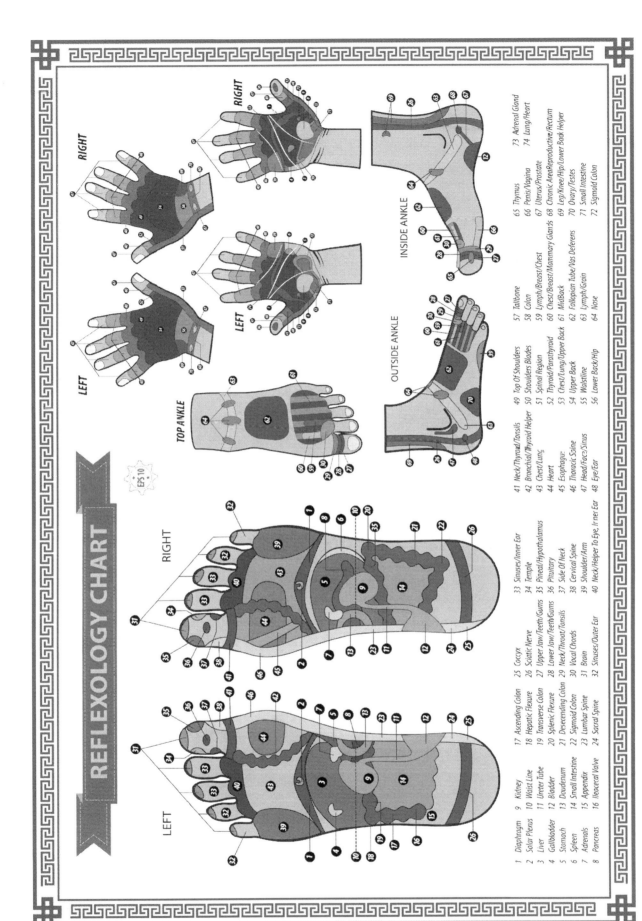

1 Diaphragm
2 Solar Plexus
3 Liver
4 Gallbladder
5 Stomach
6 Spleen
7 Adrenals
8 Pancreas
9 Kidney
10 Waist Line
11 Ureter Tube
12 Bladder
13 Duodenum
14 Small Intestine
15 Appendix
16 Ileocecal Valve

17 Ascending Colon
18 Hepatic Flexure
19 Transverse Colon
20 Splenic Flexure
21 Descending Colon
22 Sigmoid Colon
23 Lumbar Spine
24 Sacral Spine
25 Coccyx
26 Sciatic Nerve
27 Upper Jaw/Teeth/Gums
28 Lower Jaw/Teeth/Gums
29 Neck/Throat/Tonsils
30 Vocal Chords
31 Brain
32 Sinuses/Outer Ear

33 Sinuses/Inner Ear
34 Temple
35 Pineal/Hypothalamus
36 Pituitary
37 Side Of Neck
38 Cervical Spine
39 Shoulder/Arm
40 Neck/Helper To Eye, Inner Ear
41 Neck/Thyroid/Tonsils
42 Bronchial/Thyroid Helper
43 Chest/Lung
44 Heart
45 Esophagus
46 Thoracic Spine
47 Head/Face/Sinus
48 Eye/Ear

49 Top Of Shoulders
50 Shoulders Blades
51 Spinal Region
52 Thyroid/Parathyroid
53 Chest/Lung/Upper Back
54 Upper Back
55 Waistline
56 Lower Back/Hip
57 Tailbone
58 Colon
59 Lymph/Breast/Chest
60 Chest/Breast/Mammary Glands
61 MidBack
62 Fallopian Tube/Vas Deferens
63 Lymph/Groin
64 Nose

65 Thymus
66 Penis/Vagina
67 Uterus/Prostate
68 Chronic Area:Reproductive/Rectum
69 Leg/Knee/Hip/Lower Back Helper
70 Ovary/Testes
71 Small Intestine
72 Sigmoid Colon
73 Adrenal Gland
74 Lung/Heart

RIGHT

LEFT

RIGHT

LEFT

RIGHT

TOP ANKLE

INSIDE ANKLE

OUTSIDE ANKLE

RIGHT

LEFT

EPS10

The Seven Major Chakras

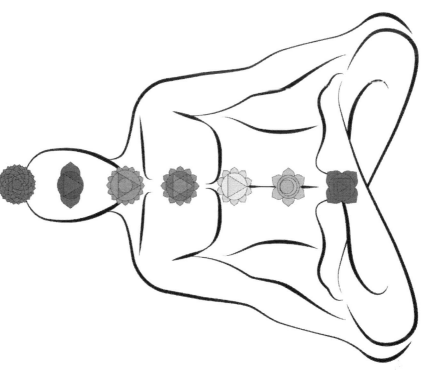

Crown Chakra

Third Eye

Throat Chakra

Heart Chakra

Solar Plexus

Sacral Chakra

Root Chakra

The Body Meridians

Two Centerline Meridians:

Conception Vessel
Governing Vessel

Twelve Principal Meridians:

Stomach Meridian
Spleen Meridian

Small Intestine Meridian
Heart Meridian

Bladder Meridian
Kidney Meridian

Pericardium Meridian
Triple Warmer Meridian

Gall Bladder Meridian
Liver Meridian

Lung Meridian
Large Intestine Meridian

posterior view

anterior view

The Body Meridians

Governing Vessel

Conception Vessel

Stomach Meridian

Spleen Meridian

Heart Meridian

Bladder Meridian

Kidney Meridian

Pericardium Meridian

Small Intestine Meridian

Liver Meridian

Lung Meridian

Large Intestine Meridian

Triple Warmer Meridian

Gall Bladder Meridian

Minerals-Rich

FOODS
Balanced diet infographics

Mg magnesium

HERBS Tea leaves	NUTS Cashew	CEREALS Buckwheat	DESSERT Dark chocolate
440 mg	270 mg	258 mg	200 mg

Mn manganese

BERRIES Rose hip	NUTS Pine nuts	CEREALS Oatmeal	HERBS Cocoa powder
54 mg	8,8 mg	5,05 mg	4,6 mg

Na sodium

SPICES Table salt	FRUITS Pickled olives	ALGAE Laminaria	SEAFOOD Lobster
39400 mg	1556 mg	520 mg	280 mg

P phosphorus

SEEDS Pumpkin seeds	HERBS Tea leaves	DAIRY Soft cheese	BEANS Soybean
1233 mg	824 mg	700 mg	655 mg

Se selenium

FRUITS Coconut	MEAT Turkey liver	SEAFOOD Shrimp	CEREALS Corn
0,08 mg	0,071 mg	0,045 mg	0,03 mg

Ca calcium

SPICES Coriander	DAIRY Soft cheese	NUTS Almond	VEGETABLES Garlic
1246 mg	800 mg	264 mg	181 mg

Cu copper

MEAT Beef liver	NUTS Peanut	SEAFOOD Shrimp	BEANS Peas
3,8 mg	1,14 mg	0,85 mg	0,75 mg

Fe iron

SPICES Dried basil	HERBS Tea leaves	MEAT Pig liver	BEANS Soybean
89 mg	60 mg	20 mg	9,7 mg

I iodine

FRUITS Feijoa	ALGAE Laminaria	SEAFOOD Squid	FISH Salmon
0,35 mg	0,3 mg	0,3 mg	0,2 mg

K potassium

FRUITS Dried apricot	BEANS Haricot	NUTS Pistachio	SPICES Parsley
1717 mg	1100 mg	1025 mg	800 mg

References

This book was created with the assistance of the following resources:

- Tappan's Handbook of Massage Therapy: Blending Art with Science(6th Edition), 2015 – Patricia J. Benjamin, PhD

- 30 Second Anatomy: The 50 Most Important Structures and Systems in the Human Body, Each Explained in Half a Minute, 2013 – Gabrielle M. Finn, Judith Barbaro-Brown

- Anatomica: The Complete Home Medical Reference, 2010 – Ken Ashwell

- Mosby's Pathology for Massage Therapists(3rd Edition) 2013 – Susan Salvo

- The Four Hour Chef : The Simple Path to Cooking Like a Pro, Learning Anything, and Living the Good Life, 2013 – Timothy Ferriss

- Gray's Anatomy – Henry Gray

- Essentials of Anatomy and Physiology(4th Edition) 2002 – Rod Seeley, Trent Stephens, Philip Tate

- Introducing Medical Terminology Specialties: A Medical Specialties Approach with Patient Records, 2003 – Regina Masters, Barbara Gylys

- Exploring Medical Language: A Student-Directed Approach(5th Edition), 2002 – Myrna LaFleur Brooks

- Basic Clinical Massage Therapy: Integrating Anatomy and Treatment, 2003 – James H. Clay, David M. Pounds

- Milady's Theory and Practice of Therapeutic Massage, 1999 – Mark F. Beck

Recommended Reading

- The Obstacle is the Way: The Timeless Art of Turning Trials into Triumph, 2014 – Ryan Holiday

- Ego is the Enemy, 2016 – Ryan Holiday

- Outliers: The Story of Success, 2008 – Malcolm Gladwell

- Tools of Titans, 2016 - Timothy Ferriss

Index

54626788R20186

Made in the USA
San Bernardino,
CA